Colophon

'*Plato tackles climate change.*'
Author: Matthew Pye
Guest Authors: Carolina Teixeira & Jules Pye
(from the 'Climate Academy')

ISBN/EAN: 978-9-08-310150-7
Published by Matthew Pye
Copyright ©2020 Matthew Pye
First edition, September 2020.

Facts & Science: Homo Sapiens Foundation
Birgit van Munster and Michael Wadleigh
(ourfutureuncompromised.org)

Cover Design: Stijn van der Pol (w7b14.com)
Proofreading: Sean O'Dubhghaill, Anthony Swallow and Moira Cronin
Design: thisissaf~ (thisissaf.com)
Cartoons: Carl Jonsson (carl-brink.com)
Photography: Katriina Surquin (katriinasurquin.com)

Plato ~~courage~~ tackles climate change.

By Matthew Pye

~~common~~
sense
superman
courage
reason
thought
openness
progress

NoCommonSense.org

From the series
'No Common Sense; Philosophy tackles climate change'

The series "*No Common Sense - Philosophy Tackles Climate Change*" mobilises some of history's greatest philosophers to bring fresh depth to our climate thinking.

Each book is written in dialogue with the strongest minds of the past and in consultation with the latest climate science data and analysis. In this book Pye introduces Plato, underlining the importance of courage in climate thinking and acting!

No Common Sense

Foreword

This book is the first episode of the marvellously profound series by Matthew Pye, "*No Common Sense; Philosophy Tackles Climate Change*". It reminds us of the fact that it was the discovery of Plato by Cosimo dei Medici that fostered the 15th century Great of Florentine Renaissance. The renaissance our 21st century is apt to mirror.

In a historically well-known type of reaction, it was Aristotle that steered us in the 18th century Enlightment and the Industrial and Capitalist Age. From Heart to Head; from the reflective intelligence to the discursive mind. And now, luckily, it is Matthew Pye who, based on an unusually profound and lucid study of Plato, prepares the ground for our thinking about the duly expected 21st Century Renaissance that will help humanity to save the Planet and itself.

As has been the case for all these periodic renaissances – studied for the Jewish/Christian or Western Civilization since 1250 BC – the coming one too is spurred on by a crisis. In Florence it was the pest that had halved the population; from 100.000 to 50.000. Also increasing the wealth per head of the population. Now it looks as if it is COVID–19. Luckily quite a bit less drastic.

The question is: are we ready for a true renaissance? With a totally new view on how to live on this Mother Earth and respect what in our more lucid moments we rightly call Mother Nature? The same Mother Nature that Spinoza saw as the Great Lawgiver? As the cause of our birth on this planet and the planner of our individual and common destiny? Are we ready to have this crisis bring us to our senses? And spur us on to use our talents fully in the service of the needs of the planet and of humanity? Or to phrase it according to the oldest human, the Vedic, Wisdom: 'to play our role nicely'? Coming to our senses. Sensibly, according to common sense and without egoism?

This eighth episode of the series 'No Common Sense', is the most common sense approach imaginable to our common heritage of Knowledge, Consciousness and Bliss – Sat, Chit, Ananda – that according to the oldest source of human wisdom, the Veda's, is our true nature. It was written and is now published – and under our nose – ahead of the edition of the full work of "No Common Sense".

Why now? Well because NOW is the time for the whole of humanity to come to its senses. Now in this so-called COVID–19 crisis, and then take 'crisis' in its true meaning of 'time of choosing', from the Greek krino, to choose, and even beyond that from the Sanskrit root kri, to act. Also a time to 'reconsider'. Literally to put in harmony with the sidera, the stars, the planets. That is what this so-called crisis demands from us. Coming to our senses and consider. Let's be grateful for Matthew's guidance and read him carefully.

Talking about Matthew, why did he ask me to write this Foreword? And help launch his marvellous and timely book. Well, it is in fact my company, aptly named Resourcement BV. And a many years long experience in outplacement and career consulting. For now resourcement, going back to source. What that source is for each of us? We spoke about that before. It is nothing other than what we heard Spinoza call Mother Nature. It was She who oversaw our 'incarnation', our birth. Your soul taking flesh in your mother's womb. She, according to Spinoza, saw that your time had come. That the time was ripe for your particular equipment, your talents, to descend to the human form in order to have your talents serve the corresponding needs arisen, or on the verge of arising, in the world, in society, in the time and place in which you were born. And beyond, in our fast unifying world, on this planet Earth.

So, an intermediate remark. Politicians in particular are talking about 'the need for repairing the economy and restoring economic growth'. How silly. The needs of the Planet demand no quantitative growth. Quite the opposite. This renaissance is there for restoring well-being by a much lighter physical burden put on the Planet. Thus quite a refining of what we regard as well being. And hence no fear for unemployment, but a call for people to truly start discovering where and how to contribute to a much healthier, materially lighter, economy.

In Outplacement counselling (of people having lost their former employment) all emphasis was on a similar exercise: discovering the link of their talents with the changing needs of the outside world. "*Entrepreneuring with Talents*" we called it. "*Becoming Master of Your own Destiny*". And the results were astounding: over 80% of these dismissed or disgruntled clients found better employment within a year. And in a position where their talents were better used to meet the needs of society. In the end nobody was worse off having gone through the crisis of job loss. A not too surprising effect of systematic training in, and application of, reflection and dialogue.

This is what this book of Matthew Pye is calling us, or perhaps forcing us, to consider: are my talents aptly used to provide humanity, and my direct surroundings, with a future on a healthy Planet Earth? This is the question Pye makes us face now. David Bohm – and others – did that before him. Quoting Bohm writing in the eighties of the last century: "And we have the danger of ecological destruction – destruction of agricultural land and forests, pollution, the change of climate and many other things. There would be a real ecological disaster within not too long a period of time if people keep doing whatever they are doing."

What is even more telling is that this great scientist, who left his laboratory and university to introduce people world-wide to the Art of Dialogue, already sums up as the major problem of our time, of our politicians first and foremost (and the financial world): "a disease of thought, of knowledge, of information, spreading all over the world". His call is then for "a deep and intense awareness going beyond the imagery and analysis…". And yes, it is as if Matthew Pye has heard that call and the fruit lies in front of you. Fruit of 'a deep and intense awareness' coupled to his years long work in teaching the international youth in the realities of History and Philosophy. As Full Member of the Club of Rome (EU Chapter). As Initiator and Leader of the Climate Academy. And now as a prolific writer – taking quite a bit of your time – but worth every minute you spend with him. As I discovered in the past few months.

This book invites you to become a true 'Entrepreneur with your Talents'. Under the Law of Three. You know that law; you find it in any creation, in any of your actions. Originally it looks like 'I and the Other' or 'I and Creation'; 'I and the work to be done'. But the Truth is much subtler. In full and true consciousness you will discover that All is One. It is just for the 'Play of Creation' that we do as if we are Two. But then the Law of Three comes in. As in I, You, He; God the Father, the Son, the Holy Spirit; Mother, Father, Child; Plus, Minus, Equal,; Acid, Base, Salt. All looking like three, in fact two for the start and the art of the play. In the end one.

The readers in the Netherlands are lucky. Soon there will be full recognition of this Law of Three in a new exciting magazine OMG (Other, Me, God) for – dare I use the term – the (spiritual) 'élite' René Guénon spoke of in his epochal book 'La Crise du Monde Moderne'. Not knowing, dear reader, he was speaking of you, of our time. Yes, we need such a Magazine – as we need all the episodes of 'No Common Sense' – to bring us to our senses. 'Remind' us. Make us deal sensibly with our world, our families, our friends and acquaintances. Put every meeting between the Other and Me under the grace of the Supreme Wisdom, Consciousness and Love we usually name 'God'. Thus 'uniting' all. Bringing us to our 'common sense'. To a much-increased social cohesion. And a careful, very careful, dealing with the gifts and needs of our Mother Earth.

And then for all of us. May this book help us to keep the wild, egoistic horse of Plato's Phaedrus in check. Spur the horse of goodness and love in us on, to lift us to the Plain of Truth where our soul will be fed by the essence of Truth. Grateful for, and much helped by this marvellous book part of that series titled "*No Common Sense*", but in fact so full of common sense that it will be our guide to a true 21st century Renaissance, changing our society from Capitalism to a true Common Good Economy. An economy in which even the politicians learn to submit the 'nomos' or rule to the wisdom of the 'logos', the all-encompassing Consciousness, some call God, some Yahweh, some Allah, some Brahman. Whatever, unlimited consciousness expressing itself in creation.

Thank you Matthew for this contemporary 'Gospel' in its true meaning of 'Good News'.

Hans Leewens,

Brussels, August 2020

Acknowledgements

Hans Leewens, at 87 years old, I suppose it is probably quite normal that you would need the occasional injection into your eye to keep them working well. What is certainly not normal, however, is the clarity and depth with which you see the world. I will always remember the summer of 2020 for all the Vedic wisdom and love (a word you rightly use unashamedly) that was shared over our cappuccini. I could say so much, but you taught me two very simple Sanskrit words that say everything that can be said, अद्वैत वेदान्त (Advaita Vedānta); the teaching of 'not two' – the basic unity of all beings.

Birgit van Munster and Michael Wadleigh, there is simply no way that this book could have been written without you both. Your understanding of the science of sustainability is just remarkable – this is not only true for the smallest mechanical detail of the data, it is also the case for the biggest themes of what is going on. The reader should be in no doubt that so many of the arguments and insights here have come from the selfless energy you have invested in all your projects. There are now dozens of young graduates of the Climate Academy that we set up together who remain so grateful for all the wisdom and knowledge that they have acquired at your ecological farm at Bryn Mawr, and also through your constant support.

Stijn van der Pol, thank you for painting my black and white docx files with the magic of your design skills and instincts. You worked on this book with real love, professionalism and dedication. Your genuine engagement and attention to the details can be seen on every welcoming page.

Rob Geursten, when I think of the number of hours that you have freely given to the birth of this book (and so much else) it causes a bit of mind melt. You are a man of many talents, sincerest thanks for all that you have invested in getting the words from my heart and mind onto these pages.

Carl Jonsson, such a modest and considered student, now a good friend (and immensely talented cartoonist!).

Sean O'Dubhghaill, thank you for knocking my raw texts into a proper form and shape with such mindfulness.

Elise Sijthoff, your work in mobilising students into the democratic space is inspirational. You were the first to publish my work and I will always be deeply grateful for that.

Anthony, Moira and Penny, my oxygen! Thank you for the meticulous final proof-reading and all the support that went far, far beyond the details of this book. Ficino coined the phrase "Platonic love", and you have been a vivid example of it to me.

Dad, you pedaled the final hard miles of this book with me with your usual dedication and humility. Superdad.

Els, Frederik, Jennifer, Pierre-Phillipe and François, so many of the ground-rules for this book were established in those meeting rooms where we wrote the Philosophy Syllabus for the European Schools.

John, you chiseled the edges off my use of all the history and art of Antiquity with expertise. Thank you.

Carolina and Jules, Katriina and Levin, and all the other Climate Academy graduates, we have shared so much; and you brought an incredible level of courage, energy and happiness to the fight for justice. You have the right to an uncompromised future.

contents

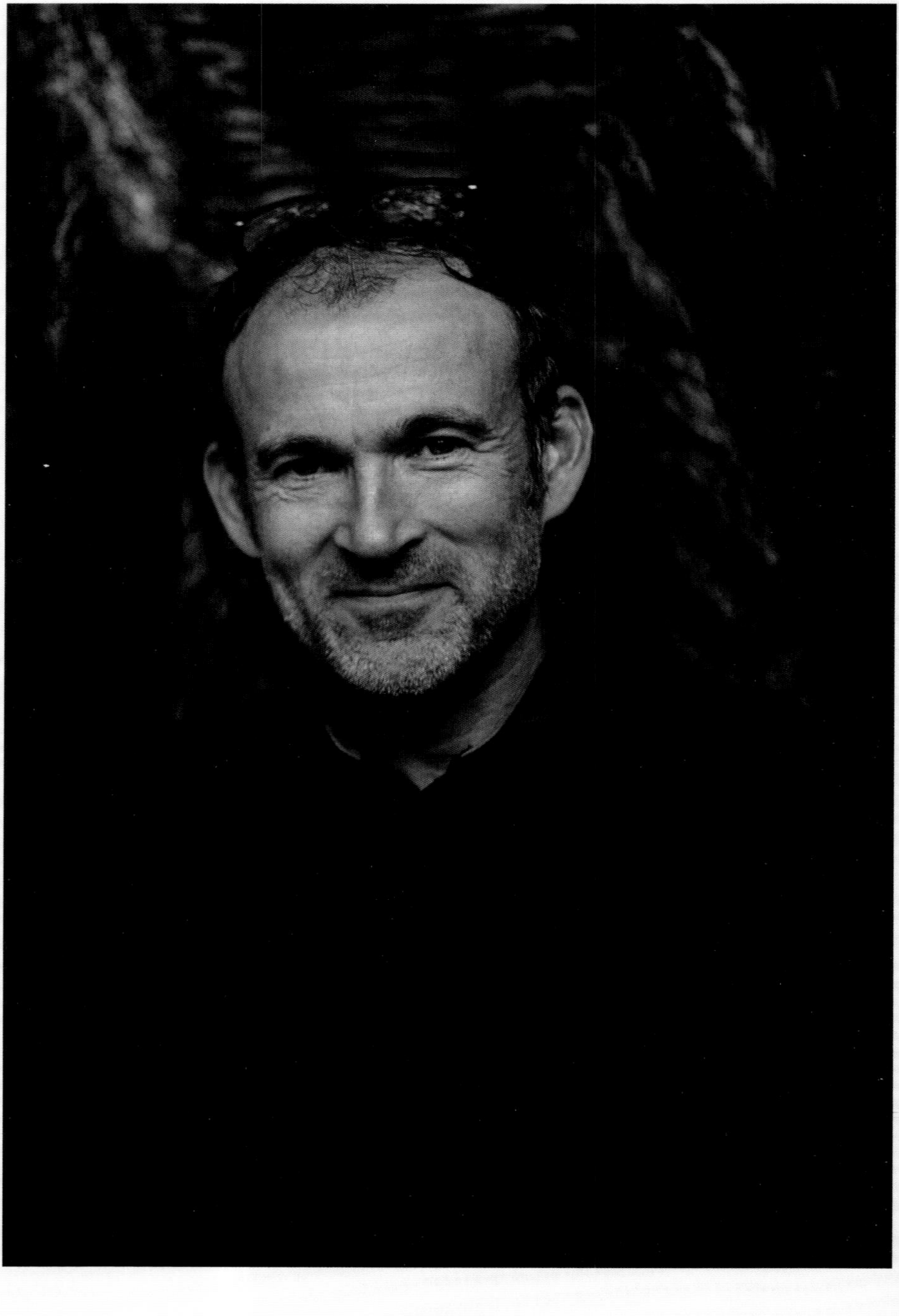

Image 2. - Matthew Pye

Preface

Crisis

This is a crisis.

A big one.

In fact, it is so big,

it is hard to see it.

Image 3. – Warming Stripes

The climate crisis is very real. However, it exists in a very dangerous blind spot of our awareness because of its sheer depth and scope. This blind spot has enabled us to carry on as if climate change was not happening.

Science can make the reality of the climate crisis crystal clear. It can summarise a vast amount of data into a small space for our eyes and brains to picture it. For example, the "Warming Stripes"[1] above demonstrate just how radical the shift in the average global temperature has been since the start of the industrial revolution. The first stripe of colour, on the left, represents the average global temperature for the year 1850; the last stripe of colour, on the right, represents the latest thermal data.[2] The contrast between the cool blue on the left and the hot reds on the right is vivid. This monumental change in our reality would be hidden from us without the work of science.

---

1 Thanks to the clarity of mind of the climate scientist Ed Hawkins.
2 The colours are rooted in the HadCRUT4 gridded dataset of global historical surface temperature anomalies relative to a 1961-1990 reference period. Earlier data sets are available for each month, since January 1850, and can be found in the collaborative work of the Met Office Hadley Centre and the Climatic Research Unit at the University of East Anglia.

Climate change is not a weather event, it is not a moment. It is something that exists far beyond our common senses. We have known about the science of a greenhouse gas effect for nearly two centuries, after Joseph Fourier first proposed the idea in 1824.[3] The atmosphere's rising heat has been the constant background theme to all of our economic and social development, all of our wars and our peace treaties; most significantly, it has been the background effect to our booming population (from 1.2bn in 1850 to 7.8bn in 2020) and to the booming industrial activity (from 7 tonnes of resource extraction in 1900 to 90 tonnes in 2020) driven by the Very High Developed nations.

Our failure to recognise and to act on this change has lead us to this moment of crisis.

There will be an awful escalation of extreme weather events in the absence of radical action at a systems level. However, the real action will not be so visible. The collapse of biodiversity and the melting of the glaciers, the destruction of the rainforests and the disruption of the Jetstream, will all happen away from our senses. They will happen as averages, as patterns and trends. If we do not make a deep and immediate response to the science, then everything will fall apart in our blind spot. How odd it is that something so devastating can happen so clearly, and yet remain so hidden.

We have already achieved an average temperature rise of 1.1°C since the start of the industrial revolution. This does not sound like a lot, but a human being suffering from a fever of 1.1°C will not feel great at all. A sustained temperature of 2°C can start to cause vital organs to fail. We are currently on a pathway for global heating of around 4°C by the end of the century[4] For a human, such a rise is a medical emergency (known as 'hyperpyrexia'), and it causes death without quick and effective treatment.

---

3   After Fourier's insight that the atmosphere must have insulating properties in 1824 and 1827, it was Eunice Foote who was the first to explain some of the chemical mechanics of global heating in the paper she read to the American Association on August 23rd 1856, "*Circumstances affecting the Heat of the Sun's Rays*". It was later coined the "Greenhouse Effect" by Nils Gustaf Ekholm in 1901.

4   The details can be found in Chapters 8 and 9.

This is only a metaphor, but since temperature is one of the fundamental co-ordinates of the biosphere, suddenly pushing it to a new level is a profoundly reckless act.

The minefield described by the scientific scenarios gets increasingly dangerous the more we allow the heating to continue uninterrupted. Tipping points lie ahead that cannot be crossed without triggering system collapses that would threaten the supply of the most basic requirements for human life, for example, food and fresh water.

The graphs of mainstream science are emphatic in their conclusions: booming material consumption is incompatible with a safe and stable future. The hard truth is that the industrial revolution is heading towards a dramatic and tragic finale.

After the economic boom, we are now facing a monumental ecological bust. This is a bust that would pull so much down around it.

This is a crisis, a systemic one.

OK Boomer.

Plato

What does a blank-faced philosopher from the past have to do with any of this? Is it not an utterly improbable Olympian long jump to bring Plato from Antiquity to the present? What use is an ancient philosopher for a modern crisis that is driven by our emissions of greenhouse gas particles into the atmosphere?

It is this book's ambition to demonstrate that Plato fully deserves our attention. Plato has a towering reputation as a genius in our intellectual history, and so we would be justified in expecting that he will have something powerfully resonant to say. Indeed, Plato has a good track record. Not only did his work have a profound impact in Antiquity, but his rediscovery through the translations of Marsilio Ficino in 1484 provided a major impulse to the Renaissance.[5]

Indeed, the Renaissance followed a time in which the traditional order of things had been profoundly disturbed by the Black Death. The surge in innovation, science, exploration and art can be helpfully understood with this trauma in the background. Luckily for us, the tragedy is ahead of us and it does not have to happen – but what is required is the courage to look at that reality and to then respond.

The storm clouds are close.

Plato the Superhero?

Plato could be the right kind of superhero for this very moment. Indeed, caped heroes always seem to arrive at the last moment, just in time to save the situation. Perhaps we will need a searchlight like the one on top of the Police headquarters of Gotham City? When their grubby, urban politics

---

5   "The Renaissance" as a period, was retrospectively coined as late as 1855 by a French historian Jules Michelet, and was popularised in 1860 by the Swiss historian Jacob Burckhardt. However, it should be admitted that there are many periods of history that can claim a "rebirth" (the Carolingian, the Ottonian, the Timurid…). For the sake of brevity, here the Renaissance is taken to signify the classical one that had really got into gear by 1500.

escalate into a major crisis, the Bat-Signal is shone onto the foreboding skies, and Batman swoops to the rescue.

Of course, this is not Gotham City. Batman does not really exist. But, Holy headache! Holy jigsaw puzzle! Holy hurricane! we have a crisis, and we could certainly use some help. After an exploration of the systemic problems that the climate crisis presents, this book will progress to identify two key aspects of Plato's work that are fundamentally important to any effective solutions to global heating.

Firstly, like all good superheroes, Plato was deeply concerned about justice and virtues. This is not some limp, sentimental statement; virtues require depth and courage, as will be explained.

Secondly, we need an urgent overhaul of the infrastructure of our society and the infrastructure of our thoughts. Although Plato was a remarkable individual, what really matters in his work is this examination of the whole, and the transcending of the individual. In a few ways, he was the anti-hero superhero, the antidote to our individualism. Plato thought about society and the self in a systemic way. His was an advocate for rational laws – the fundamental matrix of any society.

The stage is set. If this was Hollywood, then the title could be: "*Plato Returns – The Temperature Rises*". The plot? First the crisis, then the solutions. The language of this introduction will return to a normal register but, much like a movie trailer, the main scenes from the book will now follow.

Scene One – The Beginning

The Boom in the Bust

Plato (d. 347/348 BCE) was a citizen of Athens during the Greek Golden Age.[6] In fact, he was a luminous example of the astonishing progress that was being made in human culture. However, Plato was not duped by appearances. He was a thinker who could get beyond the surface of things; he could see the fault lines underneath the assets of his Athenian society.

Likewise, we also need to look beyond the imposing status that Plato has as a philosopher.

Despite his rock-hard face in the busts of Antiquity, there is a Plato behind that image who was a human being, wrestling with all of life's difficulties and contradictions. Despite his reputation in the 20th century for sanctioning tight-fisted totalitarian regimes,[7] Plato was a wonderfully open and creative man.

Behind the stony features of his bust, there is a Plato who was struggling to understand why humans can fail so ruinously. Contrary to the common view of Plato as a dogmatist, the man that sat in front of a blank sheet of papyrus to write the '*Republic*' was both playful and sensitive. He was someone looking beyond the booms and the busts, to the fundamental truth of things.

Philosophers have a reputation for being aloof. This idea then leads easily on to the expectation that they will make simplistic assessments and proposals,

6   Commonly framed as 500BCE-323BCE.
7   Karl Popper, "The Open Society and Its Enemies" (1945) is a brilliant defence of democracy. Popper underlines the fundamental importance of openness and enquiry in a healthy civilisation with tenacity and intellectual authority. However, the consequence of his work was an unnecessarily myopic view of Plato.

afforded by that distance from reality. This suspicion is particularly strong in the case of Plato because he is so high-minded. However, such a casual view of Plato is wrong. The ideals that he defends are not made possible because of his distance from reality; the opposite is true, they are born out of a full engagement with it. The *'Republic'* was conceived in the very messy details of his tussle with his world.

Indeed, it is the *'Republic'* that this book will focus on, and it was written by Plato after he watched his own city self-destruct. His writings are deep reflections on his own experiences as an Athenian who lived through the loss of the Peloponnesian War to Sparta (431-401BCE) and the loss of his teacher and mentor Socrates to a cup of poison (399BCE). Both tragedies in his life were the consequences of democratic votes and both events would have left him feeling utterly disempowered.

The climate crisis is overwhelming. Millions can see the lunacy of our inadequate response. The status quo is unravelling the seams of the ecosystems on which all human life depends. The political, social and economic systems at play overwhelm any individual response. Any reader who feels disempowered and cannot fathom how democracies could act in such a self-destructive way, will find someone that has sat in that spot before writing the *'Republic'* in Plato.

Moreover, the absurdity of both our situation and that of Plato is amplified by the fact that the self-destruction is happening under the banner of something that appears to be noble – in the case of Plato it was the Homeric values of pride and bravery in the war with Sparta, and in the name of the people (*'demos'*) in the vote to execute Socrates.

For us and our climate crisis, the most obvious and ugliest resistance to reducing emissions comes from the populist movements whose tribal pride in their nation shouts, IN CAPITAL LETTERS, over the voice of reason; Plato had an eye for the subtle things. His critique of democracy is attentive to the softer values of "choice" and "freedom". Such values are certainly noble, but just like anything, can turn toxic if they get out of hand. Plato observed how democracies tend to amp up the nobility of these values to such a high level that they morph into something destructive; they can become impossibly demanding imperatives that then drown out the voice of reason.

Scene Two – The Middle

The *Republic*

The '*Republic*' is a giant work.

To keep everything to a manageable size, this book will only deal with the first sentence, word by word. This might sound a bit limited, but the whole book can be found in microcosm inside the opening line of the *Republic*.

What will become clear in this section of the book is that Plato was searching for the organizing truth behind the clutter of all the details. Not unlike a physicist today, he was probing for the governing principles underneath all of the muddled facts about the world. Just as an architect cannot be possibly be ignorant of the laws of physics and the rules of mathematics when designing a house, so Plato thinks that a society cannot be built in a stable and durable way if the people are not attentive to some fundamental truths about reality and the human condition. Likewise, an individual cannot live a fulfilled life if it is out of sync with the essential nature of things.

The shocking truth for us is that Plato thought that a democracy was one of the worst ways to set up a society. Although he was from Athens at the time when democracy was born, he dissented from the strong cultural consensus that it was a noble form of governance. It would be easy to dismiss Plato's critique of democracy by commenting that Plato is just an angry and bitter man who scapegoated the demos (the people). As a member of the Athenian nobility, we could dismiss him as an elitist with a grudge about the death of Socrates, and for the war with Sparta.

However, this would be a cheap argument. Plato's critique of democracy is a profound one, and although this book will staunchly defend the value of democracy, it allows Plato the space to interrogate it. Our first move should be to let our guard down, and allow him to ask tough questions about the state we are in. Is it not true that climate change is overwhelmingly a problem that has been caused by nations that are democratic and capitalist?

Unless we are prepared to question these basic operating systems of our society, then we cannot expect the trajectory of the emissions to change. Is it not an openness to criticism a core strength of a democracy? Why would we not ask questions of democratic rule, and scrutinise its weaknesses? Why would we not question capitalism if it the losses it causes to us far outweigh the benefits?

The raised temperature of the planet can be understood as a metaphorical signal. In a human, a raised temperature is a symptom of a deeper problem. The body is responding to something. There are systemic problems that need urgent attention: We live in a capitalist culture that encourages us to hyperventilate on consumption, we have an energy infrastructure that is deeply entrenched in fossil fuels and we have weakened democracies and global organizations that have little leverage on problems that require collaboration, consensus and long-term commitments. Plato can offer us a sharp diagnosis of these failings.

Surprisingly, the pivotal moment in the defeat of Athens in the Peloponnesian War happened far away from the Aegean Sea. The Athenians lost almost their entire navy in a battle in Syracuse, Sicily. Warships represented Athenian dominance in the Greek world, and so when they failed so dramatically, the defeat not only caused wreckage off the coast of Syracuse, it also wrecked the symbolic order of the Athenian mind.

Therefore, after opening up the first sentence of the *'Republic'*, which is set in the Athenian harbour of the Piraeus, we will turn our attention to Plato's nautical metaphor - his 'Simile of the Ship'. Plato's depiction of a doomed pleasure cruise carries his critique of democracy further. The ship is controlled by a drunk and blind captain, who has a motley crew of men jostling to win his favour and attention, in their hapless bid to gain control over the direction of travel. The ship is owned by the people (the 'demos') and it is not on a journey that is going to end well.

Plato does put someone on board who knows what to do. This person has studied the stars, the winds and the art of navigation. It is the Navigator. The Philosopher. However, the tragedy is that nobody listens to him; he is marginalised and bullied.

Cue Scene Three.

Scene Three – The End

Virtues and Laws

The *'Republic'* argues that the best system of government is one in which Philosophers are the ruling Kings and Queens. Plato does not think that it is wise to plug the governance of a society into the short-term imperatives of our desires, but instead into the wider vision of our rational minds. Reason should be installed as the governing principle. On an individual level, this is a truth well known by anyone who has struggled to maintain a diet.

We would bristle at the notion that only some select rational elites are capable of properly exercising reason. However, there remain some important principles in his thinking once we have dissented from his rejection of democracy.

Firstly, the philosophical autocracy of the *'Republic'* is not so weird or malignant as it might first appear to us. Plato's ruling class were trained and utterly dedicated to beauty and justice and there would always be the voice of the cynic who questions if this is really possible. Plato held a genuine confidence in the transformative power of truth and beauty. It remains easy to be cynical about the power of virtues to guide human decision-making if the decision-makers are challenged by more banal desires. However, we all recognise the formidable strength of a virtuous life when we see it. This book acknowledges the wisdom and courage of Martin Luther King as an example of a leader whose convictions and vision had a revolutionary effect.

Secondly, the idea that reason should play a primary role in a state's governance is not much more than common sense to the modern reader. Indeed, we have the rule of law, bureaucracies, constitutions and courts to keep our societies well-calibrated. Decent rational laws should protect us from poisonous sandwiches and tyrannical power; decent rational laws should prevent dangerous gas leaks in schools and prevent the pumping of excessive greenhouse gases into the atmosphere.

It is true that the *'Republic'* is unashamedly antidemocratic, and so it is not a comfortable book for the modern citizen to read. However, if we want to understand why we have legislated against poisonous sandwiches, but have not legislated for greenhouse gases emissions, then we have to get out of our comfort zone. It is so absurd that we have not done so and it demands deeper thinking.

This book's two concluding principles are virtues (such as the courage to move beyond the status quo) and laws (of the most basic health and safety requirement for human life on Earth).

Indeed, ever since we have understood the danger posed by climate change, there have been countless green movements, initiatives, targets, parties, projects, policies, protests … all of which have made brave, sometimes major contributions to a more sustainable world.

However, this kaleidoscope of ambition and energy has not yet unified into a singular demand that could make a systemic difference. We need to pull hard on a lever that will reduce emissions at every level and sector of society.

We are fortunate that such a lever exists in our modern society: it is the law.

Laws are the invisible, systemic matrix that hold a society together. Laws are that hidden structure that defines boundaries, frames decision making and that provide a framework for all of our actions.

Until we have laws to limit national emissions to a safe and equitable level (see Chapters 8 and 9 for the details), we will continue to flounder in a fragmentary fashion against the rising level of greenhouse gas concentrations. The core solution to the climate crisis, around which all our creativity, interests and ambitions can revolve, is in a binding climate law for each nation.[8]

We do not offer contracts to architects that have no understanding of gravity, yet we have economists, politicians and business leaders who are designing and implementing their projects for our economic growth who have no understanding of planetary boundaries. Physics is not the last concern of an architect, but the first. Likewise, a proper understanding of the chemistry of our atmosphere and the biology of our great biota cannot be the last concern of our policy makers, but the first.

8   For 2°C heating, the U.K. the law would require an emissions reduction of 6.9% per year, starting from today. For the USA it is 16%, and for China it is 5.5%; see Cut11Percent.org for the other nations and for all of the key reasoning and scientific qualifications behind this number.

Back to the crisis

The climate crisis itself should be put into a holistic context. It is a part of a wider crisis in sustainability. This book will focus on the climate crisis because it is so acute and urgent; however, the fuller picture shows that we are in the middle of a mass extinction event. Human beings are depleting limited resources from the crust of the Earth at a formidable rate, flattening biodiversity, exhausting fresh water supplies... and yet, we look at the surface of what we are doing and casually call it "progress".

As stated at the beginning, this crisis is so big that it is hard to spot. Indeed, spotting mass extinction events is a surprisingly difficult thing to do. Such events only happen about once every 750 million years, on average,[9] so it is quite difficult to get any decent practice.

Here is one final example, from the previous mass extinction event:

Mexico. More specifically, the Yucatan Peninsula. Here there is a crater so large that it took us until 1978 to find it. It is the Chicxulub crater, and it stretches to 180 kilometers wide.[10] Half on land, half in the sea, you need a plane to notice that it is there.[11] The shocked quartz and highly unusual levels of iridium (Ir) at the site confirm to geologists that something truly cosmic[12] happened there 66 million years ago (66.043 ± 0.011 Ma).

This impact crater is where a massive asteroid marked a massive full stop at the end of the dinosaurs' paragraph of history. The dinosaurs did not get much time to see the crisis coming. How could they? The Ampelosaurus had the biggest brain of all of them, but it was only the size of a tennis ball,

---

9   The age of the Earth: 4.54 ± 0.05 billion years. The first mass extinction event was 444 million years ago (it took a while before life evolved). If there are 6 events, there are 5 periods in between, thus the average period between mass events has been 444 / 5 = 88.8 ~ 90 million years.

10   https://www.nasa.gov/missions/earth/chicxulub.html

11   A plane and some technical equipment are required. It was spotted as part of an airborne magnetic survey of the Gulf of Mexico, by geophysicists Glen Penfield and Antonio Camargo.

12   Iridium is one of the rarest elements in the Earth's crust, it is found in great abundance in meteorites. The spike in iridium levels at the K-Pg boundary is important evidence in support of the Alvarez hypothesis that a space rock, roughly the size of Mount Everest, smashed into our planet.

and their club-like feet would also have made it difficult from them to grip a telescope.

It was not just the dinosaurs who had a bad day; the bolide strike ended up wiping out an estimated 75% of all life on Earth. Who could really argue with a blast as strong as ~2 million thermonuclear Tsar Bombs?[13] Indeed, a group of fish found in North Dakota certainly did not get time to say much in response. Their fossilised remains were found in 2012 and they had been caught with their mouths open and with tiny glass beads from the blast site lodged in their gills.[14] They must have been rather shocked to see a mega-tsunami, 100 metres tall, coming towards them.[15]

By contrast, we have many reasons to be thankful. Firstly, we have more than a few seconds to react; we have a few years left. Secondly, human beings have created the problem, so therefore we can also fix it.

Plato, and Philosophy in general, offers us the chance to step back for a moment and to think with a moment of clarity about the state we are in. In the end, it comes down to this: We need the courage to demand and implement the rational laws that are required to avert the biggest bust of all. Virtues and laws are the principal boundaries that frame all the playful details of Plato's 'Republic'.

"*Plato tackles Climate Change*" simply follows suit.

---

13 Or counted in proper scientific numbers, the impact created between between 1.3×1024 and 5.8×1025 joules, or 1.3–58 yottajoules of energy. cf. Durand-Manterola, H. J.; Cordero-Tercero, G. (2014). "*Assessments of the energy, mass and size of the Chicxulub Impactor*". arXiv:1403.6391 [astro-ph.EP].

14 PNAS, DOI: 10.1073/pnas.1817407116.

15 Bryant, Edward, "*Tsunami: The Underrated Hazard*", p. 178. Springer (June 2014).

Wrapping up – What sort of book is this?

The collapse of any civilization has never been obvious to its participants. Only hindsight, and the ability to look at patterns and trends in the events, make what went wrong clear to see – this is a job that falls to historians and archeologists who can search through the rubble of what is left.

What Philosophy provides is a unique vantage point to look at our situation. It is a subject that pulls together all other subjects: history, physics, art, literature, chemistry and biology and so on. Philosophy's distinctive approach to thinking systemically and holistically gives it a certain unusual power. It does take time to understand both what Philosophy is about, and what is supposed to be happening in a Philosophy book. It takes some time to figure out the rules of the game.

It is a subject that can seem a bit intimidating and, frankly, sometimes it can just seem a bit odd.

Opposite is an attempt to draw a picture of what is going on. At the bottom right of the image is the reader – the self. This is the starting point – our everyday life. Through a dialogue with the Philosophers, we are drawn away from common sense assumptions about both ourselves and the situation. This movement out of our corner enables us to see the world from a different angle and it enables us to take a critical distance from ourselves.

The space in the middle of the triangle is where Philosophy happens – at first this unfamiliar place can be a challenging zone to find our feet in. However, through a continual 'trialogue' with the Philosophers, our world, and our own experiences, we can build up the strength and skills to become autonomous thinkers and agents.

Philosophy is not just the understanding of different arguments, it is not just the history of ideas; it is a subject that interrogates us and our world. It draws the mind and the heart out of clichés and comfortable illusions and invites us to be more fully ourselves.

In the simplest terms, as it says on the label, Philosophy is literally the "love of wisdom" (from the Greek, φιλοσοφία).

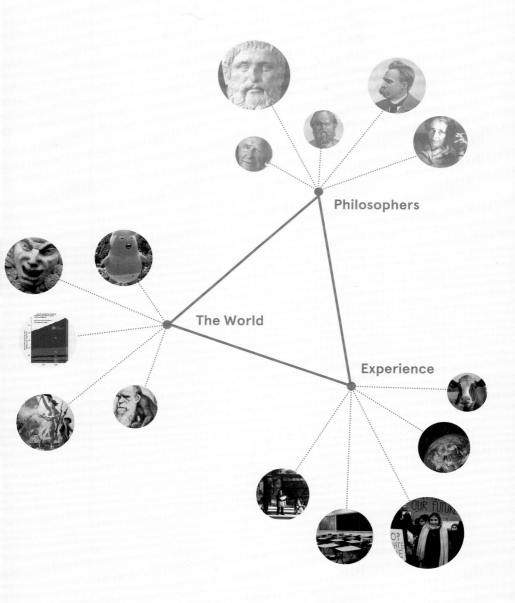

Philosophers

The World

Experience

the
boom

the
bust

Plato

Chapter One

The Boom in
the Bust

Introduction

In this famous bust, Plato appears to us as a mature and dignified man. He looks self-assured, statesmanlike and wise. Plato is a thinker with a reputation as solid as the rock onto which his face was carved. He certainly deserves the status that scholars accord to him as the Father of Western Philosophy. He was a giant thinker, whose sheer range and ambition of thought set the agenda for over two millennia – something that is agreed upon by both his admirers and his detractors. As A.N. Whitehead once commented: "The safest general characterisation of the European philosophical tradition is that it consists of a series of footnotes to Plato".[16]

Plato (b. 427 BCE) lived during the 'Golden Age of Athens' (480-404 BCE), an absolutely astonishing segment of history – a time in which so many cultural, social and political aspects of human life bounded forward together.[17]

---

16   *Process and Reality* (Free Press, 1979, p. 39).
17   Plato was born towards the end of this Golden Age and wrote most of his best-known works after 404 BCE.

Here are just some of the highlights:

Cleisthenes (in 508-7 BCE) started the ball rolling by taking the radically modern step of putting every citizen as equal before the law.[18] Pericles (b. 494 BCE) followed that up by defending and supporting the development of the world's first democracy. This was a revolutionary system of government that empowered the male citizens to the extent that: "Everyone who is capable of serving the city meets no impediment, neither poverty, nor civic condition..." These words were in fact written by Thucydides (b. 460 BCE), who competes alongside Herodotus (b. 484 BCE) for the honour of having founded "History" as the discipline that we know it as today.[19]

Image 5. - The Acropolis

18 Technically, this is referred to as isonomia. Mogens Herman Hansen, a Danish Classicist, helpfully identified three important aspects for the Greek respect for equality (ἴσος, (*isos*)), which demonstrates how deeply their political thinking went: (1) *isokratia* (equality of power) (2) *isegoria* (right to address political assemblies) and (3) *isopsephos polis* (one man, one vote).

19 Herodotus was the first known writer to attempt a chronological and systematic narrative of events from the past. Any historical account necessarily involves filters, selection of material and subjective framing, but many credit Thucydides with making the first, very determined effort to pursue the goal of objectivity in the writing of history. Thucydides also spoke of the desire for a government "for the many, not the few" (Thuc. 2.37).

Pericles also ordered the reconstruction of the Acropolis, including the Parthenon, Erechtheion and the Temple of Athena Nike, and many others. As a leading army General, he wanted Athenians to celebrate and indulge in their recent military victories over the Persian Empire[20] in style. Inside these buildings, between the imposing Doric and Ionic pillars that held open the sacred space, the gods and goddesses of Mount Olympus were captured in white marble so that they could be honoured properly[21]. Paraxiteles, a prodigious sculptor, had the ability to transform the heavy stone blocks of material into something startlingly lifelike and beautiful – all with just an idea in his head and a chisel in hand.

Myron and Polykleitos rivalled his work with their masterpieces in bronze, but it was the statues crafted by a man named Pheidias (b. 480 BCE) that stood above all others. His statue of Athena Parthenos was made from ivory and gold (the gold alone weighed over a tonne) and it was embellished with engraved gems. It stood as a 11.5-metre tall monument to his abilities. His equally massive Statue of Zeus in the Sanctuary of Olympia was judged to be one of the Seven Wonders of the Ancient World.

The more delicate and domestic Athenian art – their high-quality pottery, metalwork, jewellery and painting – have continually been dug out from the ground around the city and currently occupy exhibitions in museums all over the world. Despite the ability to preserve some Athenian marvels, the three spectacular Long Walls that the Athenians built during this period, and which connected the city to their harbours in Piraeus and Phalerum, did not survive the different tests of history and were reduced to rubble.[22]

---

20 Although the reality of the decisive Greek victories over the Persians by 450 BCE is not in dispute, the details and even existence of the official "Treaty of Callias" (dated to 449 BCE) are often contested.

21 It seems likely that the Parthenon functioned mostly as a Treasury, rather than as a religious site.

22 The walls were destroyed during the First Mithridatic War by the Roman General Sulla, in the rather brutal Sieges of Athens and Piraeus (87-86 BCE).

However, those alive in the Golden Age could have walked to the Athenian docks, all the while protected by the security provided by these immense fortified walls. Arriving at the waterside in Piraeus, the strength of their booming trade and the power of their formidable navy would have been vividly obvious. Indeed, the Athenians had overpowered the Persian Empire at the start of this Golden Age, both with their Navy and with their Hoplite Phalanx (during the Persian Wars 499 BCE to 449 BCE). After a brief introduction to this chapter, we will discover the philosopher Socrates (b. 497 BCE) at the harbour of Piraeus in the opening line of Plato's 'Republic'. Socrates provoked both intense debate and irritation, with his stubborn questioning of anyone who crossed his path, wherever he went. With less spectacle, it was also a period in which thinkers like Democritus (b. c460 BCE), godfather to the atom, Parmenides (b. 515 BCE), Protagoras (b. 481 BCE) and Zeno (b.495 BCE) were probing the nature of reality with remarkable insight.

Finally, the plays written by Sophocles (b. 497 BCE) and Euripides (b. 483 BCE), Aeschylus (b. 523 BCE) and Aristophanes (b. 446 BCE) were all performed to audiences of up to 17,000 during the Dionysia festival at the foot of the Acropolis, in the huge Theatre of Dionysus. These tragedies and comedies were poignant cultural commentaries on their own times; such was the probity of their art that these works also provided the plotlines to so much of the culture and human history that followed, once Greek power had faded away.

It was a golden period. Arguably, it has not been matched since.

And so, this bust of Plato, with its quiet self-confidence and fine features, seems to capture the gilded time into which he was born.[23]

---

23   This bust is actually a Roman copy of a 4th century original.

Just the Bust

One of Plato's central concerns was the problem of illusions.

Reality is very often not what it seems. Behind this boom, there is also another story – a bust.

The solidity and permeance of Plato's stone image betrays so much of what was going on in Plato's life and in Plato's head. Behind the power and abundance of the Athenian Golden Age there were some stress marks that would become very prominent in his early life. A more attentive inspection of these highlights is, therefore, necessary. There were some cracks in the Athenians' monumental achievements that were about to get much bigger.

Image 6. - King Leonidas

The truth is that it was not the Athenians alone who had beaten the Persians. They had fought in an alliance of Hellenic city states. Athens was the largest city by far, certainly, but this alliance included the might of the Spartan land army whose contribution was also decisive. Indeed, the resistance and heroic death of the Spartan King Leonidas I – who confronted up to 300,000 men[24] of King Xerxes I of Persia with his now famous army of 300 Hoplite soldiers[25] during the Battle of Thermopylae (480 BCE) – was a key moment in pushing Persia out of Europe. This remarkable moment in military history is summed up in the moment when Leonidas I confronts Xerxes' Persian messenger with the spitting defiance of the three words, "THIS IS SPARTA!", if you have seen the meme or the film "*300*" directed by Zack Snyder.[26]

---

24 Herodotus claimed that the Persian army had over two million men.

25 He also had 900 helots to help, and over 6,000 soldiers from other Greek city states.

26 "*300*" (2016) directed by Zak Snyder. Just to be clear, the phrase "This is Sparta!" has no root in Antiquity. It might also be noted that scholars of the Classical Period could take issue with some wider historical distortions in the film.

After the major military victories against the Persians had been settled, Athens continued to flex its military and trading muscles in the region – this involved pushing the Persians further back and consolidating its own position as the leading city state. The city states involved agreed to a formal alliance, called the Delian League, in 478 BCE.

The dominance of Athens in the Delian alliance was such that it soon became more appropriate to call it the Athenian empire. This is a reality that was confirmed when Pericles presumptuously moved the Delian League's Treasury from the island of Delos[27] to Athens in 454 BCE. Indeed, the astonishing building programme commissioned by Pericles had been heavily financed by these funds. This transfer of wealth could be described as one of history's most epic embezzlements.[28]

The Spartans were not members of the Delian League. In fact, without a common enemy, the local rivalry between the two major city states resumed its importance. As Athens grew in power, so too did the tension between Sparta and Athens. This led to the creation of two major centres within the Aegean, between which there was some heated competition.

The smaller city states were then irresistibly pulled into an orbit, one that locked them into the direction of either the Spartan or the Athenian causes.[29] And such is the logic of war, these two heavy alliances then got sucked into a conflict with each other – thereby dragging everybody into a fight. Instead of fighting against the Persians, the Greek city states were now fighting amongst themselves.

27 This was the island on which the city states had held their congresses and from which the league drew its name.
28 This was an accusation made by Angelos Vlachos, "Thucydides' Bias", p62-63.
29 This overall dynamic is known as the *"Thucydides Trap"*, although there are a few details which manage to escape this gravitational pull.

By the time Plato was born in 427 BCE, a vicious war between Sparta and Athens had already been going for four years. This was the Peloponnesian War (431 BCE-404 BCE), and it was the titanic battle of a land power (the Spartan alliance) against a sea power (the Athenian alliance). This roaming war would leave a deep mark in history and would have a profound effect on the young Plato.

This is Sparta

Seeking to deliver a decisive blow, the Athenians launched a massive offensive – the Sicilian Expedition – in 415 BCE. As a 12-year-old boy, Plato would surely have been at the Athenian harbour, clamouring for a view amongst all the wives and mothers, fathers and brothers, to wave goodbye to their loved ones as the navy rowed out into the Aegean Sea towards Sicily. The historian Thucydides[30] informs us that 134 triremes[31] (huge rowing warships) pulled away from The Piraeus following the endorsement of the Assembly vote in 415 BCE, and with the mass enthusiasm of the crowds. It was self-evident to the Athenians that they were the most advanced state of the known world.

However, the Athenians lost. Catastrophically, in fact.

A lone soldier returned to Athens for a haircut[32] in 413 BCE; seemingly Unaware of the fact that his fellow Athenians had not been informed about their defeat at the hands of the Spartans, he started to retell some of the details to disbelieving ears. His news sent total panic and shock throughout the city. As Thucydides emphatically and solemnly concludes in his History: "They were beaten at all points and altogether; all that they suffered was great; they were destroyed, as the saying is, with a total destruction, their fleet, their army—everything was destroyed, and few

---

30   Thucydides, "*History of the Peloponnesian War*", Book 6.
31   Another 73 were later sent as extra support.
32   From Plutarch's "*Life of Nicias*" p311. (http://penelope.uchicago.edu
     /Thayer/E/Roman/Texts/Plutarch/Lives/Nicias*.html)

out of many returned home."[33] Soon after, in 404 BCE, victorious Spartans imposed '*The Thirty Tyrants*' on the Athenians.This was a short lived, but brutally oppressive regime that executed around 1,500 citizens without trial[34], chased out the key democrats and plundered the city of its wealth.

It is true that ancient Athenians had many scars of warfare, but the eventual surrender to the Spartans in 404 BCE cut to the bone. It destroyed the symbolic order of the Athenian mind. It dragged everything into question. War makes a grave imprint on a young psyche, and there is no reason to think that Plato was any different. In fact, we know from his surviving personal letters that this episode deeply shook him up, even though he was not on the battlefield himself.

The historian Thucydides, whose account of the Peloponnesian War was intentionally trying to tune into the moral signals of the events, famously commented that "war is a violent teacher" (ὁ πόλεμος βίαιος διδάσκαλος).[35] He shared Plato's great mistrust of democracy.

33 Thucydides, "*History of the Peloponnesian War*", Book 7 (87,6)
34 Nails, Debra. "*The People of Plato: A Prosopography of Plato and Other Socratics*". Hackett Publishing, 2002.
35 Thucydides, 3.82.2.

This is Socrates

The other utterly disorientating incident in Plato's young life happened in his late twenties.

Plato was a student of Socrates, the mercurial sage. He was the man who was the wisest in Athens because, paradoxically, he was the one who knew that he knew nothing (according to the Delphic Oracle[36]). Socrates was hugely popular and hugely unpopular; he was both an idealist and a heretic. He was irrepressibly controversial, or as Plato himself put it, he was 'the gadfly of the State' – the annoying bug that could sting the huge, bulky state where it hurt. Socrates was so committed to the truth that he was not afraid to ask the most uncomfortable questions. This commitment to truth meant that he would engage with anyone brave enough to go to him with a question, or unlucky enough to get roped into a conversation with him around the Agora's market stalls, bars and street corners. A cross-examination by Socrates would pose serious challenges to both the brain and to the heart.

We might expect Socrates' rugged commitment to the truth to be a welcome contribution to the world's first known democracy.[37] The Athenians were immensely proud of their culture, and we could justifiably expect them to be enthusiastic about the rigorous, open debates that he prompted.

And yet, the tragic end to Socrates' life is well known. The Athenian democracy ended up silencing the voice of its most articulate thinker. This not-so-happy ending appears to be at odds with one of democracy's proudest achievements: the possibility to not only engage with dissent, but to actively harness and encourage it.

So, what went wrong? The short answer is that Socrates overstepped the line. He was an outspoken critic of the system, and he got under the skin of too many people, too often.

---

36   Plato's 'Apology', 21a-d.
37   There is no space here to discuss what classifies a state as being properly democratic.

In 399 BCE, the Assembly voted (by a narrow margin) to execute Socrates on trumped up charges of 'corrupting the youth' and 'introducing new gods to the city'.[38]

It is not clear exactly where the 28-year-old Plato was when Socrates was on trial or where he was when Socrates was brought the cup of hemlock. We do not know if he saw his teacher's slow, ascending paralysis, from the feet upwards, which eventually choked out his life. Having been inspired by Socrates to respect virtues and the truth, it would have been extremely hard for the young Plato to observe the trial. He would have heard Socrates make a reasoned defence against some dim arguments made by weak interlocutors. Harder still would have been to sit and digest the final verdict.

Plato would have also been fully aware that this was not just the battle of a man against the machinery of the state. He would have understood that there were deeply personal forces at play behind the scenes – networking and trading concessions, all for the right kind of votes.

The execution of his guru and closest friend would have been a chilling

38   The longer answer testifies to the fact that Socrates was too
     friendly with the oligarchs and anti-democratic forces.

event for the young man. To experience, so directly and intimately, the dumb potency of the state would have imprinted itself deeply into his psyche. Coupled with the shock of the recent loss to Sparta, the young Plato surely struggled to develop a coherent map of what was going on around him.

Indeed, approaching his 80s, Plato wrote his now famous *"Seventh Letter"*, in which he retroactively comments on his youth, stating: "Eager as I had once been to go into politics, as I looked at these things and saw everything taking any course at all, with no direction or management, I ended up feeling dizzy". Plato goes on to explain in this letter that the existential nausea he felt was the reason behind his decision to pick up his pen and write *the 'Republic'*.

Why Plato?

At first glance, Plato might seem like an odd choice of philosopher for a society that is faced with the particularly modern problem of reducing the concentrations of CO_2 in the atmosphere. Why pick this thinker to tackle the state we are in with climate change? Indeed, in this bust, Plato appears to us as a very remote figure. He looks like someone who is difficult to talk with, an austere and esoteric man from the past. His blank eyeballs certainly don't help us to get beyond the surface of his image. What could this distant thinker say to anyone who is trying to make sense of our modern society's collision course with reality? What might a man, famous for his totally abstract Theory of Forms, say about a problem as material and as messy as climate change?

Image 9. - Plato

The truth is that there is another Plato that lies behind his stony-faced appearance.

This other Plato experienced trauma first-hand. He witnessed the collapse of a seemingly invincible empire. Despite the Athenians' pride in their democratic government, Plato was clearly aware of how dangerously it could all fail. This was not least because he saw how the popular vote would so naturally follow the citizens' desires and instincts, and how it could turn toxic so easily. He also received some sharp lessons early on in his life about the menaces of pride, wealth and corruption.

Plato had to process the sharp psychological dissonances that living in Athens would have often thrown up: the transcendent beauty of the statues around the city, contrasted with crass or inane commentary on the world that would have taken place as different clusters of people stood around them; the high culture of the Athenian civic buildings, contrasted with the sheer idiocy of the political decision-making that took place under their lofty roofs.

Plato should not be approached as an indifferent, aloof mind. He was wrestling wholeheartedly with the same issues that climate change presents us with today. Behind Plato's look in this bust, there was someone who could see way beyond the illusions of social reality. This Plato could open the lid on the human psyche and was someone who had the ability to think well beyond the surface of things. He is a thinker who can help us see how democracies can seriously fail. He can help us to understand, with real clarity of mind, why democracies make catastrophic errors of judgement. Plato is someone who was brave enough to think far beyond the conventional wisdom of his day. He was a thinker who was totally committed to looking beyond all of the clutter and opinions to get a proper grip on the reality of a situation.

To conclude, Plato had been trained by Socrates in critical thinking and it was with formidable power that he pioneered work in Politics, Psychology, Metaphysics... (the list goes on). He was a remarkable polymath. Indeed,

Plato has something significant to say about almost every single subject found in a modern school curriculum.

Yet, perhaps the most impressive feature of Plato's '*Republic*' is the way in which he synthesises all these dimensions of his thought into one fluid, playful, and open dialogue. This is sharply relevant for dealing with the climate crisis – our modern world is so complex, diverse and interconnected. The crisis can only be solved if we are able to look at it in a holistic way. We need a thinker to link up all of the fragmentary responses that we have made to the problem and who can identify the central points around which they all revolve. The concentrations of greenhouse gases in the atmosphere have continued to climb year after year to deadly levels, despite all of the initiatives, projects and ambitions over the past decades. Somewhere, somehow, we have been missing the key points. If Plato had one outstanding skill, one that stands apart from all of his remarkable gifts, it was his ability to see beyond the details to the essence of things.

Why Dialogue?

By writing in dialogue form, Plato could indulge in his characters' peculiarities and their ideas, and at the same time he could guide the reader towards the core truths that he wanted to communicate. It was a form of writing that enabled him to be very playful. There is no question that the style of Plato's work was indebted to the Athenian playwrights. These men were the stellar heroes of ancient Athens, their scripts were hugely influential; the rumours are probably true that Plato himself aspired to be among their ranks.

The dialogue form that Plato adopts makes his writing both very engaging and highly elastic. He gets everyone involved. He has Socrates talk with a high priest, Euthyphro, about God ('*Euthyphro*'), a lowly slave talk about geometry ('*Meno*'), and he puts Socrates into an incredibly elevated version of celebrity "Love Island" to discuss the nature of ἔρως (*eros*, erotic love) ('*Symposium*') with Alcibiades, Aristophanes and many others.

Image 10. - Greek Tragedy Masks

These conversations can often assume a lot of cultural knowledge. The sheer range of characters, themes, cultural references and philosophical issues in Plato's dialogues can make it tricky to understand exactly what is going on in the text. Reading a Platonic dialogue can sometimes feel like trying to read the headlines in a foreign language newspaper – the words might make sense if you look them up, but you know you are missing out on a lot of jokes, details and allusions.

However, despite these challenges, there are rich rewards for the reader who is prepared to stick around with the conversations. Indeed, there is one important area of significance in Plato's choice to write in the style of a dialogue for this book which is concerned with climate change.

This is because the dialogue form was used in the most famous of all of the Ancient Greek art forms – the Tragedy.

Chapter Two

Tragedy or no Tragedy

Greek Tradegy

Tragedies were performed many times during the course of an average day during the 'Great Dionysia' festival, held in late March. Tragedies were not just plays, but ritual moments of collective reflection that were presided over by a priest. Written in the closest proximity to death and misery, these tragic plays were utterly unflinching in their examination of human suffering. The audience would have to grapple with the universal problems of injustice and trauma, they would be confronted with deeply flawed decision-making and tragic unintended consequences. Yet the ambition of the playwrights was, perhaps surprisingly, to send the audience home with a positive experience of 'catharsis' (as Aristotle later named it) – something close to the therapeutic feeling that we might get from crying our eyes out at the cinema.[39]

---

39 It is informative to note that the audience at the tragedy was the same one that attended the assembly in which they made important democratic decisions. This was a powerful endorsement of the virtues that were supposed to underpin their decision-making, and also a powerful endorsement of the arts' ability to do that.

The Athenians thoughtfully put on a shorter tragicomedy after the main play to help people walk home with a bit of a spring in their step. These concluding 'Satyr plays' deployed bawdy humour, phallic props and involved fake drunkenness. Perhaps the less cultured modern TV parallel of this situation would involve the following: First, a person would be required to sit through the immersive despair of an omnibus edition of *EastEnders* on the BBC. A full box of tissues and a full bottle of Merlot would be required in this case. Then, with popcorn in hand, the channel would be abruptly switched to the antics of '*Carry-On Matron*' (1972), a comic farce. Their randy humour and *slapstick capers* would surely put a smile back on your face and put the bounce back in your step, right before you head off to bed.

It is certainly tempting to frame everything as a modern tragedy when we reflect on our modern situation with climate change. Browsing through any 20 minutes of climate-related articles from a Facebook feed normally brings the universal problems of the human condition to the surface – although these feelings are not coupled with any of the deep poignancy that a tragedy provides.

Indeed, taking a cursory overview from the 20th century, we could rightly applaud ourselves for many of the advances that have been achieved in the arenas of society, culture and technology. There are many great achievements to celebrate, not least the sustained peace of the democratic EU and all of the global milestones reached in the fights against racism, homophobia and sexism. We have not only preserved and reconstructed so many assets of ancient Athenian society, from statues to statutes, we have also extended and deepened them. Our modern democracies have shown their resilience, determination and the ability to withstand the attacks of sinister empires that had no respect for our mature values or the rule of law.

What didn't kill us made us stronger.[40]

---

40 Alluding to a quotation from Nietzsche is not inappropriate for a section on learning from Greek history and culture (Nietzsche was a junkie of the Classics).

However, tragedies often deploy misguided optimism. The audience should therefore also be aware of the tragic forces of history. Given the strength and dominance of western democratic culture, like that of the Athenians, it would be easy to become complacent about what is going on beneath the surface of our successes. Empires rise and fall; history repeats itself. The real tragic action normally takes place just below the surface of things – just out of sight. This odd feature, which is how most empires operate, means that those who look back with hindsight on a civilisation are able to mock their lack of understanding so easily after everything suddenly falls apart. It would be such folly to think that our society is any different.[41]

The tragedies written by Sophocles, Aeschylus and Euripides were preoccupied with the notion of fate. Even though the characters could see their destiny coming, even if they understood the main plotlines of their own dramas, they simply could not escape. This is most famously evidenced in Sophocles' play '*Oedipus Rex*' (429 BCE) when the oracle informs the young Oedipus that he will kill his father and marry his mother.

For the rest of the drama, the more Oedipus runs away from the prediction, the more he runs into it. In the end, after murdering his father and having sex with his mother, he gouges his eyes out. These plays amplified the rise and fall of their heroes for dramatic effect, but they also did this out of a respect for the patterns of human affairs in the real world.

---

41   Barbara Tuchman's celebrated book, "*The March of Folly: From Troy to Vietnam*" (1984) is essential reading for anyone who is curious about such patterns in our history.

Climate Change is an existential threat to human civilisation. This formidable danger has been intensifying in full view – all within our technologically advanced, literate and cultured society. It seems utterly implausible that we could be failing to react to such a hostile threat. We know the direction that all of the graphs are going in and we know the consequences of inaction. And yet, since we resolved to combat the problem in 1992 (with the signing of the UNFCCC treaty), there has not even been one single year in which our greenhouse gas emissions have gone down; in fact, we are still accelerating them (by 2.0% in 2018).[42] Like the characters in the tragic dramas, despite saying all the right words, we are heading, seemingly inexorably, towards a very bad ending.

The contradiction between our public declarations and the alarming course of the crisis can be seen at many different levels. The state we are in throws up all kinds of mad contradictions. The natural world has provided a formidable set of intransigent responses to the limited gestures we have made towards solving the problem. Indeed, by juxtaposing some human activity with some phenomena from the biosphere, some astonishing dialogues can be observed that seem to sum up our tragic situation.

Some of these tragedies need us to take a seat in the back row of our amphitheatre in order for them to be seen properly; looking down on the Earth with a very wide angle enables us to view some of the major plot lines of our predicament.

Two Modern Tragedies: The Northern Forests and the Amazonian Forest

In the Spring of 2019, under the gentle reminders of longer, stronger sunbeams, the coniferous trees of the Northern hemisphere forests unsealed their dark buds. In a ritual that has been practised for hundreds

---

42   Olivier J.G.J. and Peters J.A.H.W. (2020), *"Trends in global CO₂ and total greenhouse gas emissions: 2019 report"*. Report no. 4068. PBL Netherlands Environmental Assessment.

of millions of years,[43] they slowly uncurled their baby bright green leaves open to face the sun. With biotechnology that has been perfected through eons of evolutionary practice, this astonishingly beautiful natural tapestry began to suck out billions of tonnes of CO_2 from the atmosphere with remarkable efficiency[44]. A major organ of the planet had burst back into life again on the upper side of our tilted planet.

Meanwhile, in the Southern Hemisphere, a democracy surrounded by around 3 million square kilometres of rainforest had voted into power a 'strong man' President – (Bellicose) Bolsanaro. His popularist policies included radical environmental deregulation in favour of agro-business, supported by crude claims that climate change was a plot by "cultural Marxists".

By the spring of 2019, he had mobilised his angry army of petrol-powered chainsaws deeper into the Amazonian jungle. As they sank their steel teeth into the tender timber, they were backed up by flanks of bulldozers, excavators and skidders. During the invasion, once the major tree trunks had creaked and crashed to the floor, all that the other plants and animals could do was to offer their silent resistance. The orchids and mosses, the humming-birds and the butterflies, and the thousands of impossibly complex and diverse communities of life were all conquered, square inch by square inch – at a pace of 2.2 football fields per minute.[45]

From our human perspective, it was as if one of the planet Earth's vital organs was suffering a terrifying advance of emphysema. When the machines eventually fell silent and the brown earth was left open to the baking sun, the trees were not the only thing that was left utterly stumped.

43   Fossil remains of the Wattieza tree (found near New York) date back
     to the Middle Devonian Period, c. 385 million years ago.
44   Oxygenic photosynthesis began 2.4bn years ago, resulting in the build-up of free oxygen in the
     atmosphere. Blankenship R.E., "*Early Evolution of Photosynthesis*", Plant Physiology, October 2010.
45   Deforestation was recorded at 2.6 football fields per minute in 2020.
     http://terrabrasilis.dpi.inpe.br/app/dashboard/alerts/legal/amazon/aggregated/

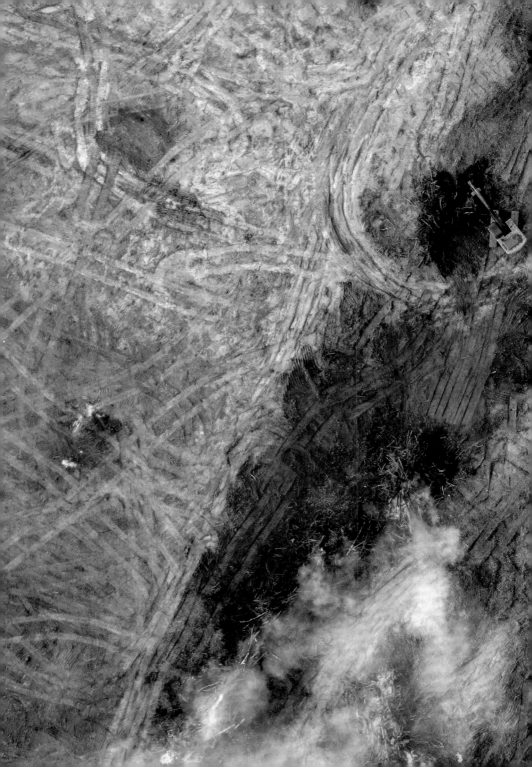

Image 11. - The Amazon Rain Forest

Perhaps the howler monkeys of the Amazon know more than we think? In the remaining lush of the rainforest, their polyphonic treetop banter makes an appropriately mocking chorus for those supposedly more evolved primates who are busily cutting down their own future. Maybe these monkeys are taunting humans who just cannot see or avoid their fate, like an Ancient Greek Chorus in a tragic script? In all that tropical cacophony of sound, the most absurd noise of all is that which continues to be made by the machines of the Anthropocene.

Indeed, there was always a natural contrast between the vast, silent expanses of Boreal forests in the Northern Hemisphere and the exotic, busy equatorial forests of the South. Yet with a glance back at the Northern Hemisphere, the same idiocy can be seen in Alaska, a state dominated by the Boreal Forest.

Republican Mike Dunleavy, Alaska's governor, abolished the state's climate change strategy commission with Administrative Order No. 309. His spokesperson explained the logic of leaving Alaska without an official plan for addressing climate change in a brief email: "For various reasons these AO's are no longer needed: they are no longer relevant, have fulfilled their intended purpose, are not aligned with the Governor's policy direction, and/or appear to have been made primarily for political or public relations purposes." The US democracy had voted Dunleavy into power in December 2018.

The absurdity of electing an outspoken climate change denier into office in a state in which the "Arctic sea ice is retreating, shores are eroding, glaciers are shrinking, permafrost is thawing, and insect outbreaks and wildfires are becoming more common"[46] is arresting. Indeed, NOAA reported that June 2019 was officially the hottest June on record for the globe. For Anchorage, it was 0.95°C above the average[47] and that Alaskan city's citizens experienced a string of astonishingly hot days at the start of July 2019 that were 12.4°C above the average.[48] Alaska, among the fastest warming regions on the planet[49] was 2.7°C hotter than average. In addition, the Boreal forests of Alaska are drier, hotter and more prone to lightning storms, which means that the number and intensity of forest fires are set to increase. This is a trend shared right across the planet's largest greenbelt.[50],[51]

In July 2019, the WMO reported that: "Since the start of June, the Copernicus Atmosphere Monitoring Service (CAMS) has tracked over 100 intense and long-lived wildfires in the Arctic Circle. In June alone, these fires emitted 50 megatonnes of carbon dioxide into the atmosphere, which is equivalent to Sweden's total annual emissions. This is more than was released by Arctic fires in the same month between 2010 and 2018 combined."[52] The CAMS added that: "A recent study found Earth's boreal forests are now burning at a rate unseen in at least 10,000 years". By August 2019, Siberia set an area the size of Belgium[53] ablaze.

46   "What Climate Change Means for Alaska", EPA publication 430-F-16-004, August 2016.
47   Global Climate report 2019 https://www.ncdc.noaa.gov/sotc/global/201906.
48   "Alaska's exceptional heat wave delivers state's hottest days on record", Washington Post, July 9th 2019.
49   US Global Change Research Programme, "Fourth National Climate Assessment". Chapter 26, Alaska 2018.
50   R. Kelly et al, "Recent burning of Boreal forests exceeds fire regime limits of the past 10,000 years". PNAS (August, 2013)
51   The average June temperature, in the parts of Siberia where wildfires are raging, was almost ten degrees higher than the 1981-2010 long-term average. WMO, "Unprecedented Wild Fires in the Arctic", July 12th, 2019.
52   Ibid.
53   "Siberia wildfires: Russians battle to contain the blazes", Steve Rosenberg, B BCEE.com (August 4th, 2019)

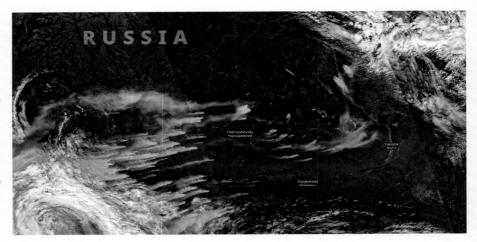

The rapidly rising trajectory of our emissions appears like a huge spoiler in the tragic plot of human civilisation – in both senses of the word.

There were so many new records and extreme weather events happening at the time of writing that just two symbolic biomes had to be selected as examples. If the reader happens to be sitting and reading these words in 2030 or beyond, then these major weather events, which have happened in our recent past, would only appear to them as smaller preliminary dots to some truly catastrophic and shocking disasters. As in classical music, the Prelude introduces the main themes that are then developed and explored. The longer the music progresses, the more assertive and emphatic those themes become.

The Fate of the Forests

The fate of the forests is tied up with the rest of humanity. If either of them collapse, human civilisation as we know it today will crash with them. Both forests perform such huge functions, as central cogs in the global biosphere. If these forests flip from acting as major carbon sinks of the planet into acting as major carbon sources, this will be a catastrophic tipping point. From such a point, all human efforts to keep their fate in their own hands will become puny, futile gestures.

The Boreal Forests are the largest single biome on Earth and make up around 30% of all forested areas. The Arctic and Boreal regions are heating up about twice as fast as other parts of the world – most recently at 0.5°C per decade, with "a potential future warming of 6 to 11°C, over vast northern regions by 2100, according to the IPCC's most pessimistic scenario, RCP 8.5."[54] "Under a globally averaged projection of a warming of 4°C by the end of this century, boreal regions could experience temperature increases from 4° to 11°C."[55]

The ABoVE research project by NASA[56] (The Arctic-Boreal Vulnerability Experiment) was launched in 2015 and works to understand this vast natural system. An unbridled melting of the permafrost is a tipping point. ABoVE wrote, without exaggeration, that this is the "the mother of all concerns."[57]

There are an estimated 1,400 gigatonnes of carbon held in the frozen earth of the permafrost[58] which, if it was released, would blow an ecological fuse and wreak unthinkable consequences on humanity. Exactly where, when and how fast this gas would be released is something that requires huge computing power and research to project. Pushing the Boreal forests towards a collapse is the last thing that we should be doing.

The collapse of the Amazon rainforest would be triggered at around 3°C[59]. We could also achieve this collapse through rampant deforestation too. Either way, such a disaster would profoundly disturb the rain, wind and ocean trends for the globe and have unimaginable consequences.

54 https://iiasa.ac.at/web/home/about/news/150821_boreal_forests.html
55 Gauthier S, Bernier P, Kuuluvainen T, Shvidenko AZ, Shchepaschenko DG (2015).
    "Boreal forest health and global change". Science. 21 August 2015.
56 https://above.nasa.gov/ gives the details to this "major field campaign"
    with 21 field projects over a decade underway.
57 Robbins, Jim "The Rapid and Startling Decline of World's Vast Boreal Forests",
    Yale Environment 360, October 2015.
58 https://nsidc.org/cryosphere/frozenground/methane.html.
59 Lynas, M., "Six Degrees: Our Future on a Hotter Planet" Fourth Estate (2007).

The Ancient Athenian democracy also voted in favour of some serious deforestation. They were under the influence of the "hawkish" and crowd-pleasing rhetoric of the famous statesman Alcibiades (their military General from 417BC.).

They voted to chop down thousands of Silver Fir trees, to beef up the size of their Navy. They sailed towards the Spartans in those dead trees. Their judgement to attack was clouded by the familiar burden of the human drive for wealth and status.

They did not see it coming, but the Athenian Golden Age was about to come to an abrupt and ruinous end. The deforestation of the Thracian forests by the Athenians is full of significance for this chapter.

i

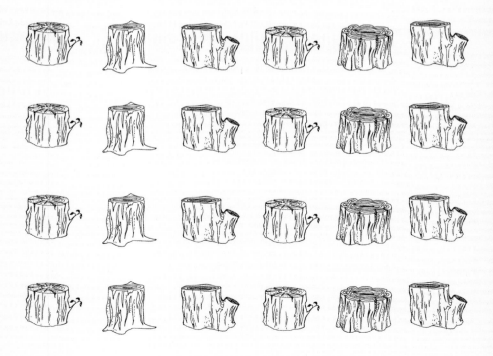

Or no Greek Tragedy?

There is a twist, though.

Plato forcibly rejects the downhill storyline of the tragedies. He copies their wit and dramatic style, but he flips the narrative trajectory upwards. Plato does not buy into dark fatalism; instead, he asserts the redemptive force of reason and the power of a virtuous life. In doing so, Plato positions himself alongside a very different kind of playwright: Aristophanes[60].

Aristophanes

Aristophanes was Athens' most famous comic writer. In fact, he holds the title for 'The Father of Old Comedy'. Embedded in Aristophanes' jokes, puns and parodies, are his fantastic dreams for a better world. He shared these dreams with Plato. They both frequently use metaphors for death and rebirth, they both often use language of imprisonment and release. They both set a scene in an underground world[61] as a prelude to a liberation into a fuller reality.

Image 14. – Aristophanes

Most significantly, for this chapter's purposes, is that they were both eagle eyed critics of democracy. They thought that it was a system of government that gave too much licence to the people's desires and too much freedom to their *thumos*.

---

60 In Plato's book on love, "*Symposium*", Aristophanes is one of the celebrity guests that is seated nearby, having a meal and debate with Socrates. He gives the wisest speech to Aristophanes – apart from the one given to Socrates of course!

61 Aristophanes does this famously in "*The Frogs*", his prize-winning comedy about how the playwright Euripides is brought out of Hades (he had died the year before the play was written).

Aristophanes often uses the metaphor of physical sickness to illustrate his view that Athenian society was morally dead and in need of new life. For example, in his award-winning play, *"The Knights"* (424 BCE) two men try and win the confidence of a disorientated old man named *'Demos'* (meaning 'the people', and in this case the Athenian citizens). The first is called Paphlagonian, an unscrupulous character who tries to use his fawning charms (and later his loud shouting) to gain the upper-hand and to achieve control over the vulnerable old guy. The second, Agoracritus is a sausage seller. His self-sacrificing attitude sets him up as a bit of a hero.

By the end of the comedy, Agoracritus emerges as the winner – and thereby getting 'Demos' back to his old self, much to the audience's relief.

Civic virtues win. Banal, self-serving, grandiose posturing[62] loses.

Image 15. - Cleon

Cleon - Cleon was the real man behind the manipulative villain of *'The Knights'*. His stage name, 'Paphlagonian', comes from the town his was born in. It is also probably a pun on the word "paphlazo" which means 'I bubble, splutter, fret' – rather like the name fated to President Trump, which also has a double meaning.

In fact, the similarities between the two leaders might not stop there. Cleon was a bombastic popularist who was famous for his warmongering attitude to the Spartans, his corrupt use of the political and justice systems for personal gain and his anti-intellectual bullying style as an orator. He was also known for his 'sycophancy'; an early example of using fake-news as a defence -- where enemies were diminished and taken out of the game with weaponised lies.

Aristophanes has the last laugh.

In the later scenes of *"The Knights"*, 'Cleon' is outflanked by a sausage seller in an Ancient Greek 'rap battle'. The low-level vocabulary used in the exchange is indicative of the regard Aristophanes' had for the intelligence and virtues of a democracy.

---

62 Unfortunately, banal, self-serving, grandiose posturing often actually works well in a democracy. The demos in America voted for Donald Trump in 2016, and 92,153 Conservative Party members voted for Boris Johnson in 2019.

Plato concurs.

Firstly, he is also not shy about the redemptive themes in his work. Indeed, his most famous metaphor, 'The Allegory of the Cave', (*'Republic'* 514a-517a) describes how a prisoner escapes his chains and illusions and climbs with virtuous determination to the real world; once there, he gets to see the full truth of things. Moreover, the *'Republic'* notably finishes with a resounding affirmation of justice and redemption. His concluding *'Myth of Er'* (614-621) concerns an Armenian war casualty ('Er') who rose off his funeral pyre (after having been dead for 10 days, but not decomposing) to affirm that those who love wisdom ("φιλόσοφοι", 'philosophers') will get their fair reward (615b-c). Er knows this to be the case because he saw it when he was in the afterlife.

Secondly, Plato also thought that democracies were set up to fail because votes in the Assembly were led by irrational desires. Plato understood how quickly values and the truth can be side-lined by those in power to keep control of the *'demos'*. From an aristocratic background, Plato thought that reason could overcome the power of our appetites and emotions, but that it would need a lot of education to achieve this.

Plato's view of voting patterns has found some modern empirical support from some recent research published in the journal, *'Political Psychology'*.[63] This study concluded that those voters in the USA with a poor political knowledge are prone to over-estimate their political understanding. This over-confidence makes them prone to a kind of tribal thinking that becomes even more accentuated when the main themes of that 'tribe' are emphasised. The lead author adds that: "This below-average group is also likely to rely on partisan source cues to evaluate the political knowledge of peers."[64]

---

63   Anson, I., *"Partisanship, Political Knowledge, and the Dunning-Kruger Effect"* (April 2nd, 2018). https://doi.org/10.1111/pops.12490
64   A fuller exploration of this issue can be found in *"No Common Sense – Popper"*, which outlined the range of dangers that such a lack of reasoned judgement poses to the healthy functioning of a democracy.

A happy ever after?

Climate change needs a positive story line at the end. This is not because we live in Disney Land and our script writers always need to put in a happy ending for us: this is the real world.[65] The positive narrative that needs to be asserted in this book is simply based on the fact that it is still possible to avert the collapse of our societies. We are still in control of our own destiny. As far as the mainstream scientific models show, we have not yet pushed nature over a tipping point.

Indeed, there are some very simple ways out of the crisis. The trees of the Boreal and Amazon forests indicate two lines in our tragic plot where the story could be reversed: the trees that we are currently slashing down are a part of the solution to climate change. Trees offer us a resource to divert or postpone the tragedy we have created.

Trees

Planting trees is one of the obvious and beautiful ways to mobilise ourselves in the climate crisis. The power of forests to capture our emissions is extraordinary, and the chemical reaction which enables them to do this also provides so much of the oxygen we breathe. Trees also act as keystones for small eco-systems and provide habitats, food and shelter. Any investment in trees is, therefore, also a significant addition to the planet's biodiversity. This aspect of the natural world is often overlooked, but without the breadth of biodiversity, the towering stack of agricultural necessities that we have can easily get tipped over (with or without the help of climate change). Just as trees need wide roots to remain stable, so it is with the biosphere.

Of all the flanks of our assault on the climate emergency, greening our environment poses the fewest political problems and offers very attractive rewards. It is simply absurd that we are not planting trees and plants everywhere and immediately. If we were in any way serious about the

---

65   Is it possible in a book of Philosophy to write this short sentence without any qualifications?

threat of climate change, this would be the first sign of dramatic action. Our inner cities, suburbia and our countryside would have their green volume turned up to the maximum. It would be the most rewarding type of warfare we've ever engaged in.

> **Mangrove trees** can sequester huge amounts of CO_2. and store it in their highly suberised roots, which are very waxy and do not decompose (suberin is the main substance in cork).
> The award-winning bio-tech company SALK is mobilising a genetic 'copy/paste' system (the CRISPR technique) to add this feature to a whole range of plants and trees, thereby supercharging their carbon capture capacity.

Image 16. - Mangrove

Ethiopia took things into its own hands recently and planted a reported 250 million trees in 12 hours on July 29th 2019.[66] It was part of a "green legacy" project to plant 4bn trees – which works out at 40 seedlings per person. The scale of the operation meant that some public services were shut down so that civil servants could also participate. The simple question arises: why are we not doing this in every nation? [67]

Tree planting is only one action in the battle of climate justice. In itself, it could only have a fairly minor contribution to the overall concentrations of greenhouse gases in the atmosphere. However, a major commitment to tree planting and rewilding would not only indicate our determination to move ahead, it would also create an essential sense of momentum for the deeper, systemic changes required (in infrastructure and energy use).

66 https://pmo.gov.et/greenlegacy/
67 Like any environmental policy, whilst it is true that trees and plants could and should be planted everywhere, each project has to be sensitive and informed about the local habitat. Trees, like anything, can disrupt longstanding equilibriums in an eco-system, or disturb the balance of our land-use. For example, trees are very thirsty for fresh water. Also, a recent study concluded that the planting of trees in the past 10 years had led to carbon emissions rather than carbon storage, due to the fact that the trees were planted in areas that were forested before, and that in general, planted trees are cut.

This change of gear might have already happened. The whole narrative of our society shifted decisively in the right direction in 2019. The momentum, created by the disarming directness of Greta Thunberg, has pushed the media into a different category of language about the problems ahead – from climate change to climate crisis and from global warming to global heating.[68] In September 2019, over 60 leading publications dedicated their front pages to the crisis.[69] Behind it all, there were also some significant legal victories. In the Netherlands, for example, 900 citizens (in the Urgenda Foundation) successfully sued their governments for their inadequate actions.

The fact is that most people are genuinely concerned about ecological issues, and that that majority is growing. As a small example, in a 2018 IPPR survey[70] over 70% of British people wanted the UK to at least maintain or increase its renewable energy targets when presented with the possibility of post-Brexit deregulation. This was a statistic that was underlined across Europe by the significant rise of Green Party votes in various nations during the European Parliament elections of 2019. There are millions of people who participate in environmental projects; they are conscious of their carbon footprint, and they take a lot of care in the hundreds of gestures to try to live sustainably. It is easy to feel isolated with ecological angst, but the thousands that have joined 'Extinction Rebellion' around the globe are a vivid demonstration of the depth and breadth of the anxiety and anger that exists about the current ecocide.

This positive narrative is fully aware of how limited and short-sighted democratic decision-making can be, but it is also conscious of all of the tragic forces at work that pull us deeper into the Anthropocene. There remain so many people and systems that just do not recognise what is going on, and how close we are to the edge. However, some things have started to

---

68 https://www.theguardian.com/environment/2019/may/17
/why-the-guardian-is-changing-the-language-it-uses-about-the-environment
69 https://www.cjr.org/covering_climate_now/
70 www.ippr.org/files/2018-02/1519061948_leaving-the-eu-not-the-european-model-part1-feb18.pdf.

change. We have not yet passed the point of no return, and we will always be capable of reason.[71] We are still capable of getting a hold of our desires and impulses and reining them in with common sense.

To conclude this opening section of the introduction, this book is not written as an echo of the Greek tragedy. It will follow Plato in the opposite direction. It shares with Plato an optimism about reason's power to provide us with a proper view of the state that we are in. It shares with him an emphatic affirmation that we are capable of responding to our deep sense of justice and beauty.

These assertions about our ability to transcend our situation are not written lightly.

Plato did not write his utopian *'Republic'* blind to the dangers and folly of the human condition. He experienced terrible tragedies in his own life. He wrote it in full awareness of our weaknesses and failings.

Plato lived through the best of times and the worst of times, and he arrived at some powerfully constructive conclusions.

It is now time to read the first line of his book.

---

71 In Book 10 of the *'Republic'*, Socrates argues that whilst it is possible to blunt a knife, it is not possible to blunt human reason – because reason is the very essence of what it is to be human. This argument is not without its problems, and so it will be left down here in the footnotes.

t
mi

e
dle

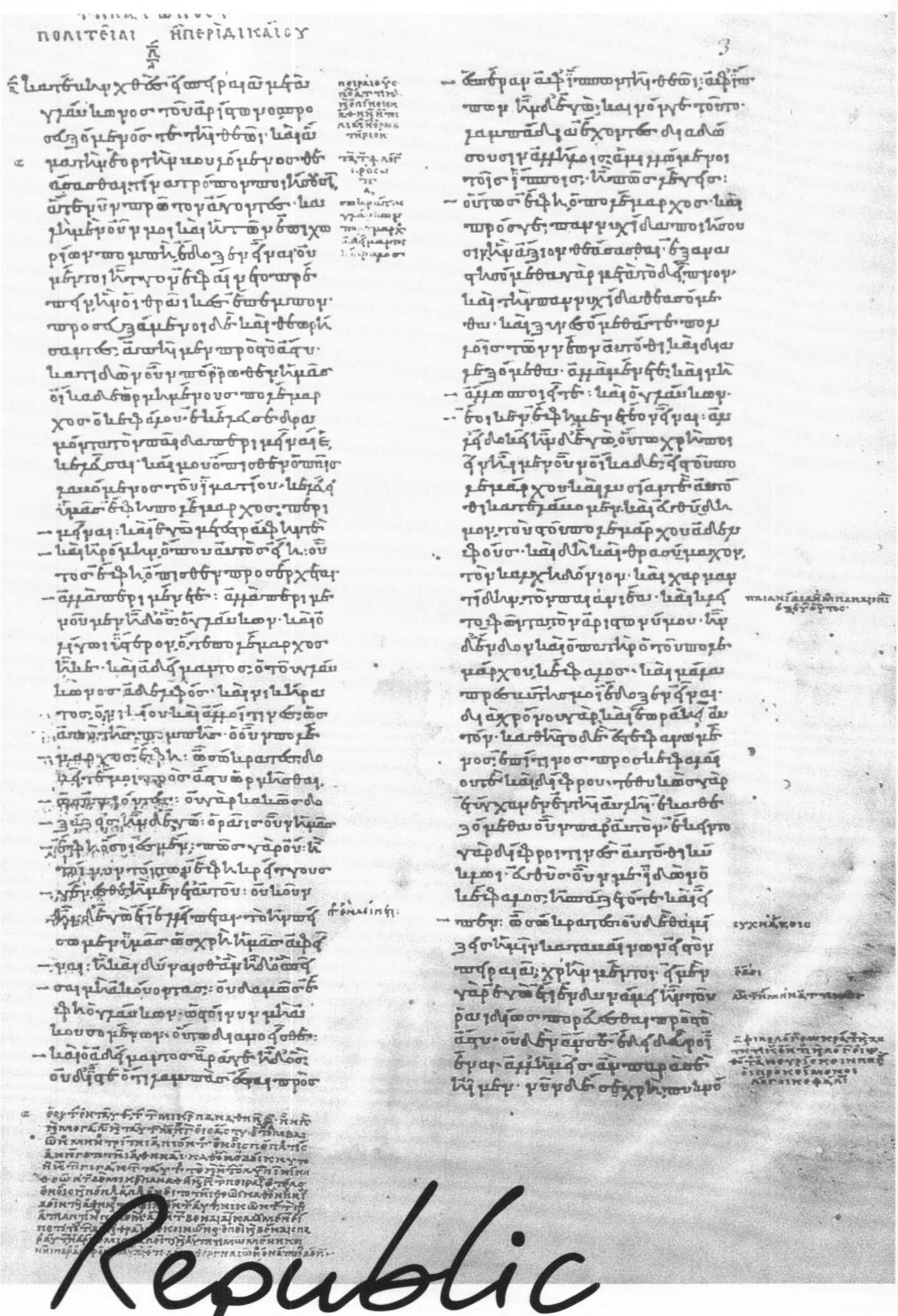

Image 17. - First Page of the 'Republic'

Republic

Chapter Three

The Opening of 'the *Republic*'

Having established the importance and background to Plato's *'Republic',* the only problem facing anyone wanting to plug into this extraordinary piece of literature is the simple consideration of where to start. The book works on so many levels and is so complete. Therefore, the best approach is to simply bite off a very small piece of text at the beginning to keep things straightforward and to demonstrate the richness of the text.

Here are the opening lines of the *'Republic'*. Arguably, they are also the opening lines of Western Philosophy:

Socrates: I went down to The Piraeus yesterday with Glaucon, son of Ariston, to pray to the goddess; and, at the same time, I wanted to observe how they would put on the festival, since they were now holding it for the first time. Now, in my opinion, the procession of the native inhabitants was fine; but the one the Thracians conducted was no less fitting a show. After we had prayed and looked on, we went off toward town. Catching sight of us from afar as we were pressing homewards, Polemarchus, son of Cephalus, ordered his slave boy to run after us and order us to wait for him. The boy took hold of my cloak from behind and said, "Polemarchus orders you to wait." And I turned around and asked him where his master was. "He is coming up behind," he said, "just wait." (327a)

Given the status of this text, a reader fresh to the book would easily feel rather deflated, even a little bemused. It all seems a bit trivial. For a cultural masterpiece, we would expect more impact from the outset. The sonic assault of Beethoven's *5th symphony* and the confrontation of Munch's primal "*Skrik*" grab the cultural moment and immediately interrogate us; the colossal beauty of "*David*" by Michelangelo and the directness of Camus' opening line in "*L'étranger*" creates an instant poignancy. Yet, here in the opening lines of the '*Republic*', rather like the stone bust of Plato, a reader might think that not much is going on. There are alien names and cultural practices, and we are dropped into the middle of conversations that seem a bit banal and blank.

However, just as with the stone face of Plato, there is real depth behind the surface of things. After all, the foundations for the rest of the book are being set up in these modest looking lines. Therefore, like with the bust of Plato, it is rewarding to retrace your steps through the text[72] more slowly.

In fact, really slowly.

Here are the first four words (seven words if you count in English).

They are hugely important:

---

72 My French colleagues use the word 'texte' to signify anything that can encourage philosophical discussion, from paintings to music, from a newspaper cutting to a clip from a film.

"I went down to The Piraeus yesterday..."

A film would call this opening line "the establishing shot". It is the moment at which the basic co-ordinates for the rest of the action are put in place. It provides the key location, establishes context and concepts. In classical film styles, it is often shot from a distance, from an aerial angle.

For example, in the opening to Hitchcock's' *Psycho*" (1960), a panorama of a cityscape rolls from left to right, and over the long drifting minute of slow zoom we are informed that this is 'Phoenix, Arizona'..., 'Friday December the Eleventh', ... 'Two Forty-Three P.M.' and then we are taken through an open window to see our central character, Marion Crane. She is half-dressed with her boyfriend, and neither of them knows that the next time she has a shower, she will be stabbed to death with a kitchen knife by a cross-dressing psychopath called Norman.

This opening line of Plato's *Republic* is his "establishing shot". It provides the place, the time and the characters, the significance of which will become clearer over time.

The text will be slowed down, from left to right. At the pace of one word at a time:

(1) "κατέβην" – (katebēn), "I went down".

It is no use if Philosophy remains just an abstract, aloof subject.[73] Socrates might have understood some elevated truths, but his understanding of higher values and reality needs to have an impact in the real world – otherwise, Philosophy might end up being viewed as mysticism. Indeed, after the Delphic Oracle informed him that he was the wisest man in all of Athens,[74] Socrates did not withdraw to the ascetic life of pure contemplation.

He spent his time down in the Agora of Athens, sharing his Socratic wisdom with everyone, from sausage sellers to Army Generals.

In fact, the opening word "κατέβην" (I went down) functions as a big arrow that points to one of the central metaphors of the whole '*Republic*': Plato's famous 'Allegory of the Cave' (514a-517c). In that allegory, a chained prisoner escapes from a cave, gains enlightenment, and then goes back down (κατέβηκε)[75] to inform the others about the full reality of things. It is an allegory in which Plato thinly veils Socrates as that prisoner.

His ascent and the descent are marked by struggle throughout. Firstly, there is the struggle to get out of the cave. Secondly, there are problems of perception. The prisoner needs to adjust his eyes to the bright light: from the dim shadows to the firelight, from the gloom of the cave to the outside world and its dazzling Sun – then, on the way back down, we go from the brightness to the darkness again. Thirdly, at each phase of his ascent there

---

73 This is not to denigrate the more formal and more exclusively abstract traditions of Philosophy, but simply to remember that even within mathematics, for every pure mathematician there is an applied mathematician too. Philosophy as a subject is characterised by a quest to discover the whole picture of reality.

74 In Plato's "*Apology*" he is informed about this by Chaerephon, whereas the writer Xenophon in his "*Apology*" has Socrates go up to the Oracle himself.

75 To point at another layer of meaning that is at play here, the journey to the underworld is known as a κατάβασις (*katabasis*) in Greek.

is a struggle to understand the new realities that the prisoner encounters. The prisoner must grasp an entirely new order of things at every step of the dialogue; each new level of experience utterly undermines the previous one and flips the old understanding into a disturbing illusion. After the mental overload of being under the full light of the Sun in the world outside of the cave, the allegory supposes that the prisoner would return back down to those who remained in the dark – to liberate them from their enslavement and deception. Yet, this leads to one final struggle. How can he communicate his new-found understanding? How could they understand or appreciate what he is trying to tell them?

In a very telling conclusion, the allegory concludes that the others would kill him in order to preserve the status quo of life in the darkness. Those in the cave prefer their illusions. They do not want to be disturbed. It is a brutal finish to the metaphor. The notion of struggle fits with our common sense of what it is like to try and understand the world. However, the killing of the well-meaning prisoner can seem a bit overstated at first glance. Are we really so viscerally attached to our understanding of the world? Can we be so agitated by an offence to our pride and common sense?

However, Plato was mindful of the hard fact that Socrates was executed in 399 BCE – a shockingly jarring end to an inquisitive and playful life. As detailed previously, Plato lived through that event and it exposed some of the human condition's base drives to him. Indeed, some moments of reflection on either our personal lives, or on human history, will expose how they are both littered with examples of how deeply our cerebral understanding of the world is wired to our guts. The entire 20th century makes no sense without this insight. Plato is not being bitter here; he is simply bringing some key issues to the surface.

It is intimidating and confusing to be told that everything that you have accepted as true so far in your life is an illusion. It is very disturbing to have the basic coordinates of your life pushed to the side. What the prisoners in the cave are being told is impossible to conceive, unless they were to go out of the cave. It is understandable that they are offended and push back against these alien and intrusive claims.

Philosophy is often a disturbing subject; it should be. Radically new perspectives on life necessarily cause us to recalibrate our relationship with others, with society and with the world. But once the shadows have been seen for what they are, they cannot be unseen. Although the facts of our life might remain the same, Philosophy can utterly change all of the sinews that connect them. Philosophy has the power to flip our experience of the world, to upend our thinking and to entirely change the texture of how existence meets us.

This power cannot be appropriated without a struggle – but once it is plugged into, Philosophy serves as a formidable ally in understanding the world.

Likewise, after understanding human society within the frame of climate change, everyday experiences take on another texture and another meaning. It quickly becomes obvious that most news reports do not frame the problem realistically, do not appreciate the fundamentals and simply skim over some of the key issues at play; this is if they report on it at all. These key problems in the quality of the media reporting on the climate crisis are frequently mirrored in chats down at the pub, in the office, around a dinner table or on a bus.

A real engagement with Philosophy and with the climate crisis can radically alter how we experience and think about our everyday decisions and our connection with the world. The transformation of our views can be quite exhilarating at first, but the sense of alienation that follows on from a new understanding can play itself out at many levels of social life. Having the basic organising principles of your life reorganised because of something so seemingly abstract and distant is, to be frank, a bit awkward sometimes. After getting a handle on the depths of the climate crisis, it can be hard to state the essential points of the climate crisis within the normal rubric of a conversation without seeming a bit intense. Explaining different consumption choices and lifestyle changes (to those who notice them), without appearing to be over-zealous or idealistic, can be a prickly exercise.

Of course, not every conversation has to take on a Socratic intensity; chatting about the football or latest Netflix release does not need to be related back to a debate about Free Will versus Determinism, not every news item has to be coupled with an examination of the importance of the climate crisis. Normal life carries on.

Both Philosophy and the daunting realities of climate crisis throw us into a strange new world. They can both transform the head and the heart. Everything is rather different outside of the cave. These new realities simply have to be assimilated, they demand discussion, no matter how difficult they are.

After the going up, there is always the going down.

"Κατέβην" is one simple Greek word. But if the zoom lens of our imagination is pulled right back to the widest view, it is hard to imagine a more appropriate word for the start of Western Philosophy.

(2) "χθὲς" – (χthes)[76], "yesterday".

"Yesterday" indicates that Plato wanted his readers to cast their minds back in time. The question that comes to the fore is: how far? By the time that Plato wrote the 'Republic', in c. 380 BCE, the Athenians had lost the war with Sparta. It quickly becomes clear that the "yesterday" here signifies that Plato wants us to go even further back in time to understand the proper context for the book.

That is because one of the characters in the opening lines, Polemarchus, was executed[77] by the Spartans when they took over the city.

---

76   The X here is a guttural, best expressed as a 'ch' in English.
77   He was forced to drink hemlock.

By 380 BCE, he had been dead for 24 years. Having this well-known metic raised from the dead, to perform in his dialogue, would have snagged his readers' attention. Indeed, his father, Cephalus is also mentioned here – he lost all of his property under the rule of the 30 tyrants. Putting these two

Athenian losers[78] at the start of the book was not without symbolism. Plato did not just come up with two random names; instead, he is making a point about how insubstantial the wealth and the honour of the current moment is. It is so easy to forget how transitory the material world's pleasures and pride are.

Indeed, in this opening scene down by the harbour, everything seems very relaxed and comfortable. The conversations are entirely normal, the characters are in the most ordinary of settings. The stage that Plato sets here must, therefore, be sometime during the heady democratic days of the Athenian golden age. It must be a moment before the results of the disastrous Sicilian Expedition of 415 BCE.

Any reader of Plato's '*Republic*', looking at these two well-known Athenians[79] talking happily with Socrates, would see the ominous dark black clouds just over their shoulders. These two merchants do not know what is coming and what is coming will not be pleasant for them.

If this were a modern horror film, then the viewer would see a man running ever closer towards them holding a kitchen knife. This approaching danger would be framed over the shoulder of the unsuspecting victim, who is idly talking towards the camera. Rather like watching the shower scene in '*Psycho*', we know all too well that the shower curtain is about to get ripped back.

78   They certainly lost under the Spartans. Calling them losers here emphasises this fact to provoke debate and reflection about why democracies can fail so spectacularly. Plato has this target in sight, but his representation of these two characters in the dialogue comes with different shades and angles.

79   Technically, they were not Athenian citizens, but "*metics*" – foreign traders who resided in Athens.

This narrative viewpoint adopted by Plato in The Piraeus will seem familiar to those who are properly informed about the climate crisis. This is because the consequences of pushing nature into a truly hostile state will be monstrous, and those who understand these outcomes are naturally highly attentive to the persistent idleness of our response. Looking out on the normal world, this seems anything but normal.

Runway or Runaway?

Short-term economic plans are often put forward without any acknowledgement of the deep transformations that are required to spike the curve of our emissions downwards. Planning in this way, with our backs turned to rapidly encroaching ecological threats, is far too common; in fact, it would not be an exaggeration to say that it is almost universal.

For example, in the UK, the dispute over whether to expand Heathrow Airport provoked much debate: about the effects on air and noise pollution, the jobs created or the homes lost and the advantages or the disadvantages of expanding other airports. These conversations did not put the fundamental questions at the centre of the discussion – is a planet with thousands of extra flights compatible with the requirements we have for reducing emissions? If the UK needs to reduce its emissions by 6.9% per year, every year, starting from today (2020),[80] where will the other reductions be made, in order to off-set the highly potent greenhouse gas effect of air-travel? Air travel accounts for 7% of the UK's emissions.

---

80   See Chapters 8 and 9 for the details, or the short summary
      available at: www.Cut11Percent.org.

In the absence of low-carbon planes, it is a reckless move to develop more air-traffic volume and to not put firm plans in place to at least halve our airmiles. For those who respond that this is not realistic, the question must be asked: what kind of an economy will be possible at all with unmitigated climate change? The laws of science will not change – if we had invested in genuinely green infrastructure decades ago, when we knew what was coming, then the transformations required could have been much more gradual.

> **"It is not enough to be busy. So are the ants. The question is: What are we busy about?"**
>
> – Thoreau, *Letter to H.G.O. Blake* (1857).

Yet, as recently as 2007 when the third runway was proposed,[81] it was still only a relatively small number of well-informed climate activists who had the conviction to push this question into the debate. Their annoying reminder of planetary boundaries was widely considered as a fringe concern, compared to the imperatives of consumer demand and economic growth.

The robust court case brought by 'Plan-B' in 2018 was an attempt to cut through the hubbub of the democratic debate and to highlight the basic irrationality of building more airport capacity.[82]

Whilst human civilisation is approaching catastrophic climate change by the end of the century, we have our heads lost in the details of short-term plans, and our hearts have been distracted by other things.

---

81   *"Industry backs third Heathrow runway as consultation opens".*
     Flight International. 22 November 2007.
82   The case failed, but a hearing to appeal the original decision
     was granted by the High Court in July 2019.

Hindsight

Plato is setting Cephalus and Polemarchus up to show the dangers of an unreflective life. Socrates is going to find it tough to talk with both Cephalus and Polemarchus on a meaningful level. People are going to brush him off with clichés and rather limited responses throughout the rest of Book One of the '*Republic*'.

Yet, it is not that difficult to have some sympathy for both of them – especially as the 'dot-to-dot' of history was not clearly pointing to such a shocking outcome for the Athenians against the Spartans. Right up to the moment of the defeat in Syracuse (Sicily), there were not that many reasons to doubt that the prosperity and glory of the Athenian status quo was about to collapse. Indeed, we all know how hard it can be to think through our complicated situations from a decent vantage point. Even with the very best intentions of doing the right thing, we are easily trapped inside a messy tangle of perspectives. Life is just busy, with short term practical problems and immediate emotional struggles.

With respect to climate change, it could be argued that we are in a much more privileged position. The science is vividly clear; the dot-to-dots that researchers have completed lead, without ambiguity, to a catastrophic set of circumstances. However, to imagine that we can see things clearly is to underestimate the lack of clarity that there is in the media about the dangers ahead, and involves forgetting that all the psychological filters that exist that prevent us from seeing and accepting that reality.

So, Philosophy is a subject that has a unique power to offer a holistic vision of the state that we are in. It can lift the lid on reality and can put things into their proper perspective. It is unusually competent to provide us with some common sense about our situation. That is not to say that everybody will listen. We continue to discuss our economic ambitions with casual attention to climate science. We will always remain contradictory and unpredictable in our decision-making. However, Plato helps us to get a precious moment of clarity.

For those who are looking at the on-coming disaster, it is deeply disconcerting to talk with people who have their backs to the climate crisis. It is often said, with no small amount of irony, that hindsight is a beautiful thing. That is precisely what Plato is providing by setting the '*Republic*' "yesterday" in The Piraeus. Hindsight. Deep hindsight. Not only for those readers who held the first copies of his book in Athens, but more importantly, for every reader who came after. This includes us.

(3) and (4) "εἰς Πειραιᾶ" – (*eis peiraia*), "to The Piraeus".

The symbolism of a place: the Piraeus

Islamic State terrorist bombers struck Zaventem Airport and Maelbeek Metro station in Brussels on the morning of March 22nd, 2016. For months afterwards, and even today, there is a lingering shadow of those attacks. Certainly, in the weeks and months after the bombs, those places held a strong symbolic meaning for anyone passing through. This phenomenon is true everywhere in the world, and the greater the tragedy, the deeper and longer the symbolic resonance it acquires. We rightly remember the names of Passchendaele, My Lai, Hiroshima and Nagasaki, and so on.

Image 19. - Passchendaele

Passchendaele, Belgium. Or what T.S. Eliot would depict so powerfully as '*The Waste Land*'.

Australian gunners on a duckboard track in Château Wood near Hooge. October 29th, 1917. Photo by Frank Hurley

For any Athenian reading the '*Republic*', The Piraeus would have held a strong double representation. Before the humiliation to both the Syracusans (413 BCE) and Spartans (404 BCE) it would have signified their trading and military strength. After the debacle, it was transformed into a symbol of their shattering loss. The higher the rise, the harder the fall.

The Piraeus was the hub of the Athenian naval empire and most of the goods and people that came to Athens were funnelled through its port. The population of Athens was huge during Plato's time. It had an estimated population[83] of 50,000, enough to fill a football stadium, whereas almost every other city state had a population of somewhere between 500 and 2,000 (with the exceptions of Sparta, Corinth and Thebes). It would have been strikingly cosmopolitan to any visitor landing at the port, and quite an edgy area to hang around – the perfect place for Socrates to 'get down' to his Philosophy.

The most obvious symbolism of The Piraeus was that it grew up as a vivid illustration of Athenian trading power. The harbour would have been teeming with traders and travellers preoccupied with their business. In fact, in these opening lines, we join Socrates and his friends as they are invited back to the house of Cephalus – a wealthy metic.

It is in this house that Socrates will engage with the three interlocutors over the question of "What is Justice?", in a conversation that would go on to fill up the pages of Book One.

Metics

Metics were principally economic migrants to Athens. They were mostly merchants (some were artists or freed slaves). They made up nearly half of the total population. Most were poor, but some were the wealthiest people in Athens – and had considerable indirect influence. They had to pay extra taxes and did not enjoy the full civic rights of native Athenians.

---

83   The population of the full Attica peninsula is estimated to be between 250,000-300,000. Thorley, John (2005). Athenian Democracy. Lancaster Pamphlets in Ancient History. Routledge. p. 74.

A bit of town planning

There is a further significance about the location of Cephalus' house that should be noted. Plato's choice of The Piraeus carries an interesting symbolism for a reader of the '*Republic*' who is thinking about climate change.

The Piraeus (shown underneath*) was the first city to be designed – the streets were mapped out with grid straight lines from the hub of the Agora, the marketplace. The Piraeus is, therefore, the first example we have in history of town planning. The architect of those plans was a man called Hippodamus (Aristotle, *Politics* ii.8).

Image 20. - The Pireaus

Although getting roads to run at right angles to each other does not sound like much of an achievement, Hippodamus' project was much more significant than that. He was thinking through how a city could optimise its infrastructure, land use and housing.

At least in this sense, the city represented something more than just a blind following of the appetites. Hippodamus showed the value of putting some thought into the path taken by economic growth and how to make the best use of the resources. This rational step away from just the ad-hoc consequences of economic development is a notable step in human history. Town Planning might not sound like one of the most stirring achievements of the Ancient Greeks, but it was another significant 'first' for Athenians.

GDP

For all of the advances in our civilisation, we seem to lack so much imagination and wisdom when calculating our progress. The standard measure of economic development across the globe is GDP. GDP is a hopelessly reductive valuation of what we all get up to every year. It was first introduced as a key indicator by the Nobel Prize-winning[84] statistician and economist Simon Kuznets during an address to the US Congress in 1934. GDP has been criticised ever since as a clumsy and narrow measure of economic growth. Indeed, Kuznets himself warned that the simplicity of GDP would make it prone to abuse by those who might benefit from oversimplifying matters. However, despite all of the criticism,[85] we seem to be stuck with it.

It might just be a statistic, but the formative effect that this blunt measure of human progress has had on our policies and thinking must not be underestimated. The quarterly reporting of GDP is a key pivot around which so much government planning and media attention moves. It is a measure that is blind to countless stores of wealth that are held in the biosphere, in families and in communities.

The ambition to sustain GDP growth at around 3% per year is never squared with the fact that we live on a finite planet.[86] Homo sapiens are now so populous on the Earth, and our technological power is so extensive, that continual conventional growth in GDP is simply impossible. Astonishingly, the next 35 years of resource extractions and fossil fuel emissions are projected to equal the cumulative extractions and emissions of the past 300,000[87] years, figures that "represent an unsustainable future... a trend that is not in any way sustainable."[88]

---

84   He was awarded the Nobel Memorial Prize in Economic Sciences in 1971, "for his empirically founded interpretation of economic growth which has led to new and deepened insight into the economic and social structure and process of development."

85   Most famous here was Bobby Kennedy's criticism in his speech to the University of Kansas in March 18th, 1968.

86   A 3% growth per year, using the simple mathematical equation of 'the doubling time' means that we will have doubled our economic activity in 23.45 years. A growth that would further increase the resource extractions of our limited resources.

87   Figures calculated by OurFutureUncompromised

88   United Nations Environment Programme, International Resource Panel. *Decoupling natural resource use and environmental impacts from economic growth.* (2011)

In fact, right now we are currently living through the Sixth Mass Extinction Event in the shadow of our GDP growth. Although, as it is no passive accident, George Monbiot is surely right to call it the "First Great Extermination". We are pushing species into extinction at between 100 and 1,000 times the pre-human, or 'background' rate.[89] Some might be happy to live in a world just full of cats and dogs and the occasional bird or pig; however, such a crippling loss of biodiversity would surely make any kind of human civilisation at all quite impossible.

Image 21. - Northern White Rhino

Yet, these appalling acts of ecocide do not make a significant impact on our economic policies or mainstream media. Somehow our imagination about what is valuable and significant seems to have been cropped down to an absurdly small picture. Continually citing GDP as the vital statistic for the health of our economies is evidently utterly inadequate – yet we still do it. It is just one statistic, but it is symptomatic of the fact that we just don't have a

89   *"Conservation Biology"* Volume 29, Issue 2 (April 2015) p452-462.
     (https://doi.org/10.1111/cobi.12380)

plan for a sustainable future. We are just getting on with business as usual; somehow, we still manage to call it "economic growth" without flinching.

In light of all this, Hippodamus' plan for The Piraeus was actually a significant moment for civilisation. It demonstrated that we can think ahead. It showed that we can plan our development. Hippodamus' designs for the harbour area offered the Athenians a bird's eye view of what they were doing, and he provides us with the reminder that we should do the same. It is unconscionable that we still do not have a global plan in place for a sustainable economy. The Sustainable Development Goals published by the United Nations are no more than a shopping list or broad intentions, listed in no particular order. The 17 goals have no strategic coherence, and yet at the same time the United Nations is producing devastating assessments of the trajectory that we are on, towards an ecological catastrophe.

Kallipolis – The Beautiful City

The 'Republic' is a book that is not shy about pointing to the dangers of short-sighted and superficial economic thinking. Plato also warns us against allowing our thirst for status to govern our actions. Our appetites and pride, our guts, are neither a stable, nor a virtuous starting point for political decision-making. He argues that in order to establish a truly stable city you cannot think from the bottom up.

Indeed, Plato's ambitions are much greater than a simple rethinking of GDP. His vision of human society is much deeper than the administrative thinking of Hippodamus. His Philosophy demands far more than just tinkering with the status quo. Plato wants to push beyond just urban efficiencies and practicalities. The 'Republic' calls for holistic thinking, not piecemeal reactions to problems.

Plato is calling for a root and branch reformation of society. He wants to do Town Planning at the most comprehensive level. His Philosophy is sharply relevant for the climate crisis because unless we are prepared to look at the big picture, and ask some very basic questions about what direction we are going in as a society, we will surely not hold global heating to well below 2°C. We cannot pretend that the markets will recognise external costs on their own. We cannot ignore the threat that narrow nationalist thinking poses to the global threat that we all face. The climate crisis will be intolerant of further delay and obfuscation; Plato might have been a utopian thinker, but we need something to jolt us out of our fragmented, cynical approach to the problem.

Are we prepared to root our reasoning and actions in a reverence for the truth? Are we willing to share the responsibility for the emissions reductions in a mature and thoughtful way? Are we prepared to examine the basic values and priorities that we live our lives by? Plato named his ideal republic "Kallipolis," the beautiful city. What will become increasingly clear in this chapter is that Plato refused to reduce human life to a simple, one-dimensional level. A harmony is established between all three aspects of the city of Kallipolis – the appetites, the spirit and reason.

He did not consider economic thinking to be a separate domain to thinking about virtues. He did not allow patriotic pride in his city to be unrelated to a reflective set of values. His 50-year training programme for the Philosopher Kings and Queens was as much about sharpening their critical thinking skills as developing their respect for 'The Good'.

The ideal city

With striking boldness, Plato argues that society has to get things right from the top down.

Reason first, not last.

Values integrated into decision-making, not simply an ad-hoc afterthought.

The Characters

Indeed, it is not just The Piraeus that carries a clear symbolism in the 'Republic'. Each of the characters that Socrates talks to throughout the book plays a definite role in its structure. Plato is setting up this structure in the opening Book of the 'Republic'. Rather like in a chess game, the opening moves cannot be executed carelessly – each piece, and its location, have very strategic roles to play. Having clarity at the start of a game makes all of the moves that follow more secure and powerful.

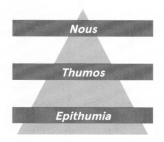

Plato's 3-fold division of the self

Cephalus, Polemarchus and Thrasymachus

The three main interlocutors in Book One (Cephalus, Polemarchus and Thrasymachus) all carry a definite symbolic meaning. Each of them represents a part of the human psyche. Starting from the bottom:

1. **Cephalus**, the first person that Socrates has a real dialogue with, represents the simple human appetites (ἐπιθυμία, *epithumia*) – for sleep, food, drink, sex and material wealth.

2. His son, **Polemarchus** represents what Plato summarises with the word (θυμός, *thumos*) – which is often translated as "spiritedness". It could be described as the emotional aspect to our virtues, for example the desire for revenge or glory, or a thirst for recognition. In the bluntest language, *Thumos* insists that we are important.

3. The third person, **Thrasymachus**, represents the highest human faculty, human reason (νόος, *nous*). This 'superpower' enables us to understand the world at a universal level, far beyond the particulars of everyday life.

This sequence of three also communicates the different ranks of each part. Plato puts *Epithumia* at the bottom, *Thumos* in the middle and *Nous* at the top. In the text, he does this by giving the first extended dialogue to Cephalus in which he hands the old metic a bunch of rather lame clichés to fend off Socrates' questions about justice. Next, the son Polemarchus enters in the dialogue with a more combative set of responses to Socrates – although these points do not stand up very long to interrogation either. By contrast, in the final section of Book One, Thrasymachus is scripted with the very best arguments that even match Socrates' insight and skill. Such is Thrasymachus' talent for reasoning, Socrates cannot bring the discussion to a decisive finish about the nature of justice, and Book One ends in aporia.

This three-fold pattern and structure will be sustained and developed throughout the rest of the '*Republic*'. Plato will develop his arguments as to why Reason should be primary, and why it should govern the other two drives. However, it is in fact outside of the '*Republic*' that Plato gives his most concise expression to his three-fold division of the psyche.

In his work, '*Phaedrus*' Plato installs Reason as the charioteer that nobly attempts to steer two winged, wild horses (245c-249d). One horse (*epithumia*) is pulling towards the Earth, and the other (*thumos*) is pulling towards the heavens – and the wise driver (*nous*) who has seen the truth, harnesses and guides them.[90]

Yet, Plato does not deny the value of the simple pleasures and necessities of the body by giving Reason the highest status. It is self-evident that a mind needs a body. Indeed, Plato endorses these physical drives, he even argues that they have the capacity to inspire noble qualities. For example, in his remarkable work '*Symposium*', Plato has a group of celebrity Athenians reclining around a banquet table in a speech contest. Each emphatically

---

90 Aristotle would later label the three parts of the psyche as: Pleasure, Honour and Knowledge. He would also assert that man's fullest nature is expressed when he exercises his reason and takes his place in civic society. The "He" is no accident of traditional grammar here; Aristotle takes a big step backwards from the gender equality in Plato's community of Philosopher Kings and Queens.

affirms the value of sexual desire (eros).[91] Erotic love is praised for inspiring health, justice, courage and many other virtues. In the final speech, Socrates elevates Eros to a demi-god, who can inspire the mind to transcendent values and wisdom. Most notably for the political context here, Socrates even ascribes to Eros the power to make 'the art of civic order' (209a) clear.

Inspiring words. But perhaps the men around the table had been drinking too much wine... Maybe it was the testosterone, not the neurones, that were talking? The guests around the table even found pug-nosed Socrates to be a bit of a diva. Maybe Plato was being sarcastic? Maybe he was offering us a parody? Plato leaves it wonderfully ambiguous. Either way, the *"Symposium"* is a literary masterpiece and it leaves us in no doubt that although Plato was a deeply religious man, he also understood the importance of physical drives. Plato's mind might have been compelled to search for higher truths, but rather than deny the material world to get there, he thought it was possible to get to universal reality through it.

Image 22. - *"Eros", Piccadilly Circus, London*

Indeed, Plato's overriding aim in the '*Republic*' is to argue that human life is much richer and more complex than a simple, physical level of existence. He wants to insist on the noble role of rationality in human affairs, not outside of them.

91 By contrast, ἐπιθυμία is used throughout the New Testament to signify something negative. Most influentially by the Apostle Paul: "Therefore do not let sin reign in your mortal body so that you obey its evil desires (ἐπιθυμία)" (Romans 6:12). It could also be noted that Neo-Platonist thinkers did pick up on the priority that Plato gave to reason over the senses and, combined with the direction of thinking that the Early Church took, the body tended to lose out in the Western culture that followed.

The focus of this section is to establish that both the location (The Piraeus) and the characters carry a definite message: The most basic requirements of human life (*epithumia*) and our hard-wired drive for recognition and meaning (*thumos*) find a healthy balance in the good life. Such an equilibrium is established in both the individual and the state by the guidance of reason (*nous*). Below is an illustration of what is going on; it frames everything that Plato wants to communicate in his '*Republic*':

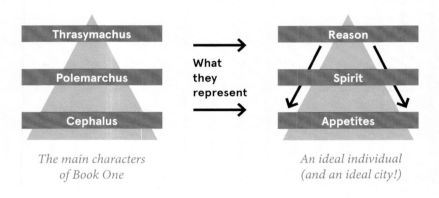

The main characters
of Book One

An ideal individual
(and an ideal city!)

Cephalus

Plato wants to get further in his thinking, beyond the appetites. He wants to think with more than just his lower organs. Indeed, Socrates is warmly welcomed when the group of friends get to Cephalus' house in The Piraeus (by line 328b), but the conversation immediately gets dragged into all sorts of worldly concerns.

Cephalus starts by informing Socrates that he did not see the festival because he has grown too old now to go trekking down into town too often. He elaborates on his situation by thinking back to the good old days when he was more mobile and able to follow the prompting of his desires. He tells Socrates about his friends: "When they meet, most of the members of our group lament, longing for the pleasures of youth and reminiscing about sex, about drinking bouts and feasts and all that goes with things of that sort" (329a). Socrates tries to push the conversation past jovial banter about these base appetites, but Cephalus brushes him off. Cephalus is a businessman who does not see the need for deep reflection. He could crudely be labelled as 'a bourgeois philistine' today.[92]

It is revealing that Socrates finds it very difficult to make progress beyond the surface of this rich man's thinking. He pursues him for a good understanding of 'Justice', Socrates wants to get further than just a transactional view of human life. However, after Cephalus chucks out a few throwaway comments (that Socrates dismantles with ease) it is obvious that the old man is just not interested in those kinds of questions, and so he goes off to the garden to make his daily offerings to the gods.

The message is clear: he is happy, he is a traditional guy and Socrates should just follow the customs of Athens and relax a bit. Socrates is asking too many questions for his comfort.

Relax a bit!

This pushing away of reason is an easy gesture to make by politicians. Votes can be won by appearing to be 'pragmatic' and by appealing to moderate, practical thinking. Populist or libertarian commentators often caricature those who are engaged in reforming our society into a sustainable civilisation by setting up a false opposition between ideals and practicalities. They talk as if they are the pragmatists, standing in contrast to the unreasonable ideologues – not the other way around. "It's the economy, stupid!" is supposed to stop a debate about climate change with a face slap.

---

92 Nabokov describes a Philistine as: "A full-grown person whose interests are of a material and commonplace nature, and whose mentality is formed of the stock ideas and conventional ideals of his or her group and time". (Nabokov, *Lectures on Russian Literature*, essay Philistines and Philistinism).

But "How realistic is it to pursue degrowth in our economies?" only looks like a reasonable question to ask if we ignore the fact that shunting the Earth's systems into a profoundly different state will cause catastrophic and uncontrollable degrowth anyway.

Rather than dealing with the systemic problems raised by global heating, these cynical commentators point at small practical details to distract from the bigger picture. For example: "[Greta] also pushes the flight shaming narrative, which encourages people to give up air travel. Good luck getting to Hawaii or Iceland in that case..."[93] In the echo chambers of modern social media, the intuitive appeal of such comments enables them to stay afloat.

It seems absurd to anyone who understands the bigger picture about climate change that the economy could be used a put down in a conversation about the crisis. Such a dismissal can often be indicative of a scepticism and tribal thinking that was explored in *"Popper Tackles Climate Change"*. If these problems are the case, then there might not be much point trying to get past first base in a dialogue about the climate. A dogmatic refusal to think beyond the status-quo is a major conversation stopper.

Plato has Cephalus appear on stage first for a reason. Like anyone who has met a brick wall in a discussion about climate change, Plato knows how this can feel.

93   https://www.theamericanconservative.com/articles/by-all-means-lets-criticize-greta-thunberg/

Cephalus has a son: Polemarchus

Cephalus lived in The Piraeus with his son, Polemarchus. It is this family home that Socrates goes to visit. These two characters and their house provide a very helpful first couple of steps in understanding the '*Republic*'.

The short-sightedness that often shapes our thinking is embodied in Cephalus. Early readers of the work knew that he had all of his property confiscated under the 'rule of the 30 Tyrants' after the Spartan defeat. A society that simply pursues "the greatest good for the greatest number", and which reduces all virtues to a crude pursuit of pleasure, is vulnerable to a number of dangers. It might be true that trade and prosperity can lubricate some stiff joints in a civilisation. However, allowing wealth to take over as the primary force in a society to the point that it can dictate terms to everything else, seems like a ruinous set-up.

Why recap the significance of Cephalus? The reason is that these basic appetites can quickly morph into more advanced, complex ambitions that are concerned with status, ambition and pride. In other words, Cephalus has a son: Polemarchus. He represents a 'spiritedness' and thereby embodies a second threat to a stable civilisation.

A society that is driven by a thirst for vengeance (like Germany under the Third Reich[94]) or a lust for recognition (like North Korea under its different despots) is rightly called degenerate. These kinds of passions can sometimes consume all of the thinking and occupy all of the plans of a state – just like they can in the life of an individual. Polemarchus has a clear function in Book One. He is the symbol for this powerful energy in the human condition that demands recognition.

Socrates also pursues Cephalus with questions about what justice is. His answers are almost as shallow and dismissive as his father's answers. In contrast to Cephalus' transactional view of justice, Polemarchus instinctively thinks about justice as necessitating vengeance.

---

94   "*Nazism and War*" (°°), II, is a very engaging review of how the Third Reich was overwhelmed by a lust for revenge and warfare.

He remarks that justice is, "to give to each man what is due to him" and "to benefit one's friends and harm one's enemies" (332d). He is thinking with his heart, not with his head. Socrates cannot get him to think beyond this impulsive and polarised view of people and he cannot draw his thoughts to the bigger picture.

Again, the early readers of the '*Republic*' would have known that the fate of Polemarchus was even worse than that of his father's: the 30 Tyrants had him executed.

A symmetry between the soul and the city

To return to the structure of Plato's thinking (illustrated above with the triangles), there is a symmetry throughout the book between individuals and society. What works for one, works for the other. What is right for the polis is right for the soul. A balanced healthy city will be just like a balanced healthy person. Each class of people in his '*Republic*' had an important role to play, just like each aspect of our human psyche is a key function. Crucially, Plato places everything under the control of reason, both for the city and for the individual alike.

For those who might wince at the notion of putting philosophers in charge of a State, Plato should be given the chance to justify his argument. For the moment, it is enough to note that common sense informs us that a life given over to the desires or 'spiritedness' are probably less than ideal.

As a caricature, slobbing out in front of the TV with pizzas and beers everyday carries serious dangers to our physical and mental health (a crude example of a modern Cephalus perhaps[95]). Likewise, a life geared exclusively to avenge a wrong or to acquire a certain status comes with serious health warnings as well (a modern day Polemarchus).

---

95   To be fair to Cephalus, he would more likely be a red wine drinker and opera-goer. I will leave the issue of whether or not there is any ethical difference up to the different traditions of Utilitarianism to argue about this.

Plato would argue that there is nothing intrinsically wrong with our appetites and or passions. It is just that they have to be framed by the nobler judgements of reasoning.

And so it is with a city.

The scenery and the main plot lines for the '*Republic*' are now set.

(5) "I wanted to observe how they would put on the festival, since they were now holding it for the first time"

Anyone paying attention should notice that this short section (5) should not be here. The plan was to deal with only the first four words of the '*Republic*'. However, it is worth getting all the way to the end of this first sentence of his book, because this is where Plato really seems to square up to the Athenian democracy.

With this clause of the first sentence Plato pulls together his major complaints about democracy: its warmongery and its ignorance. Not only did the democracy vote to go to war with Sparta, they also voted with vindictive stupidity to execute Socrates. The very man who has gone down to The Piraeus to get people to reflect on what a good city is, is the same one that they voted to kill with hemlock. If the Athenians had been willing to think more openly about what they were doing, and why they were doing it, then they could have avoided some major mistakes.

Extinguishing reflective people from your society is a bad step. With the words, "for the first time", Plato really hammers his points home.

Recall from earlier that Socrates was found guilty of two crimes: 1. "corrupting the youth" and 2. "impiety" (ἀσέβεια, *asebeia*) (which had two prongs to it: "failing to acknowledge the gods that the city acknowledges", and "introducing new gods to the city").[96]

---

96   Plato, "*Apology*" 24b.

Let's deal with the first accusation quickly. The case for him corrupting the youth is an debatable one. The value of civic unity was deeply respected by the Athenians, as was the status of the elder citizens' wisdom. To actively encourage young people to put difficult questions to the establishment could have been considered quite toxic. Boys were not men. Indeed, Socrates' philosophical project could easily be viewed as a dangerous corruption because young people might take some time to understand the value of certain rules and traditions, given that they might imprudently test the boundaries.

Today, the impudence of Greta Thunberg is welcome in our fuller democratic times. Raising basic points of common sense about the lack of climate actions against our current political leaders is a potent and healthy example of how such simple questioning by young people can be. Indeed, Greta is evidently not corrupted – quite the opposite. Her Asperger's syndrome is one of the major reasons for her remarkably uncluttered and straight view of society and of what is going on. On this charge, for better or worse, Socrates was more or less guilty. However, whatever the virtues of teaching children to question authority, this first accusation is not the concern here.

Plato has got the injustice of the second accusation about "introducing new gods" firmly in his sights.

This is because in this opening line of text, Socrates is on his way back from the festival of a new god that he knew nothing about. ("I wanted to observe how they would put on the festival, since they were now holding it for the first time"). Plato is underlining Socrates' innocence. He categorically was not impious; he categorically did not introduce new gods to the city. He was curious about what the festival would be like.

Moreover, it was well known who did it and well known why they did it: It was the Athenian democracy that did it. The authorities introduced a new god into the city as part of their 5th century BCE Realpolitik.

The new god in question was the Thracian goddess of the moon, 'Bendis'.[97] To introduce a new deity into a Greek city was highly unusual, because to bring another god into the city could upset the original god. In the Athenians' case, this was Athena. However, in 430-429 BCE, under the extreme stress of a plague that wiped out an estimated 25% of the population (including their hero Pericles), the Athenians reached out in desperation to a local god, Asclepius. He was the Greek god of medicine, from the nearby city of Epidaurus – a small city with a big reputation for healing. In the chaotic circumstances, it seemed like a risk that was worth taking.[98]

Therefore, it was extremely odd to find the Athenians welcoming another deity, this time a rather exotic goddess from distant Thrace. If it is already a bit weird to ask your long-standing wife to accept another man to the marital bed, it is even weirder to invite another woman too. Although the Athenians were polytheistic, a new god had only been introduced twice in the entire fifth century BCE: once for Bendis, once for Asclepius.

The Athenians took this unusual step because the Thracians had something that they really wanted. To the north,[99] Thrace was blessed with abundant forests: forests make trees, trees make wood, wood makes boats and boats can really help you wage war – especially if you are a naval power like Athens. Behind the high words of the religious ceremony, there was a more basic agenda. Behind the noble sentiments expressed in the political speeches of the Athenian assembly, a very different game was being played out.

---

97   Bendis, not like Beckham.
98   Bendis was formally accepted into the Athenian polis in 420 BCE.
99   Today the area of Thrace is split between Northern Greece, Bulgaria and Turkey, and apart from the forests, this area represented a key strategic location as well.

The Athenians were eager to prove their muscles to the Spartans, and they had been busy building up their naval strength. Therefore, The Piraeus did not simply represent the trading ambitions of the Athenians of the time. It also carried the powerful symbolism of their ambitions: trade and war. How often has the first given rise to the second? Any proper context to the trigger of World War One in Sarajevo will trace the roots of the crisis back to the trading alliances made between the European powers during the scramble for Africa. This is the simplest example that could be cited by historians, but human history is littered with others. 'Desire' and 'Spiritedness' under one roof: an appetitive father often leads to a combative son. In Plato's simple metaphor here, Cephalus was the father of Polemarchus and they both live under the same roof.

Indeed, this family house in which the dialogue in Book One takes place, was just next door to the shield manufacturing business which they owned – a large enterprise that employed 120 slaves.[100] Plato was communicating something important by housing them together in The Piraeus.

In summary, not only did the Athenian democracy falsely accuse Socrates in his trial, their dangerous move to officially install Bendis in Athens was completed for their own misguided appetites and for the purposes of war mongering. The war with Sparta was a huge miscalculation from the start.[101] Trading priorities and military hawks had pushed the Athenians into a catastrophic war. Desires and spiritedness had driven the Athenians' way of thinking, and reason had been pushed aside.

This was Plato, in his opening lines, setting the record straight.

Slam.

---

100 Lysias, "*Speeches*", 12.19.

101 Three years before the first ceremony for Bendis was celebrated at The Piraeus (on 19th Thargelion (May/June) 429 BCE) the Athenians had agreed to let some Thracians construct a small shrine inside the city walls. A smart pre-emptive move before the Peloponnesian War kicked off. (See Janouchová, P., "*The Cult of Bendis in Athens and Thrace*", GRAECO-LATINA BRUNENSIA 18, 2013, 1. Page 97).

Conclusions from the Opening of the 'Republic'

Plato was a profoundly metaphorical thinker. He held the ambition to identify the universal truths in particular things. It might seem as if this section has just too much content for such a small amount of text. However, this would underestimate how much of the 'Republic' is so consistently built upon these first blocks.

Moreover, it would also underestimate how committed Plato was to understanding the inner nature of everything and how committed he was to capturing the truth in allegories that can live on beyond his own time and culture. It has been said that Martin Heidegger, when he started lecturing, took a whole semester to get through the 'Republic', but the last time in his career that he taught the work he never got past the first sentence.[102] Indeed, a slow reading of Plato never goes unrewarded because he was able to make the particular details of his own situation resonate with universal value.

Plato picked up his pen to write the 'Republic' because he wanted to point out some fundamental dangers that he could see in the way his society was set up. The reason why he sent Socrates "down to The Piraeus" in the opening line was that something had gone deeply wrong with Athenian common sense. These dangers could not easily be seen by someone who might become lost in the details of their life – so Plato decided to pick up those details and to make them resonant with the big issues.

Climate change throws at us the most extra-ordinary contrast between the realities of the scientific conclusions and the social responses to it. And yet, we seem to get so lost in dull details. We have media campaigns about plastic straws, we fixate on polar bears and political personalities.

---

102 Yale Professor Steve Smith tentatively offers this anecdote in his excellent lecture series on Political Philosophy (Lecture 4, "Philosophers and Kings: Plato's 'Republic' Books I-II").

These are not the details that can resonate with the deep structural problems that we face. We need writers, artists and broadcasters who can bring the big questions that climate change confronts us with to the surface. Crises offer us the chance to re-examine the big stuff, the fundamentals of what we are doing. For a civilisation that is caught up in the middle of the sixth mass extinction event, we need a public debate that goes far deeper than simple virtue signalling about recycling and waste.

ENTIRE ECOSYSTEMS   THE ECONOMY   MILLIONS of DEATHS   THE POLAR BEAR

Chapter Four

The Allegory
of the Ship

The metaphorical symbolism of The Piraeus, and the characters that Socrates meets, are implicit. However, sometimes Plato was explicitly metaphorical. He enjoyed setting up Similes (or Allegories) to make his points. The Allegory of the Cave (mentioned previously) is his most celebrated example. In fact, the '*Republic*' contains five key similes. Three of these are mainly concerned with issues of Epistemology: The Cave, The Sun and the Divided Line. The other two are mainly concerned with Political Philosophy: The Large and Powerful Animal and The Ship. All five similes are interconnected.

Given the limited space of this one chapter on Plato, the lens used to look at the '*Republic*' will be restricted to an exploration of only one of these Similes. Since some strong nautical themes are found in the opening lines of the '*Republic*', it seems best to advance Plato's thinking with climate change through his Allegory of the Ship.[103]

The reasons why Plato chose a ship to deliver his barbed criticisms of democratic rule will now become clear with a closeup examination of this famous allegory.

103 Excerpt from Book 6, lines 487d-488e, translated by Desmond Lee [New York: Penguin, 2003 [1955]

The Allegory of the Ship

'Suppose the following to be the state of affairs on board ship or ships. The captain is larger and stronger than any of the crew, but a bit deaf and short-sighted, and similarly limited in seamanship. The crew are all quarrelling about how to navigate the ship, each thinking he ought to be at the helm; they have never learned the art of navigation and cannot say that anyone ever taught it them, or that they spend any time studying it; indeed they say it can't be taught and are ready to murder anyone who says it can. They spend all their time milling round the captain and doing all they can to get him to give them the helm. If one faction is more successful than another, their rivals may kill them and throw them overboard, lay out the honest captain with drugs or drink or in some other way, take control of the ship, help themselves to what's on board, and turn the voyage into the sort of drunken pleasure-cruise you would expect. Finally, they reserve their admiration for the man who knows how to lend a hand in controlling the captain by force or fraud; they praise his seamanship and navigation and knowledge of the sea and condemn everyone else as useless.

They have no idea that the true navigator must study the seasons of the year, the sky, the stars, the winds and all the other subjects appropriate to his profession if he is to be really fit to control a ship; and they think that it's quite impossible to acquire the professional skill needed for such control (whether or not they want it exercised) and that there's no such thing as an art of navigation. With all this going on aboard aren't the sailors on any such ship bound to regard the true navigator as a word-spinner and a star-gazer, of no use to them at all?'

(*"Republic"*, 488a–489d)

This is a picture of a society that is in deep trouble. The captain can hardly see or hear, and his crew are involved in all sorts of tricks and plots to gain control of the direction of the ship. It is a drunken pleasure cruise – and drunk people tend to act in an exaggerated way with their emotions and appetites, regardless of reality. Indeed, the drink has made their minds so slippery they would not be able to hold the truth, even if they tried to.

Anyway, the priorities on board this ship are nothing to do with knowing anything or understanding anything. Truth is mocked and side-lined, like in the Navigator's situation. This is a ship on board which all that really matters is control. The competition between the crew members reduces everything to a farcical contest of popularity and power; it reduces everything to the present. The truth simply does not matter. The destination does not matter.

In fact, the truth is seen as a direct threat to their manipulative games and they are 'prepared to murder anyone' who claims otherwise. Such a rudderless ship might be lucky to avoid sailing into storms or the rocks – but it would only seem to be a matter of time until it did.

Plato wrote this passage in observance of the failings of his own democracy, but he captures many of the perennial problems that are systemic in any democratic rule. What is to stop a democracy voting into power people with a dangerously bent moral compass? How can democracies be protected against deception and fraud if they are set up to reward what is popular, rather than what is true or what is right? Are democracies not hazardously wired into our emotions, rather than our heads? And so on.

Indeed, Plato was aiming some of his arrows here at the Sophists of his time – highly paid men who tutored politicians in the art of rhetoric, the most famous of which were Gorgias, Thrasymachus and Callicles. Their role in Ancient Athens has clear equivalences today, but perhaps the closest fitting job title for their occupation would read 'Spin Doctor'.

The word 'Sophist' is rooted in the Greek for 'wise', σοφός (*sophos*). However, although the original Sophists certainly provided a knowledgeable education alongside their training in public speaking,[104] the word came to denote something negative. Today, 'sophistry' is defined as "the clever use of arguments that seem true but are really false, in order to deceive people".[105] This shift in meaning from Homeric times to today is mainly due to the heavy criticism that Socrates, Plato and Aristotle[106] levelled at them.

The guidance that the Sophists gave had nothing to do with measuring yourself or a situation to the truth; it had everything to do with winning an argument and winning the popular vote. When the crew on board Plato's ship were not involved in vicious fights between them, plotting manipulative and dirty tricks, they deployed all of their sophistry with the captain to gain control over the direction of travel. Here, on board the allegorical ship "Demos", Plato installs the Navigator as a contrast to that culture. Philosophers literally love wisdom (philo = love, sophos, wisdom). It is a discipline that yearns to uncover the true nature of things; Plato would insist that this search was connected to something deeper than mere opinion and something more noble than word play or trickery.

---

104 Sophos is derived from σοφίζω (sophizo), which means "to instruct or make learned."
105 Cambridge English Dictionary.
106 Aristotle's criticism of the Sophists was not that well received because he himself was a tutor (to the young man who became Alexander the Great).

On Board USS Bush

"I know how hard it is to put food on your family."
(New Hampshire, Jan 2000)
"Rarely is the question asked: is our children learning?"
(Florence, S.C., Jan 2000)
"There's a huge trust. I see it all the time when people come up to me and say, "I don't want you to let me down again."
(Boston, Oct 2000)

Fifteen years ago, it used to be amusing to quote various "Bushisms" in a classroom presentation on the 'Republic' to illustrate Plato's concerns about 'mob rule'. However, it was important to remain very sober about how costly a lack of respect for the truth and an appetite for war could be: After the 9/11 attacks, the swashbuckling George Bush Jr. strode through the swinging saloon doors of the White House and announced a game of Cowboys and Indians in the Gulf.

"Operation Iraqi Freedom" started to blow up Iraq's infrastructure and make huge holes in the lives of millions of families on March 20th, 2003.
The decoupling of foreign policy from the facts about Saddam Hussein's WMD capacity, the trespassing of the boundaries of international law and the undermining of international institutions, all caused major damage to the validity of western democratic rule.
The real forces that were at play in Iraq were clearly identified by Plato in The Piraeus: appetites and spiritedness. Noble reasoning was notably absent. Regrettably, this episode was a prequel for what was to come. "Bushisms" now almost read like old jokes from a more innocent generation. Trump and Bolsanaro, Farage and Boris, have taken populist sentiment to a new, grotesque level. Indeed, it is not only the level of language that has dropped to new lows. Where language leads, actions follow. The catalogue of the damage they are causing continues to bulge...

Plato's maritime parody of politics is bitingly relevant today, in an age of populist fantasies and FAKE NEWS.

Politics has always had a creative relationship with the truth. However, within just a handful of years that flexibility has gone much further into a world of post-truth and alternative facts. The techniques that are most frequently used to score political points in our culture today have little to do with literary skills or knowledge, and much more to do with sheer pugnacity. This is TOO BAD!

However, the consequence is the same: truth has been pushed heavily to the side. The Navigator on board, with a genuine understanding of seamanship, is marginalised. He is SO BORING!!!

Moreover, Plato went one step further. It is not only Plato's concern that truth would be challenged by '*epithumia*' and '*thumos*', he went as far as anticipating that a democracy could dismiss the relevance of truth and reality altogether. The crew vying for the captain's attention cannot even tell the difference between truth and fiction. Indeed, they do not want to know the difference.

Truth decay is a serious condition for any state. We mostly think that this rot is something that affects totalitarian regimes that invest in 'thought police' and big wheels for their propaganda machines. The central insight of Plato's Allegory of the Ship is that democracies are also prone to truth decay.

In addition, whilst Trump and Bolsonaro represent the most rotten examples of truth decay, it is important not to miss Plato's fundamental analysis of democracy by being distracted by personalities. His critique of democracy is a systemic one – Plato does not think it is wise to organise a state by wiring the decision-making process into the desires.

Indeed, emissions were just as bad in a world that had Obama, Blair and Merkel as leaders.

There are three different aspects to this condition that all have direct relevance for climate change:

Truth Decay 1 – Sophistry

Plato actually names one of his works after a Sophist, "Gorgias". In that dialogue, Socrates ends up sharing a dinner with him at another Sophist's house (Callicles). The conversation is, perhaps unsurprisingly, concerned with rhetoric itself – something that Gorgias concedes early on "is persuasive but not instructive about right and wrong." ("*Gorgias*", 455a)

Socrates argues that sophists have no real skills or depth – they just know a few tricks. He points out that they do not develop the powers of analysis nor nurture virtues – both of which are fundamental to the art of statecraft.

POLUS: So you think oratory is a knack?

SOCRATES: Yes, I do, unless you say it's something else.

POLUS: A knack for what?

SOCRATES: For producing a certain gratification and pleasure." (462c)

A few lines later, Socrates insists that they simply have a knack that "guesses at what's pleasant with no consideration for what's best". (465a)

As the dinner and dialogues progress, Socrates reflects with sardonic humour on his upcoming trial:

"I won't have anything to say in court…For I will be judged as a doctor would be judged if a pastry chef accused him in front of a jury of children." (521e2-4)

He is sure that democracies are not set up to vote in favour of actions that are either difficult or unattractive. Like children, they do not easily understand the virtue of being told to undergo some bitter treatment for their own good, especially if on the other hand they are presented with a handful of treats as an alternative. Furthermore, they cannot tell the difference between the advanced skills of a doctor and the kindliness of what is sometimes translated as a 'sweetshop owner'. Therefore, Socrates does not go with much optimism into his trial; without the use of "flattering rhetoric" (522d) he is sure that he will be sentenced to death.

Ouch.

In fact, the dialogue ends in a darkly amusing way. One by one the guests leave or just stop talking to Socrates the value of what he is saying is not appreciated. And so, by the final section, Socrates ends up alone, just talking to himself (505c-509b).

The unfortunate fact about populism is that it is easy to take pot shots at complexity and nuance with blunt accusations and polarisations. Indeed, populist ideas gain votes by using this simple 'sweetshop' approach in which difficult and complicated situations are reduced to the cheap rewards of slogans and tribalism. This political advantage held by populists will be familiar to those who watched the torturous Brexit process with horror and the repugnancy of Trump's Presidency with despair, an advantage made more pronounced by the shrinking number of words or minutes that we are accustomed to in our consumption of the news.

William Davies, author of "*Nervous States: How Feeling Took Over The World*" (2018) asks: "What happens if sections of the news media, the political classes and the public insist that only sovereignty matters and that the complexities of governing are a lie invented by liberal elites? For one thing, it gives rise to celebrity populists, personified by Mr. Trump, whose inability to engage patiently or intelligently with policy issues makes it possible to sustain the fantasy that governing is simple."[107]

107 New York Times, "*Boris Johnson, Donald Trump and the Rise of Radical Incompetence*", July 13th, 2018.

Not surprisingly, the politics of climate change have been affected by these features of populism too.

At an event inside the Solvay Library of Brussels in 2017,[108] Donald Trump's climate change advisor, Myron Ebell, launched an astonishing attack on climate science that actually drew audible gasps from the small Conservative audience. The sharpest intake of breath was taken when, in the context of his own childhood in the rural Mid-West of the US, he said: "There is a belief among the elite that they know better how to protect the environment than people who actually live in the countryside... Time and time again 'experts' have theoretical, but no practical knowledge." Finishing with a flourish: "Whenever you hear 'environmental expert', think 'urban imperialist'".[109]

108 1st February 2017, *"Conservatives make the best Conservationists"*
     (organised by the ACRE group of MEPs).
109 From the notes taken by our 'Brussels Climate Academy' journalist, Carolina Teixeira.

At surface value, it is easy to see that Ebell was setting up an opposition between Trump's rural voting base and the liberal, cosmopolitan voters in the cities. However, Ebell's polarisation of 'Red Neck' versus 'White Collar' workers was not just about appealing to different voter profiles.

The far right populist's deeper intention is to make 'the environment' into an entirely tribal issue – totally divorced from a fight between true and false. Their strategy is to push to the side any possible scenario in which reality is discussed. Their aim is to create a political arena within which all truth claims are equally wrong or right, so that all judgements are reduced to mere opinions. Trump's petulant and grotesque insistence on the mainstream media being the "Fake Media" is part of that same tactical plan.

It has been a very successful ploy; it often seems as if politics has transformed itself in the last few years from being a professional Boxing match into being a showbiz Wrestling match. There are clear rules in Boxing; there is a skill set, training and a genuine fight to decide who is the better sportsman. Wrestling is just a fake fight for commercial profit.

"We are building the walls of God's house..."

Any meaningful discourse about climate change between a scientifically informed politician and a populist would be embarrassingly short and damaging for the populist. Climate change scepticism has been utterly debunked (see "*Popper Tackles Climate Change*"); therefore, any match-up framed by reality needs to be avoided by those who want to preserve the status-quo. What Ebell was trying to set up in the Solvay library was just a phony Wrestling match.

Indeed, the event was designed to provide sound bites for the news, and a few quotations for Twitter, Instagram and Facebook. Ebell did not take questions. Like in a wrestling match, everything was staged for maximum audience satisfaction, where money decides the script and in which personalities matter more than genuine skill. Indeed, Donald Trump's whole approach to politics has strong parallels with his time with the WWE.

Flattening truth to relativism and reducing public debates to mere tribalism is one of the first lessons in the far-right playbook. It provides them with a space to make the most outlandish or toxic claims about anything with impunity. It also makes it easier for them to weaponise information and to spread misinformation. It is no surprise that Donald Trump has shunned facing up to experienced and informed journalists in the White House press briefings – he prefers to shoot from the hip with his Twitter gun.

Beyond all of the noise, the problem is this: climate change is stubbornly true. It will not be charmed, brushed away or manipulated. It cannot be ignored. It is just there, and we must deal with it. All our economic and social ambitions are governed by the laws of physics and chemistry. These laws are absolute and utterly intolerant of hubris and sophistry. In a culture that inhabits virtual worlds more frequently, a consumer society that likes to mask and evade limits and a political climate that increasingly indulges fake explanations, it is rather a shock to the system to be confronted by an absolute fact. This is especially hard for us to accept from nature since we have spent centuries dominating and manipulating the biosphere for our benefit. It is a bit alarming to suddenly be put in front of an immovable fact that is not willing to negotiate.

Distracted, we have allowed our democratic ship to sail into threatening unchartered waters. Our modern, advanced societies have got into the habit of not dealing with reality. We have been side-tracked by the pastry chef on board and have grown inattentive to the doctor. In fact, the climate crisis is so far advanced that scientists and other very normal people have started to glue themselves to buildings in an attempt to have their concerns about the collapse of human civilisation recognised. Something is evidently not right if citizens have to resort to volunteering for arrest just to establish some points of common sense.

We are surrounded by ecological tipping points and the route to safer waters requires us to tack against some strong headwinds.

Plato foresaw the kind of trouble that a loose mind-set to the truth would bring. Furthermore, he thought that this casual attitude would be exaggerated in a democracy. This is because the democratic drive for equality and freedom would quickly override the search for truth.

The details of this analysis are examined in the section that follows.

Truth Decay 2 – Truth Flattening

What is interesting about Plato's claims about social structure is that he thought that the manner in which a society was set up would affect the way that people thought about the truth. He was anxious that a flattening of the social structure into a democracy would lead to a corresponding failure in people's minds – in which an understanding of truth would get flattened. Plato could see a significant connection between the fundamental organisation of a society and the way in which the people in it think.[110]

Plato came from a noble background. There is no question that he was an elitist and there is no question that the 'Republic' endorses an authoritarian regime. He will be lambasted by later philosophers for proposing

The ideal city

110 This was not the only aspect of Plato that filtered down to Karl Marx.

a state with seemingly unaccountable leaders at the top and for promoting propaganda to keep everyone in their place.

Sidestepping these prickly problems for the moment, the important issue to note here is that Plato thought that social structures should match the fact that everything has an order and a rank in the big scheme of things.

Some things were right, some things were wrong. Some things were more real, other things were less real. Not everything can or should be levelled. Reducing fundamental questions about life, ethics and society to merely an emotional, instinctive level was dangerous. He thought that democracies would make our hearts and minds go hazardously soft.

Plato was anxious that the democratic drive for equality and freedom would easily overflow and go beyond a transformation of social structures. He anticipated that it would eventually dissolve everything to those standards – including truth claims. He feared that democracy would level everything. Plato seems to have equated democracy with a moral relativism, as if it was an embodiment of the notion that there are no absolute moral values, and that all opinions are equally valid.

By contrast, Plato argued that there was an absolute, higher reality that humans needed to try and understand and come to terms with – a world of truth that exists independently and above human ignorance and human opinions: the "Forms".

Plato understood that there was an absolute inner nature to all things, a basic glue to existence which could be seen in the idea that mathematical truths do not shift according to time, place or culture. He even saw higher truths beyond the world of mathematics, a level of truth even more absolute. Plato named this ultimate reality: the "Forms". These abstract, 'cosmic gingerbread cutters', shaped all the different material of the world. Behind every hamster there was the "Form" of hamster. Indeed, everything participated in a truer Form of itself, from the 'Form of Cat' to the 'Form of Dog', from the 'Form of Circle' to the 'Form of Square'. Most significantly, the 'gold' citizens of his ideal state aspired to understand the highest forms of all – the 'Form of Beauty', the 'Form of Justice' and, ultimately, the 'Form of Good'. Knowledge of this unqualified quality was needed for anyone who was to use their wisdom in legislating for the polis.

The ambition of Philosophy was to examine the particular details of the world and work out its inner nature. Practising Philosophy for Plato was rather like trying to hack into a benign Matrix. The philosopher exercised his reason to gain access to the fundamental operating systems of existence.

He put reason and the senses in opposition to each other. If all of the philosophers in history were to be lined up, according to if they were more invested in reason or the senses to work out what was real, Plato would be one of the most prominent Rationalists.

What follows from this is that at the other end of the truth scale from the abstract Forms, Plato thought that the material world was just an inferior copy of reality. Art could be found at the opposite end of the scale; after all, art is an imitation of an imitation. For example, a painting of a dog is not even a dog, it is a fake dog; a statue is merely a copy of a boy; History is an incomplete and distorted view of a series of events.

Image 26. - Cute Dog

The 'Form of dog'
I was astonished one day outside an Ice Cream Café when my son Jules, just over one year old, pointed at a very scrawny chihuahua and said: "Dog!" Every parent is proud of their child's first words. But this was different. Having no dog in the house, and no friends or family with dogs, his only direct experience of dogs was through an impossibly thick picture board-book of animals. There was a dog in there – a huge golden Labrador that I would point at and go "Woof!", "Dog!" and (maybe once or twice) pant.
To make the mental connection between this imposing canine and the tiny animal that scuttled past the café was remarkable. Plato would say that he was remembering the 'Form of Dog' – noting the inner reality that all dogs share. He was connecting with the Forms that cannot be known by the senses – they are known by the intelligence. They are not seen, they are "intelligenced".

Any attempt to assign "dogginess" to a particular feature of dog is doomed to failure. (Cats have four legs, not all dogs have pointed nuzzles, some dogs are mute, some have lost their tail in an accident...) We can all intuit what makes a dog a dog, but the "dogginess" of a dog cannot be put into words. Plato would argue that it was exclusively an innate understanding of reality that prompted Jules' to correctly declare: "Dog!" #proud.

Some truths are more secure and valid than others. Not everything is equally right or wrong.

Central to Plato's political Philosophy is the idea that those who understand the inner nature of reality, who have a secure understanding of higher truths and values, should also have a fully independent role to play at the top of the state.

Hierarchies of truth were to be matched by social hierarchies.

Plato was, therefore, nervous about disconnecting the political order from this metaphysical order.

There is a lengthy discussion in Book One of the 'Republic' between Socrates and Polemarchus[111] in which Socrates insists that running a state is a skill (techné). For Plato, it makes no sense to have a state run as a democracy in the same way that it would seem absurd to run a hospital as a democracy. Imagine a doctor walking into a hospital ward, and then asking the patients to raise their hands in a vote as to whether the man in Bed 17 should have his leg amputated or not. Who knows how people would vote? Maybe the man in Bed 12 knows that the injured man is an athlete, and an amputation would end his career. He is thinking that it would be better to give him at least a chance of recovery. Maybe the woman in Bed 9 is a bit squeamish and she cannot imagine voting for such a drastic procedure. It is also possible that the woman in Bed 18 has just had a dark thought flash across her mind – she is thinking of voting for the amputation because she is so angry with the injured man. She has not slept for almost a week because of his reverberant snoring. Others, with the best interests of the man at heart, admit to themselves that they are simply guessing and hope they get it right.

In this imaginary hospital ward, the incompetent doctor notices that the fellow patients are hesitant to cast a vote; therefore he encourages them to go with their gut feeling or just simply to follow their instincts. The doctor himself knows that the operating theatre is quite overbooked and he has been set targets to keep the operational costs of the hospital down.

111 'Republic', 335.

As he proposes the vote, he phrases the options and tilts his voice in such a way as to incline the voters to vote against the operation.

This is no way to run a hospital. Handing the decision-making process over to people who will only vote from ignorance, and largely by sentiment, is both dangerous and dim. Decisions about medical care require a set of skills and understanding that only a medical degree and years of experience can provide. Only doctors have this techné, and they swear a Hippocratic Oath to offer the best possible treatment to the patient. There is a hierarchy of understanding, most importantly between doctor and patient, but also within the medical profession itself.

Medical degrees take years to complete and clinical expertise requires decades. Thankfully, Plato did not propose Student Loans for his Academy, as graduation from the world's first university in Athens for those being skilled in the art of statecraft would take 50 years. These 'Philosopher Kings' would take decades to acquire the wisdom, autonomy and understanding to make just decisions for the citizens. Plato forcibly argues that those who run a state should be required to do so by paying genuine attention to reality. As he puts it in the Allegory of the Ship, they should proceed with an understanding of the "seasons of the year, the sky, the stars, the winds".

By contrast, Plato sees a lack of respect for the truth and knowledge in a democracy as something potently dangerous. If all truth is flattened in the name of freedom or desire, then the democratic ship is in trouble. In Book 8 of the '*Republic*', he argues that democracy's desire for freedom would lead its citizens to drink "too deep from unmixed wine[112]" and a dangerous lack of distinctions would emerge throughout such a society. For example, where "the father habitually tries to resemble the child and is afraid of his sons, and the son likens himself to the father and feels no awe or fear of his parents." (562e). Plato also forecasts that students would no longer respect their teachers, the young copy the old and vice-versa (563a), and [sic] slaves

---

112 The Ancient Greeks mostly mixed their wine with water. The God Akratos was the demi-god, attendant on Dionysus, who drank unmixed wine – and is understood to be the god of 'festive excess'.

and masters, men and women, become equal before the law.[113]

This section finishes with a striking conclusion: "Then, summing up all of these things together," I said, "do you notice how tender they make the citizens' soul, so that if someone proposes anything that smacks in any way of slavery, they are irritated and can't stand it? And they end up, as you well know, by paying no attention to the laws, written or unwritten, in order that they may avoid having any master at all." (563d)[114].

"*No Common Sense*" on both Nietzsche and Arendt deal more fully with this tricky issue. Briefly:

Despite its modern ubiquity and seemingly cozy and tolerant approach to life, the maxim of moral relativism "there are no moral absolutes" is highly problematic.

Firstly, it fails to notice its own absolute claim that there are no absolutes. Moral Relativism is an incoherent position. Secondly, the fact that there are so many millions of people who still hold such a moral outlook in the modern world as if it were just common-sense, points to the sort of hazy, casual thinking that worried Plato. It was the type of thinking that could cause shipwrecks. Similarly, Nietzsche wanted to wake people up from a moral apathy. Arendt was preoccupied with how a banal "thoughtlessness" could colonise an individual and a society – with devastating consequences. Both modern thinkers shared with Plato a deep ambition to think beyond cultural clichés.

113 Plato has been held up as a champion of women's rights (mainly following the texts in Book 5) as they are affirmed as Philosophers for the community of the Guardians. However, much ink has been spilt both supporting and disputing his feminist credentials.
114 Bloom, A, "The '*Republic*' of Plato". Second Edition, Basic Books, (1991). p240-242.

Plato pushes the speculative narrative to a conclusion[115]: this lack of social hierarchy and order would not be sustainable, and from this state of chaos where no authority or boundaries are accepted, people would cry out for a simple ruler that would just take away all the mess, complications and difficulties. Indeed, Plato thought that democracies were prone to collapsing into dictatorships. All of which justifies his previous claim that: "The excess of liberty, whether in States or individuals, seems only to pass into excess of slavery..." (562c).

It is easy to dismiss Plato's fears about the in-built weakness of democracies to crumple into dictatorships by simply noting that the most stable, balanced and advanced states that have emerged in the last centuries have been democratic.

However, even though his ideas sound repellently authoritarian and impossibly traditionalist, it is worth allowing his diagnosis of democracy to remain standing. Plato should still be allowed to interrogate our current democracies. His writing might seem out-dated now, but Plato might have spotted something important behind the surface of things – something of real value for understanding our inertia about climate change.

The acute case of democratic truth decay that we are currently experiencing does matter and Plato offers a helpful view on the causes of our troubles: Plato's link between social structures and mental structures is an important contribution to our intellectual history.[116]

Whatever the right stance is between these two poles of Social Theory, it is evidently true that there is an interrelation between how a society is socially

---

115 For those readers who are familiar with Freud's view of 'Civilisation and its Discontents' (1930), this short extract from The 'Republic' shows that there are more parallels between Plato and Freud than just a three-fold division of the psyche. The essential point of contact here is that Freud also thought that people crave a place of meaning within a hierarchy. This is something that Lacan would later call a symbolic order.

116 As a more recent example, in the 19th century, Marx argued that the way we think is determined from the economic base upwards – whereas Weber saw everything the other way around, with beliefs determining our economic reality.

organised and the shape and the priorities of its thoughts. Although the interplay of both democracy and capitalism on our psyche will always remain ambiguous and complex, it does seem possible to put forward some tentative observations:

The language of capitalism naturally puts the self at the centre as the measure of things. A famous principle of the retail business is that: "The customer is always right". However, it is one thing to put consumers at the centre of their shopping choices, when the reduction of everything to an opinion or a taste does not really matter. The difference between a blue tie and a red tie, a Latte and a Cappuccino, is not of universal significance. However, this mode of thinking in a clothes or coffee shop can quickly transfer, unnoticed, from one zone of human life into another; from the private, economic sphere into the public, civic sphere. Major moral and social issues cannot be reduced to a question of taste – it is categorically not the same to declare a preference for a Latte over a Cappuccino compared to expressing a preference for consensual sex over rape.

There is a major difference between supporting a capitalist economy and endorsing a capitalist culture, but when the boundary between the two is so confused it can make having a clear debate about civic questions rather difficult.

If we are continually exposed to a type of thinking that habitually appeals to our desires or pride as the final measure of our judgments in the economic sphere – it is hard to switch gears when thinking about our civic space. In a culture that places an emphasis on the value of choice and the self, it is then easy for those in the political world who are pushing for environmental deregulation to appeal to our instinctive offence at boundaries, laws and limits.

Indeed, the influence of wealth on the decision-making process was a significant part of Plato's thinking and deserves greater attention. Having examined the indirect threats of wealth to a just society, it is now appropriate to look at the more obvious, direct threat of wealth to warp our civic thinking.

Truth Decay 3 – Buying the Truth

It is informative to revisit a few lines from the Allegory of the Ship again: "They spend all their time milling round the captain", they "lay out the honest captain with drugs or drink or in some other way, take control of the ship, help themselves to what's on board, and turn the voyage into a sort of drunken pleasure-cruise" (488c).

Our desires and spiritedness are so potent. They can quickly override our reason. Moreover, their capacity to overwhelm our thinking becomes amplified quickly when wealth and property are introduced into the scenario. This is equally true for both individuals and for society. Indeed, Plato's interest in how social structures affect our thought processes was later explored further by Marx, who also understood how much wealth can corrupt our thinking. Both Plato and Marx saw how much property lies at the root of civil unrest.

It was for this reason that Plato wanted to prohibit the Philosopher Kings and Queens from ownership. Plato puts them into an entirely separate community, thereby insulating them from the dangerous blusters of desire, and from any storms of pride. His measures are not moderate: such is his concern about the capacity of money to destabilise a society, Plato advocates the complete elimination of property from the ruling class.

The outlawing of property for both the "Guardians" and the "Auxiliaries" was to be explained to the citizens through the Myth of Metals: they are forbidden from touching gold or silver, because it would be impious to mix the divine metal of their soul with that of the Earth. They are not permitted to even be under the same roof with it (417a).

Furthermore, the Guardians do not have a private room (416d-e), they share their meals (which are provided by the workers), sexual partners[117] and they even share their children (457d). No form of ownership would distract them from their civic duties.

The love of wisdom was to be their overriding concern. Their lives were to be not unlike that of a monastic community, in that they were to live and work in seats of learning and contemplation. They were to devote themselves to the highest ideals, without the temptations and distortions of worldly concerns. The difference was that they were there to think about the City of Man, not the City of God.

Plato's ambition to hold public and private interests at the maximum distance possible from each other for the ruling class might seem radical. However, it would not have been such an alien idea to his early readers. The ancient Greeks made a clear distinction between private and public interests in both their minds and in their institutions. Male citizens ran their private concerns with absolute authority – a patriarchy that covered all members of their family, their slaves and their estate. However, these domestic affairs were left behind when they entered into the public space (to debate, to vote or to fight, for example). As citizens, when they acted and spoke on behalf of the polis, it was understood that they did not fix their thinking and voting with any private concerns from their home.

In the modern world, the boundaries between these two spheres of human life have become increasingly smudged. The gap between what is a private interest and what is a public interest has largely been lost – mostly due to colonisation of the public space by private interests. The contrast between ancient and modern political thinking is explored with great insight by Hannah Arendt who laments the erosion of a genuine public sphere for debate and action (see *Arendt Tackles Climate Change*).

---

117 Sex was actually regulated amongst the upper classes so as to maximise the chances of breeding optimal children. This programme of eugenics was to be played out behind a fake lottery (460a), a sort of Ancient Greek 'Spin the Bottle'.

Therefore, the autonomy of the Navigator on Plato's ship, detached from the shenanigans of the crew, is an important reminder of that boundary. The Philosopher is the key person on board, because he is the only one who is attentive to reality ("the sky, the stars, the winds"), he is the only one who is committed to the truth and the ship's welfare. Plato puts him on the ship because he is fully aware of how corrosive wealth can be to the clarity of thoughts that we have about truth and justice.

The emphasis here on the autonomy of the Navigator ("The Guardians") is not written in order to defend the Platonic intention to eradicate money from the political decision-making process. Plato might have to forgive this take on his Philosophy, but it seems reasonable to use his utopian thinking as a way to sharpen our diagnosis of what is wrong with our current political order. We can fully engage with Plato's radical analysis and can allow him to interrogate our society, without subscribing to a full implementation of his plan.

A long time after Plato, the Enlightenment retuned into the importance of reason. This time, a confidence grew in the ability of the common people to think about the state they were in, and so modern societies increasingly took on the collective responsibility of democratic decision-making. In the same period, industrialisation and capitalism made huge gains.

The spectacular growth of these three aspects of modern civilisation are not necessarily incompatible. Democracy, industrialisation and capitalism could all serve each other. However, we must continually ensure that our democratic institutions are safely insulated from the dangers that accompany the atomisation of people in industrial societies and which insulate them from the misuse of the power of money. The point of this use of the Allegory of the Ship is to underline the fact that certain firewalls, between the civic and the private spaces, must be maintained. It is a gap that the ancient Greek society respected with good reason.

Money is a form of power, it is not just a method of transaction. This is an issue that requires real attention, given the vast size of some private pockets of wealth that exist in the modern economy. If these interests grow to form such a formidable strength that they pose a genuine threat to the authentic functioning of our democracies, then we should be willing and able to ask uncomfortable questions about their place in society of those individuals with that wealth.

Basically, nobody onboard our democratic ship should be able to buy the truth.

Capital Flows

Modern western societies have moved far beyond the ancient Greek slave society and Feudal system into a capitalist world in which major businesses hold huge amounts of capital. In this context, the chart on the following page illustrates how money can flow through different aspects of our democratic system in a feedback loop that amplifies the wealth of those in power at the expense of some public interests.

Major corporations spend millions through Lobbying, Political Campaigns and various traditional Media and Social Media channels to influence the way in which citizens vote. The political parties that then form a government either protect existing legislation or change legislation (often simply by deregulation); this favours the interests of those corporations. The extra capital is then reinvested into reinforcing public opinion, which leads to votes and then legislation. This feedback loop continues to gather strength to the advantage of those in that jet-stream.

The key area of the chart is in blue on the left where the media and elections are in play. This area is where a society gets to reflect and think about the direction in which it is travelling. It is the zone inside which governments are held to account. If those with the most wealth in a democratic society get too much control of this area, then the most important component in the democratic system is compromised.

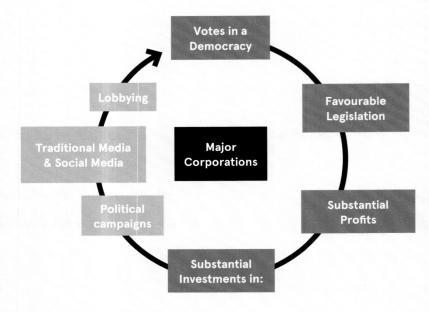

Not included in the flow: 1.   A Concern for the Truth and Justice
Critical Journalism,   2.   Minority Rights
which protects: 3.   The Commons

Additional notes for the chart:
° In nations like the USA "Political Campaigns" have a greater significance as there is only modest amount of legislation to limit how they are funded. Severely restricting this umbilical cord between the business world and the political parties they support would significantly improve the depth of democratic representation in all nations, especially in the USA.
° Likewise, the box for "Lobbying" will vary from nation to nation according to the legislation around it. No matter the legislation, there are always soft forms of lobbying that find their way into the political bloodstream.
° There are also vulnerabilities from outside the system, in the case of the Brexit Referendum and the US Elections of 2016, Russia invested millions into social media channels to achieve an outcome that would cause the maximum damage to the cohesion of Western democracies.

A free and critical media is fundamentally important to any democracy – it is the journalists who carry the noble burden of holding a government to account over issues of truth and justice, the rights of minorities and crucially for climate change – The Commons.

Another crisis of representation

Arguably, our democracies have arrived at another moment of crisis, another crisis of representation. This time it is nothing to do with race or gender, it is about money, once again.

The Peterloo Massacre of Manchester in 1819 celebrated its 200th birthday recently. It was a pro-democracy demonstration that was symbolic of an age. The bulging populations of northern towns had an absurdly small voice in the Parliament of the United Kingdom. In protest, around 60,000 men, women and children gathered in St Peter's Fields to demand reform.

Image 27. - Peterloo Massacre Memorial

The battle to enlarge democracy has always been fought between those with wealth, influence and a vote against those who were without all three. Now that we are 200 years further down the democratic road, most people have been given their legitimate space on the political radar. The new challenge is to make sure that the votes do not get bought out by money.

There are a whole range of reasons why there has been so much 'trickle-up' of capital in recent years – rather than the commonly expected effect of 'trickle-down'. In the hugely popular work, *"Capital in the Twenty-First Century"* (2013), Thomas Piketty provides a detailed account of how this consolidation of capital occurred. Whatever the causes, the increasing divide between rich and poor within the advanced democratic economies of the planet is not just an issue of social justice[118] – it also poses a serious threat to some fundamental principles of democracy itself.

The concentration of wealth into a small corner of an economy does not just afford those with that capital the luxury of buying products and services, it can also buy political influence – both directly and indirectly. If a few narrow business interests (including the banks) end up with an unaccountable level of control over the workings of a democracy, then the state would be more fairly described as a de facto Oligarchy.

The precise point at which a critical loss of power happens will always be ambiguous.[119] However, without the proper exercise of democratic checks, which should be evident in a genuinely free press and free elections, a democracy would exist in name only. As Yanis Varoufakis commented: "It is possible to be a government in power today, but not in power". How close are we to such a point? Who knows, but there are strong indicators that point to dangerous levels of democratic erosion.

How could we have got into such a predicament with climate change if everything were functioning well? Just a brief look at the science graphs and the continued investments in fossil fuels is such an offence to common sense. The sheer absurdity of it all indicates that there is a major fault with the system. There should be no need for books of Philosophy to peel away different layers of our psychology to see something so utterly basic.

However the climate crisis ends, those in the Public Relations business for the fossil fuel industries will be credited with the extraordinary achievement of successfully camouflaging such a narrow, private interest

---

118 Some have criticised Piketty for assuming that inequality is necessarily wrong. These criticisms have not just been drawn from neo-liberal economists, but also from Rawlsian scholars whose primary focus is the welfare of the poorest – and this is not incompatible with inequality.

119 There is a field of enquiry in Philosophy that is interested in this ambiguity. It has a technical name: the problem of 'Vagueness'. Scholars in fields as diverse as Logic, Metaphysics and Semantics have puzzled long and hard over a proper understanding of situations where there are 'No Sharp Boundaries'. The problem of vagueness is of crucial importance at the psychological level of Political Philosophy – as readers of Thomas Hobbes will understand.

for so long. The depth of destruction that is taking place to our shared environment is a grotesque reality. Yet it is somehow happening with near impunity. Such a situation must not be brushed-off with a casual attitude towards the balance of public and private concerns in a society. Any genuine democracy cannot have the political sphere colonised by the private interests of so few. The ideals in Plato's '*Republic*' simply serve as a reminder of the importance of civic thinking and decision making away from the potency of cash.

Having fought so hard and sacrificed so much to make democracy work, the Western World cannot afford to stop making large investments in it.

A most dangerous creature: The Kochtypus

On April 2nd, 2014, the Supreme Court of the United States handed down a ruling in the case of "*McCutcheon v. FEC*". The details are fiendishly complex, but the core conclusion was that limits on the contributions that individuals can make to political parties and individuals were unconstitutional. The decision was split 5-4, with Judge Clarence Thomas providing the decisive vote.

The lawyers who tried to defend the laws that limited the financial contributions expressed their disappointment at the ruling: "The response of today's decision eviscerates our Nation's campaign finance laws, leaving a remnant incapable of dealing with the grave problems of democratic legitimacy that those laws were intended to resolve."

Even without this ruling, the openness of the American political system to the influence of money should surely just be called 'bribery'. If the name, flag and context of the USA was taken out of view, any outside observer would see a political system that is so predisposed to narrow financial interests that they might easily conclude that it was a country struggling to move from a dictatorship to a democracy. The USA offers one of the most striking examples of how money can warp the democratic process. Every nation is vulnerable to having their democratic ships hijacked by treasure hunters, but the USA provides one of the clearest examples of this threat.

One detail of the "*McCutcheon v. FEC*" case is very informative: Judge Clarence Thomas had some significant links to the Koch Brothers. Prior to this case, Judge Thomas had already been challenged about his impartiality in rulings about political financing, as he had attended several of the Koch Brothers' events and retreats. The court files against Thomas had been compiled by the organisation "Common Cause.[120]" It was neither the first nor the last time that a tentacle of the 'Kochytpus' had been spotted in public affairs.

The Koch Brothers provide a vivid example of the threat that money poses to the health of a democracy. They built one of the most astonishingly powerful corporations in the world, and at the same time invested billions of dollars in trying to shape the political world to fit their own private interests.

Charles and David[121] Koch made their joint fortune of over $100bn in the fossil fuel and chemical industries, in finance and trading, in paper and pulp, in fibres and fertilisers and many others. Even more diverse, however, is the system of influence that they have developed to protect those same interests. The "Kochtypus" has eight tentacles, including key people in the courtroom and in congress, key 'Astroturf agencies' and academics and important outlets of their Libertarian ideas through media personalities and numerous think tanks. The full details can be viewed easily online.

120 Common Cause describes itself as: "a nonpartisan, grassroots organization dedicated to upholding the core values of American democracy. We work to create open, honest, and accountable government that serves the public interest."
121 David Koch died on 23rd August 2019.

The fossil fuel industry, exemplified by the Koch Brothers, has strategically invested their resources into undermining and suspending definitive climate action. they have pumped their dirty money into all the pipes of our democratic thinking under the auspices of democratic virtues of 'freedom', 'tolerance' and 'individual rights'.

As Plato observed with the isolated Navigator on the ship, they are willing to do anything to marginalise the truth. They have been playing the game of denying the climate science for so long that "they think that it's quite impossible to acquire the professional skill needed for such control (whether or not they want it exercised) and that there's no such thing as an art of navigation".

The Kochtypus sting
Under the Kochs' umbrella group "Americans for Prosperity", an army of activists "armed with iPads full of data and a fiery script" came to Nashville to create a groundswell of opposition to improvements to the local public transport system. In a city with consistently gridlocked roads, a plan to invest $5.4bn in trains and buses was popular with businesses, the mayor and the locals. However, the Koch Brothers have developed a huge national database called "i360" which identifies who might be predisposed to their worldview about 'small government'.
After 42,000 strategic phone calls and 6000 tactical door knocks, the transport plan was defeated by a landslide on May 1st, 2018.

Plato makes the rather alarming assertion that those on the ship are willing to kill anyone who makes informed truth claims. This might look rather like an overstatement. However, those who have experienced how far vicious populist politics can go in the fight for control of the social narratives, would want the visceral nature of politics to be remembered.

In the absence of philosopher's being made into Kings, Plato proposed making Kings into Philosophers. The good news is that the basic realities of climate change are not complex at all. The modern democratic decision-makers (voters, shareholders and consumers) should be informed about the key points of science and the changes that need to be made. The way forward out of the crisis should be simple to see. However, in order to make our modern voters (or "King Makers"[122]) more reasonable in their decision-making, there remains a $100bn Kochtypus in the room that we have to talk about.

A Zombie Walk?

Pause a moment.

Is this not going a bit too far? Are our minds really that soggy? Does a stronger flow of capital inside a consumer culture really make such a difference? Are we really that slow to understand our situation? Are we that easily duped by a small group of corporations? Would we treat a Navigator on our ship in such an ignorant way today? Perhaps we have indulged Plato's elitist view of society too much? Does capital really bend the tubes of our brains that much? Surely, we can make the distinction between a casual opinion about a product and the robust conclusions of a scientific research?

Have we been transformed into zombies again[123]?

It has to be admitted that in 2012 on October 13th, 15,458 Zombies did walk through Minneapolis (USA). It was a world record. There are a rising number of Zombie marches throughout the world, and a growing interest in Zombie culture.

---

122 "The proudest now is but my peer, The highest not more high; To-day, of all the weary year, A king of men am I. To-day alike are great and small, The nameless and the known, My palace is the people's hall, The ballot-box my throne! ... To-day let pomp and vain pretence, My stubborn right abide; I set a plain man's common sense, Against the pedant's pride. To-day shall simple manhood try, The strength of gold and land, The wide world has not wealth to buy, The power in my right hand!". John Greenleaf Whittier, "*The Poor Voter on Election Day*" (1848).

123 The first major zombie attack happened in 1968, in "*The Night of the Living Dead*" (dir. G. Romero).

Indeed, Wikipedia defines some Zombie characteristics as:

• Mobile but technically dead, without a heartbeat or other vital signs;
• Non-communicative;
• Contagious: a person that is bitten by a Zombie will become a Zombie;
• Unemotional, with no mercy toward victims;
• Clumsy and violent;
• Vulnerable to destruction of the brain, which kills them;
• Unaffected by injuries, even normally fatal ones
  (as long as they do not hurt the brain too much).

Image 28. - Zombie Walk

With over 100 nations of the world achieving a literacy rate of over 90%[124], it seems implausible that we could be in such a muddle about something as simple as the heating effect of atmospheric CO_2. It is equally implausible that a rational society would push its civilisation so close to catastrophic tipping points. How could we be so empty-headed?

Plato has certainly been criticised for underestimating our general level of thinking skills. Many have rebuked him for his Myth of the Metals in which most people in the Athenian polis were given inferior Bronze souls. Some have seen the shadow of Plato's elitist thinking in the reluctance of western democracies to enlarge their voter base (note Edmund Burke's assessment of the working class, following page).

124 https://data.worldbank.org/indicator/se.adt.litr.zs?most_recent_value_desc=false

Has our democratic consumer culture really made us that brain dead? Is the Allegory of the Ship not too alarmist about the dangers of pleasure cruising? We all have our faults, and every form of government has its weaknesses, but are things really so bad that we have to start asking fundamental questions about democracy's value?

Edmund Burke, on us 'berks'
Edmund Burke (b. 1729) was writing at the time of the Enlightenment when we might expect more optimism about the universal human faculty of reason. However, the attitude observed in this often-quoted text shows that Plato's anxiety about the masses remained commonplace. He writes: "The occupation of a hair-dresser, or of a working tallow-chandler, cannot be a matter of honour to any person—to say nothing of a number of other more servile employments. Such descriptions of men ought not to suffer oppression from the state; but the state suffers oppression, if such as they, either individually or collectively are permitted to rule. In this you think you are combating prejudice, but you are at war with nature". "*Reflections on the French Revolution*". The Harvard Classics. 1909-14. Paragraph 80.

Unfortunately, any engagement with the science graphs will inform us that as a body of people we are indeed behaving rather like zombies. This is not a comment on our intelligence. This is not a call for the abolition of democracy. However, it is an invitation to take a moment of sober reflection about what we are doing. Plato helps us to analyse how democracies can fail, sometimes catastrophically.

This should not come as a surprise. We have walked into global disasters before. The march of nationalism and other social forces looked like a zombie walk to many commentators in the build up to the outbreak of war in 1914. Norman Angell's work, "The Great Illusion" (1911)[125] was written

125 It was originally published in the UK as "Europe's Optical Illusion" in 1909. It has been rebranded, reprinted and often misunderstood ever since.

to point out the sheer self-destructive idiocy of war. It was an immensely popular book. Many people read it and took comfort from the fact that his reasoning was so solid, they concluded that no sane person in power could actually allow something so truly bonkers, like World War, to ever happen.

But then, 1914 happened.

In fact, as it turned out, Igor Stravinsky had already published the riotous soundtrack for the war, a year ahead of time. With almost prophetic foresight, in his ballet, the '*Rite of Spring*' (1913), a juggernaut of sound accompanies the dance of an innocent young girl to her death. Tellingly, her final moves are performed as a circle of sage elders watches on.

Plato's '*Republic*' is an invitation to be honest about where we are up to. The global transfer of capital to a tiny group of people has occurred at such a great pace (especially since the global financial crash of 2007-2008) that it is sure to have wider implications than just the raw numbers in different bank accounts. The enhanced ability of this small subset of society to affect our thoughts and patterns of behaviour is an entirely predictable consequence of this shift. It is surely not outlandish to claim that how we see and respond to the climate crisis will be strongly influenced by this centre of gravity.

As Thrasymachus cynically commented to Socrates in the opening book of the '*Republic*', "... justice is nothing other than the advantage of the stronger" (338c). There has not been time to explore the arguments that were put forward by Thrasymachus in the first exchanges of conversation in The Piraeus. However, his reductivist claim that justice was just a word that would be continually hijacked by those in power, to mean whatever suited their interests, remains a bracingly relevant idea.

This whole section about the dangers of any one faction of a society being able to buy the truth could be reduced to Thrasymachus' basic insight – now often captured in the aphorism that 'Might makes Right'. Money can buy you the smart thinking and smart strategies offered by those with the brains to manipulate our perception of reality.

This does not require us to get carried away by whacked-out conspiracy theories or extravagant sci-fi films to entertain the idea that we have been somehow turned into walking zombies by a consumer culture that has a group of immensely powerful multinational corporations at its core. They are wired to maximise profit for the quarterly reviews of investors, they will logically invest their money in the direct and indirect control of their consumer base. More subtly, for all the failings of Marxist societies, Karl Marx deserves perennial respect for his probing diagnosis of how an economic 'Base' affects a society's 'Superstructure'.[126]

Our democracies might not be collapsing into military dictatorships, but we must be alert to the dangers of getting hijacked by a small minority of private interests. Such a type of soft oligarchy, made up of a concentration of global corporate powers, can gain a decisive level of control over the mainframe of our thought. Perhaps the problem is that we mostly associate tyranny and oligarchies with violence and terror, and with stringent military and police control. Such an association is entirely understandable given the brutal power that 20th century tyrannies have unleashed on civilisation. We were right to defend ourselves and our values when faced with the atrocities that these regimes brought with them. By contrast, we are now faced with the oddest of situations in which the existential threat is not only concealed in a benign looking system out there, it is also at work internally, in all of us.

---

126 As Marx and Engels succinctly commented: "The ideas of the ruling class are in every epoch the ruling ideas, i.e. the class which is the ruling material force of society, is at the same time its ruling intellectual force." (*The German Ideology*, Part 1, 1846)

"We have met the enemy, and he is us"[127]

How utterly bizarre that while all of this destruction was taking place, we were not engaged in a fight against some invading alien force. As this demolition continued to happen, we did not resist an odious ideology. On the contrary, we were all just being fairly nice to each other and generally trying to have a bit of fun. Therefore, when the graphs that illustrate the current ecocide are put side-by-side with some snapshots of our mainstream culture, it is very difficult to reconcile the two images. Worse still, the destruction of the ecosystems of planet Earth is on the margins of our consciousness and this could actually turn out to be the most destructive of all.

Image 29. - The Matrix

Maybe the Zombie Walk record will get smashed in around 2036 if more than seven billion people do not act decisively to prevent CO_2 levels in the atmosphere reaching a level that will lock in a 2°C rise.

127 This has been taken from the Earth Day, 1971 poster. However, the phrase was first used as a parody by Walt Kelly in 1953 in his critique of McCarthyism. Kelly had played with the message sent by US Commodore Perry back in the war of 1812, after they had captured an enemy British ship: "We have met the enemy and they are ours; two ships, two brigs, one schooner and one sloop".

For us to have arrived at such a sharp end game of ecological decision-making, without any previous show of decisive resistance or rebellion, demonstrates that dysfunctional thinking is at play at all levels of the system. This view is evidenced both in the external social systems and in our internal systems of thinking and acting. It is easy to ridicule politicians who seem to have lost the distinction between truth and lies because it suits their ambitions and egos.[128] It is easy to point an accusing finger at the CEOs who run their corporations for the narrow interests of shareholders. However, this misses the point of Plato's critique of democracy. We are all participants in a system that is set up to primarily serve our desires.

We live inside a culture in which truth has diminished in value. We are increasingly unanchored from external realities and led towards a progressively virtual world of sentiment. In the e-based consciousness of today, our detachment from the actual world means that our expectations and thinking are less regulated by natural boundaries. Such a scenario makes us more vulnerable to manipulation by those who control the coordinates of those worlds.

In October 2019, the BBC launched an upgrade to its News service. A listener can now say: "Alexa, give me the news with extra Jacob-Rees Mogg", to select views which they prefer, thereby filtering out content which they do not like. Indeed, whole topics can be removed – which some with COVID-19 or Brexit fatigue would currently welcome. However, those who are concerned with the amplification of Echo Chambers in the media see this as a cause for concern.

---

128 It would be very interesting to read the mind of some of the leading populist politicians as they lie on their pillow at night, processing the day's events. How much of their thinking is performed as a Machiavellian strategy: conscious, skilful and purposefully manipulative of the truth? Or have they suppressed truth and reality so deeply, under the weight of their political ambitions that they cannot tell the difference anymore. the (highly) Conservative parties in Europe about their environmental and climate policies in the Solvay Library (cf. pages 42-43), it seems that the latter is the case.

Soma so good

Here is the big irony to bring this section about truth decay to a close.

In the first half of the 20th century, and in the aftermath of the World Wars, the US government was anxious to curb the evidently violent and irrational instincts of human beings and sought to bring about something placid and constructive. One World War was bad enough, but having to bludgeon our way through a Second World War really did pose some uncomfortable questions about human nature.

The US turned to the psychiatric insights of Freud's nephew, Edward Bernays to help them understand the chaotic and destructive forces that must be at work under the surface of things. Apart from leading the push for the establishment of legal frameworks for peace through the United Nations, they also invested millions of dollars in mollifying our primal instincts through the soft comforts of consumerism. The details of this sub-plot to American culture can be found in *Arendt Tackles Climate Change*".

However, here is the irony. That pacification of our human impulses had the double effect of dulling both our critical thinking skills and our civic skills. So now, as we face a new existential threat, we somehow can't really see it. When we look at it, our minds are so doped up on 'Soma'[129] that we do not really react to it.

For the moment, far too many people see increased recycling and reduced plastics as somehow relevant to the sheer scale of the dangers we are in. The gigantic churning up of the earth for resource extraction continues to accelerate, as does the pace of the planet's bio-diversity loss. The asymmetry between the science and our actions is so pronounced that clear-minded, mature and highly educated people have started to give up their jobs and glue themselves to trains and buildings.

How utterly bizarre that such an action is so rational.

"What you need is a gramme of soma."

"All the advantages of Christianity and alcohol; none of their defects."

...

"Take a holiday from reality whenever you like, and come back without so much as a headache or a mythology."

"Take it," insisted Henry Foster, "take it."

"Stability was practically assured."

"*Brave New World*" (1932), Aldous Huxley (Chapter 3. 218–26)

---

129 "*Soma*", (Sanskrit, "सोम") is an ancient ritual Vedic drink made from an uncertain plant base. What is certain is that this drink produced hallucinogenic thoughts. It is the pill that is popped by those in Huxley's Brave New World for those moments when their thoughts and emotions need soothing.

Philosophy in the fight against Truth Decay

There has never been a time at which Philosophy was not relevant. However, given the global scale of the problem, the holistic thinking needed to get us out of it and the existential nature of the crisis, it is difficult to resist the temptation to state that this really is a uniquely relevant moment for the subject.

It is important not to forget the trauma that Plato went through as a young man. He did not idly write his 'Republic' out of some speculative, dreamy ambition to make the world a better place. His utopian 'Kallipolis' was conceived in a crucible of suffering. He had witnessed something devastating.

By setting the scene in The Piraeus, and by choosing a ship to carry one of his central messages, Plato was skewering Athenian society where it hurt most. To criticise the Athenian democracy with a naval image was a biting piece of satire. There would be no mistaking the explicit reference that he was making to the Athenian vote to take on Sparta with their navy.

They sailed their expeditionary force into the bay of Syracuse, under the influence of strong appetites and 'spiritedness'. It all seemed so heroic at the time. Indeed, their pride and energy had been channelled towards Sicily by their military general, Alcibiades.[130] His charisma and pumped up rhetoric elevated the expectations of the Athenians – until they lost.

Plato had also been crushed by a personal tragedy with the death of Socrates. His critique of democracy was not written as some off-hand, elitist dismissal of the working class. Plato's analysis of democracy is informed by a probing analysis of individual psychological dynamics and

---

130 Alcibiades was voted into office as the Athenian military General in 417 BCE. A military 'hawk', he increased the size of the Athenian commitment to Sicily from a fleet of 60 ships to, "140 galleys, 5,100 men at arms, and about 1300 archers, slingers, and light armed men". Plutarch, « *Lives of Illustrious Men* », Volume 1 (trans. John Dryden), p392.

how these play out as social forces. He invites us not to underestimate these irrational energies.

The USA and Brazil have lurched in recent years towards many of the darker consequences of democracy that Plato foresaw. Post-truth politics have ripened into a very 'Strange Fruit' in both of those nations. Yet, despite the election of Trump and Bolsanaro, it remains hard to look at our modern democracies and imagine that Plato could be substantially right in his analysis because we hold our open system of government in such high esteem.

In our cultural memories, democratic rule still stands in noble contrast to two utterly appalling alternatives. In the twentieth century, the heinous rage of the Third Reich was overcome by our deeper commitment to democratic tolerance and peace. The stifling totalitarian oppression of the USSR, which hung over Eastern Europe for decades, eventually permitted the fresh air of democracy in, following the collapse of the Berlin Wall. Democracies really do embody so many of our most treasured values, and we rightly fought with blood to defend them.

It is, therefore, a major psychological challenge to take on Plato's *Republic* and to allow ourselves to think about democracy in such negative terms. However, it is a leap in thinking that we must take.

The natural world is being flattened at a savage speed. Millions of species are clinging to the last fragmentary pockets of habitat that our great vacuum cleaner of 'civilisation' has not yet hoovered up. Under the watch of democracy there has been a rapacious destruction of thousands of extraordinary ecosystems. Our democracies have tacitly endorsed the evisceration of a bewildering array of biological niches, all for the sake of things as banal as a packet of cheap supermarket ginger biscuits. Such is the scale of human population and our consumer expectations, we have even brought entire biomes to the brink of collapse.

Until we are prepared to ask ourselves some acutely painful questions about the failings of our system, there is little reason to suppose that we will be able to stop the irrational power that is taking us deeper into the Anthropocene. The aerial shots of the Canadian Tar Sands and the Palm Oil plantations of Malaysia provide us with the footage of the most important battlegrounds for the years ahead. With an attentive look, we can see the ghosts of Passchendaele in the churned-up chaos of the Tar Sands and an echo of the Third Reich in the industrialised uniformity of those long lines of oil palm trees.

Invoking such horrific episodes from the past is not written lightly. They need to be brought to the surface of our memories because what we are facing is the possibility of a global collapse that will cause devastating consequences for millions. They both happened on democracy's watch. Having the 'Democratic' label on your civilisation does not guarantee any protection from human lunacy or the dark drives of our psyche. Just because we live in a system that celebrates so many important values and virtues does not mean that something profoundly destructive is nonetheless happening anyway.

We have been utterly irrational before. We cannot afford to be complacent.

Conclusion to the Allegory of the Ship

Utopia

After all of this analysis, what conclusions about the Allegory of the Ship can be drawn?

Probably the first thing to note is that Plato's '*Republic*' never happened.

A cursory look at the history books will inform us that the crew on board never passed control of the ship to the Navigator. The just city ruled by a small group of Philosopher Kings never got off the pages and into the real world. Plato's utopian vision remained literally that: οὐ τόπος (*ou topos*), literally "no place".

Perhaps the closest it ever sailed to reality was (a little ironically) in Syracuse, Sicily. Towards the end of his life, Plato was invited there by the tyrant Dion (408-354 BCE) who was a committed Platonist. Dion's invitation was issued with the ambition to make the King (Dionysus I) into a philosopher.

However, in the blustering winds of court power that involved the three tyrants Dion, Dionysus I and Dionysus II, the visits of Plato to the island were nothing much short of a disaster. Dion might have had some good intentions when he used his influence as the brother-in-law of Dionysus I to bring a strategically minded Philosopher to the island in 387 BCE.

However, when Plato invited Dionysus I to think about the limitations and failings of despotic rule, it seems as if the rather impetuous ruler did not fully appreciate the value of an examined life. Indeed, he commissioned the assassination of Plato, and from Plutarch's account, it seems that Plato was lucky to escape Sicily alive.[131] According to this account, even though Plato managed to sail away, he got sold into slavery.

Not a great start, Plato.

---

131 Plutarch, '*The Life of Dion*' 5:6.

It is easy to think that he was a bit naïve to imagine that his ideals could cut through the egos of some tyrants in an ancient Hellenic city state, who lived amongst "vulgar luxuries" in regimes that "count pleasures and excesses as the highest good".[132] However, this would be to miss the remarkable conviction Plato held in the redemptive power of the truth, and his commitment to a set of values that he understood could transform individuals and a society. So, the ambition to turn Kings into philosophers failed.

The alternative, to make philosophers into Kings, did not work out either. In fact, the consensus of Western civilisation has pushed away from Plato's elitist utopia with increasing conviction. We have emphatically rejected the idea of rule by a King, or by a small unaccountable elite. We now have mature liberal democracies that find Plato's politics rather bracing.

The West has concluded that we don't need an office of rational or irrational caretakers to manage our desires and spiritedness. Despite our flaws, we have shown that we are capable of making reasoned and informed judgements, more often than not. Indeed, the great democratic thinkers of modern Philosophy (Paine, Rousseau, Bentham and Mill) were not unaware of the pull of our appetites. But despite their different reservations, they all had enough confidence in our informed common sense to endorse democracy as the ideal form of government.

This confidence was keenest in the work of Thomas Paine. He wrote his revolutionary "*Common Sense*" (1776) as a loud, straight-talking, wake-up call to the American Colonists. His pamphlet wanted to shake awake those readers who were dozing under a number of false assumptions about their King and about their Parliament (see "*Paine Tackles Climate Change*").

132 *Ibid*, 4:5.

However, having given ourselves the mandate to rule, this confidence now faces a stiff test with climate change. This crisis requires that our reasoning assume an unusual level of control over those appetites and drives. Despite being far off course with our emissions reductions, the dangers ahead do not seem to be commonly understood. It can be deflating to discuss climate change with people who have not yet grasped how deeply embedded the problem is in both our political and economic system. At the shallow end of the problem, they might still causally think that their agency in the problem only reaches as far as small individual actions. At the deep end, there are many that are engaged in high-tech solutions, but who might not be mindful of the fact that there are limited resources to make all that stuff in a closed mass system.[133] Moreover, these solutions themselves will create massive emissions to manufacture.

The illusions that we labour under as emissions continue to rise are not unlike those that Paine tried to deconstruct in his combative prose for the American colonists. Perhaps the strongest parallels can be found in the illusions that those in power have the best interests of the people in mind when they make their decisions, and that they fully understand what they are doing. Yet, despite the deeply ingrained myths of his society, Paine found the courage and the confidence to empower his readers with some plain truths.

We are so easily ensnared by a limited view of the problem that it is hard to defend the idea that our democracies will wake up from their deep slumber on time. The drives behind our escalating emissions are formidable.

133 The Second Law of Thermodynamics – known to its friends as Entropy –
     is always undermining our efforts in this arena.

Turning the ship towards the wind

And yet.

Revolutions are not oddities of human history; they are regular and inevitable. There is so much at stake with climate change that it seems utterly absurd that we could really allow such a mundane chemical truth, discovered two centuries ago,[134] to be the thing that unravels us (and much of the natural world).

Rather than a Zombie film, perhaps the ending to the climate crisis will be like a conventional Hollywood action film? Perhaps the hero will emerge from the burning building in the final scenes, scarred and exhausted, but with the mission completed. Such films might be fictional, sometimes laughable, but they do appeal to something within the human condition that is very real. Human beings can transcend their situation, with guts and reason.

We urgently need to look beyond the surface of things. We must identify where our democratic culture is dangerously failing us. This does not require us to dig out our democracies from the turf of our societies. There is no need to supplant them with Plato's aristocracy of philosophers. However, we must allow Plato to interrogate our society with the full force of his thinking.

Indeed, this capacity for wholescale examination is precisely what makes democracies so resilient and healthy. Not only does a democracy encourage dissent and debate within itself, it also allows dissent about itself. The first of these virtues was recognised by E.M. Forster when he wrote: "So two cheers for Democracy: one because it admits variety and two because it permits criticism". And the second virtue is recognised when Forster was free to add the famous qualification in the next line:

"Two cheers are quite enough: there is no occasion to give three."[135]

134 Joseph Fourier, "*Théorie Analytique de la Chaleur*" (1822).
135 E.M. Forster, "*Two Cheers for Democracy*" (1951), 'What I Believe'.

These key virtues of democracies have enabled them to limp forward through different crises in the past. Indeed, it is especially in moments of crisis that they advance most strongly.

The explosion of internet traffic has supercharged our capacity to consume and it has amplified social divisions; there are strong tides of media flow that are pushing us away from dealing with the climate problem. However, our rationality enables us to go against the tide in any political system. Therefore, although we do not have a system that supplies and installs philosophers as our statesmen and stateswomen, what we do have is a wide and extensive system of education and media that is able to appeal to the rational part of us all. Both education and the media need genuine transformation to not fail in their role in the crisis, but they will be key to any authentic response we make.

This is not something that is compatible with the model proposed by Plato in the '*Republic*', because for him the whole logic of a democracy is that it is fatally rooted in the appetites – however, given that democracy is the system within which we are going to have to work out our solutions to the climate crisis, it is worth taking this helpful reminder from Plato about the importance and the power of reason and the power of education to transform our lives.[136]

Indeed, Greta Thunberg has provided a jolt to the usual media currents. Her directness and depth have provided a vast democratic space for millions of others to occupy. There is an impetus and energy that has enabled the crisis to break important ground in our thinking, most notably through the strong female voices of Anuna De Wever and Adélaïde Charlier (Belgium), Hilda Flavia Nakabuye (Uganda), Marie-Claire Graf (Switzerland), Louisa Neubauer (Germany) Alexandria Villasenor (US) and many others.

---

136 Plato himself seems to soften the sharp ideals of the '*Republic*' in his more pragmatically minded work, "*Laws*". A book written at the end of his life.

Image 30. - Hilda Flavia Nakabuye (Uganda)

These young people, alongside the strategic actions of Extinction Rebellion, have helped bring a beautifully wide range of homo sapiens who are committed to deep change to the surface of the media.[137] In some cases, these people have committed to a genuine transformation of our societies for decades, perhaps most notably in the figure of Jim Hansen.[138]

When the first pages of my previous book were written four years ago,[139] this book on Plato was planned to be the closing part of the "*No Common Sense*" series. The conclusion that was envisaged was the only way through the climate crisis would be through the courts. This was for a few key reasons: only the courts could respond quickly enough and only the courts could approach the issue in a rational, non-partisan and objective way. Indeed, contrary to the toxic populist tropes, the courts are a critical part of the democratic machinery, as they place everyone as equal before the law and they uphold our human rights.

By contrast, the slow democratic processes of educating, voting, legislating and implementing was just incompatible with the time frames that the science was demanding. Four years ago, the notion that people could hit the streets in massive numbers demanding radical change was quite unthinkable. However, the demonstrations of public anger and hope have become an important pathway to the radical change that is needed.

---

137 One unsung hero is Jonathan N Fuller (who you can find on Facebook), who has been publishing forensic assessments of the British Media's coverage and framing of the climate crisis for months.

138 The Adjunct Professor directing the Program on Climate Science, Awareness and Solutions (Earth Institute, Columbia University) and so much more that does not fit into a footnote.

139 I could be a slow writer, but being a full-time teacher and all the rest makes me even slower...

The millions of people who hit the streets in protest across the globe in 2019 demonstrate that once people start to envisage change it can become highly contagious. Indeed, there does seem to be an awakening in recent months of just how irrational we have been in our actions. Although we have only ever increased our greenhouse gas emissions, there is still a window of opportunity to turn our ship to the opposite direction. This could be the moment, just on time, when these essential virtues of democracy enable us to shift course. It seemed utterly implausible a short time ago, but this could be the moment at which we could regain our common sense.

There is a chance that later commentators on the history of climate change might look back on these years as a social tipping point. Indeed, it is not hard to imagine how public opinion on climate change could suddenly flip – the evidence is so incontestable and the costs so savage that once common sense about the crisis gets some traction, it could tighten very quickly. It seems also as if major change only requires a minority of people. Erica Chenoweth's recent study of non-violent movements concluded that once 3.5% of a population are fully engaged in the cause, success appears to be inevitable.[140] This 'magic' trigger number is derived from a study of 323 violent and non-violent movements in which every non-violent movement that achieved the 3.5% participation, succeeded[141].

In "*The Tipping Point*" (2000), Malcom Gladwell writes: "The success of any kind of social epidemic is heavily dependent on the involvement of people with a particular and rare set of social gifts."[142]

2019 was, if nothing else, the year when the subtitle of Gladwell's book seemed very true for the climate crisis: "How little things can make a big difference." However, as Greta herself points out, nothing meaningful has changed yet at a systemic level. On a more positive note, there is so much built up tension and stress behind the scenes in the climate crisis that it would not be a surprise to see a sudden, dramatic movement.

140 Chenoweth, Erica; Stephan, Maria J. (2011), "*Why Civil Resistance Works: The Strategic Logic of Nonviolent Conflict*", Columbia U. Pr.
141 cf. also, Chenoweth, E., "*Civil Resistance and the 3.5% rule*". TEDxBoulder, September 21st 2013.
142 Malcolm Gladwell, "*Tipping Points*", 2000. p33.

Chapter Five

The Seventh Letter

We know why Plato picked up his pen to write the '*Republic*' because he tells us why.

As an old man, Plato reflected back on his youth, and in a rare auto-biographical moment, he wrote the now famous '*Seventh Letter*'.[143] Rather remarkably, it is a letter that history has preserved for us. In this Epistle, Plato recalls some of the darker memories from his youth: the debacle of the Sicilian Expedition, the brute force of the 30 Tyrants and the horror show of Socrates' execution. He tells the reader that the '*Republic*' was written in response to the political turmoil he experienced in his young life. It was the product of a profound struggle with the injustices and chaos of the world.

Plato has often been characterised as an aloof thinker. This is perhaps because of the central importance of the abstract world of 'Forms' in his work, or perhaps because he recommended that the rulers of a state should live in a separate community. Certainly, this view became prominent after Popper marked out a historical dot-to-dot exercise from 20th century tyrants all the way back to Plato.

143 Although the authenticity of the letters has been debated, there is enough scholarly confidence in this famous Seventh Letter to simply quote it without further qualification

This view of Plato, as detached and dogmatic, is misjudged.

The 'Seventh Letter' offers us the chance to see the 'Republic' from a wider perspective and to pull some of a key issue to the surface. The letter helps to consolidate our understanding of what he was thinking when he wrote the text, given that the 'Republic' is written as a series of dialogues in which Plato himself is absent.

The letter is full of insights, but one section in particular is sharply relevant to the current climate emergency.

"I looked at this, you see, and at the men who were in politics, at the laws and customs. And the more I looked and the older I grew, the more difficult it seemed to me to administer political affairs justly. For you cannot do so without friends and comrades you can trust. In such men it was not easy to find. For the city, you see, no longer lived in the fashion and ways of our fathers. Eager as I had once been to go into politics, **as I look at these things and saw everything taking any course at all with no direction or management, I ended up feeling dizzy.**

...I did not abandon my interest in politics to discover how it might be bettered in other respects, and I was perpetually awaiting my opportunity. But at last, I saw that as far as all states now existing are concerned, they are all badly governed. For the condition of their laws is bad almost beyond cure, except for some miraculous accident. So I was compelled to say, in praising true Philosophy, that it was from it alone that I was able to discern any justice. And so, I said that the nations of the world will never cease from trouble until either the true breed of philosophers shall come to political office or until that of the rulers shall, by some divine law, take the pursuit of Philosophy."

Plato's 'Seventh Letter', 325d-326b.
(trans. Professor Steve Smith, Political Philosophy Lecture 4, Yale University)

Today, at a time when so many young people can see democracies failing them in a profound way, it is easy for them to feel nauseated. Not only are young people presented with a mountain of financial debt, they are also confronted with an ecological debt that is monumentally large. This is a debt that has built up off the media radar, but which now surrounds our vulnerable democratic ships. Although it lies mostly beyond the senses, a moment of reflection will force a fresh voter into a struggle to understand why the situation was not managed with any direction at all before they came of age. Dizzying.

The most astonishing example of this mismanagement could be seen in the display panels that lined the "Blue Zone" of the conference at COP25 in Madrid. First, perhaps due to the sheer weight of intimidating scientific reports, or maybe due to the 'Greta effect', this ecological debt was recognised in all its brutal force.

There were panels stating, "Miami disappearing under the sea is not change", "75% desertification of Spain is not change", "143 million people being climate migrants by 2050 is not change."... and after each panel, the same conclusion was made plain: "Don't call it change, call it CLIMATE EMERGENCY".

Yet, although the slogan for COP25 was "#Time for Action", the final two display panels summed in two short texts why the world has not managed to ever decrease its greenhouse gas emissions.

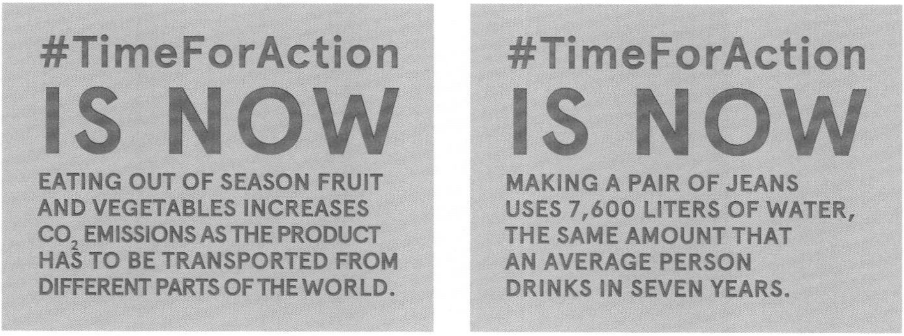

Image 31. – Courtesy of Homo Sapiens Foundation

#TimeForAction
IS NOW
EATING OUT OF SEASON FRUIT
AND VEGETABLES INCREASES
CO_2 EMISSIONS AS THE PRODUCT
HAS TO BE TRANSPORTED FROM
DIFFERENT PARTS OF THE WORLD.

#TimeForAction
IS NOW
MAKING A PAIR OF JEANS
USES 7,600 LITERS OF WATER,
THE SAME AMOUNT THAT
AN AVERAGE PERSON
DRINKS IN SEVEN YEARS.

Anyone with an understanding of the depth of the change required in agriculture would find the first panel ridiculous. And it takes some squinting of the mind to even work out the relevance to climate change for the second panel. Why pick on these two points anyway? When faced with the systemic problem of climate change, to point out only a couple of individual action points, of almost insignificant detail, is a lamentable response. The UNFCCC is tasked with pulling together the best scientific brains, human and material resources in the world to tackle a global threat to human civilisation – and yet these were the two panels that were chosen.

It is difficult to know what causes the bigger brain-melt. Is it just the superficiality of these panels? Or is it the fact that so many thousands of people, including hundreds of journalists, activists and negotiators walked past these panels without a second thought?

Maybe we have forgiven Al Gore by now for the absurdly limp finish to the original "Inconvenient Truth" back in 2006; after graphically illustrating the existential threat posed by climate change, the film finished with the promise that the climate crisis could be solved with astonishing simplicity. Viewers were prompted to a zero-carbon lifestyle with the imperatives to "buy energy efficient appliances", "change the thermostat" and, most inanely of all, to "recycle". What the gods who installed the 2nd law of thermodynamics into our universe thought of it all, as a solution to the emergency, is probably not publishable. It had taken nearly two decades for the USA to wake up to the alarm sounded by Jim Hansen's testimony about anthropogenic climate change to congress in 1988.

Al Gore's film was long overdue, but it was at least a welcome recognition of the problems. It was just a God damn shame that someone fell asleep at the typewriter at the end when it came time to address the solutions required.

However, there can be no room for tolerance with the UNFCCC in 2019. Humanity is still moving at high speed into a minefield of irreversible tipping points and we have continually accelerated our emissions for over 30 years. We are much deeper into the crisis now. Yet, the best panels that COP25 could produce to underline their commitment to reducing emissions still only made the most impossibly flaccid points. There is simply no time anymore for mistakes, platitudes or clichés. We have to immediately engage in policy details that are centred on specific science-based numbers. The negotiations cannot be held in a comfortable place anymore where superficial deals are traded between UN member states.

To push out the same empty gestures in 2019 is just not OK.

The scientific data has always been available[144] to policy makers, they have just preferred to look over it to more palatable measures. The reason why the UNFCCC did not say something more intelligent or realistic on the panels and in the opening speeches is because they did not want to say it. There is a well understood 'budget' of greenhouse gases that we could safely emit into the atmosphere.[145]

There is also a very simple way to divide up the emissions reductions we need to make. The details can be found explained in "The Science" of the appendix (or at www.Cut11Percent). These numbers are based on the most basic *per capita* responsibilities that can be deduced from the openly available data that is regularly updated by the different scientific bodies, such as the IPCC, UNEP and WMO.

The reason why I attended COP25 in Madrid was because a couple of my students were supposed to be part of a presentation that would put these key numbers to the world, during the opening ceremony. All the preparation and planning had been done by 'Our Future Uncompromised' – who pulled together a wide range of ministers and science academies in support. The students were going to set out a singular, transparent target for each nation; in contrast to the standard fog of confusing promises and slogans, and instead of a range of carbon neutrality targets that are not measured against any scientific projections.

At the time, the UK needed to reduce its emissions by 6.6% per year starting immediately – and there were some nations with more work to do (e.g. Belgium -13%, Singapore -19.4%) and some with much less (Panama -3.6%, Uruguay -1%). Indeed, some nations have such a low *per capita*

---

144 Arguably, the greatest achievement of AR5 in 2014 was the calculation of the remaining carbon budget with a robust confidence. It is a number with a great many nuances and qualifications, and it is continually updated by the results published in scientific journals.

145 The details are given in Chapters 8 and 9 and in the appendix. Although if you are a fish in the Great Barrier Reef reading this, or a citizen of a nation that will go under water with just a 1.5°C average temperature rise, then your understanding of what is meant by the word "safe" will be different.

carbon footprint that they could even afford to increase their emissions for the global average to not go over a 2°C budget[146] (Nicaragua +2.8%, Tanzania +3.1%). These are numbers that get to the heart of the problem.

Our Future Uncompromised was supported, among many others, by the President of the UN Climate Conference 2019, by COP25, by Chile's Environmental Minister Schmidt and host country Spain's Ecological Transition Minister Ribera. The numbers had been printed, the banners made, and a time slot of four minutes was reserved in the opening session on December 2nd, 2019. Our slot fell somewhere between António Guterres and Ursula Von der Leyen.

But it never happened[147]. No YouTube or Google search will allow anyone to find it. At the last moment, empty protocol restrictions (the flammability of the paper) were cited.

But the students understood precisely what was flammable.

Until the UNFCCC is ready to look at the science-based targets that are based on some basic principles of common sense, we cannot expect to see our emissions decrease. The UNFCCC has one goal and it is defined in Article 2 of the convention. It pledges the "...stabilization of greenhouse gas concentrations in the atmosphere at a level that would prevent dangerous anthropogenic interference with the climate system...". How can an institution of such massive human resources and expertise make such a bad effort job of fulfilling its own mandate? If the UNFCCC was any self-respecting business, then it would want all of the key data and targets mapped out and all of the strategies blocking progress to be examined. Otherwise, the key data gets covered up in a pile of clutter.

---

146 See www.OurFutureUncompromised.org for all of the important
     scientific qualifications to this ambition.
147 To be precise, it happened elsewhere, later in the conference. The videos can be found
     on the UNFCCC website and at ourfutureuncompromised.org.

For the moment, either the organising committee is profoundly lost in slogans or with piecemeal concerns, or there is a wilful resistance to look at reality. The reader is free to draw his or her own conclusions about where the truth resides between these two obstacles to actual progress.

Returning to where this mini-section started, the blue display panels produced by the UNFCCC should have provoked a sharp reaction in any onlooker. For a thinker that can seem so distant to us, reading line 325e of Plato's Seventh letter again pulls him much closer, "as I looked at these things and saw everything taking any course at all, with no direction or management, I ended up feeling dizzy..." (325e).

Plato dug in deep to write the '*Republic*' after feeling like this and, in so doing, he has left us something of lasting importance.

the

end

Plato

Chapter Six

The Key
Problems

There appear to be three fundamental problems with the state we are in with climate change, and two key solutions.

Using the word "solution" might seem overly optimistic. It might imply that these measures are easy to implement. It is true that the word "solve" is at home in the world of mathematics, where mistakes can be identified and deleted easily, and where there are neat boundaries between a problem's different components. Yet, although the word might seem a little simplistic when used to talk about something so organic that is entwined into so many different aspects of our society, it is important to be brave enough to use it, because there remain solutions to the crisis. They are tough, and complex to implement, but they are solutions nonetheless.

Our fate is not inevitably dark. If we act with urgency and depth, then we can avoid sailing into the impossibly strong tides of nature's tipping points.

First however, the problems.

1. Capitalism

Plato was not afraid to ask the biggest questions about society. He was bold enough to question the fundamental organisation of the world around him, and this included the system of democracy. His magnum opus, the 'Republic', is an invitation to do the same. The two main operating systems of our global village are democracy and capitalism. After having looked at them both, this is the moment to pull some conclusions together.

Plato helps us stay awake about the dangers of democracy. He identifies where it is vulnerable to corruption or failure. However, this book remains defensive of democracy, despite Plato's withering attack on it in the 'Republic'. Overall, it seems more than reasonable to assert that the benefits of democratic rule far outweigh the risks involved in ditching it. For anyone who wants to engage in public life in our modern society, it seems clear enough that we still have the capacity and the resources within our democratic system to change course. We can educate democratic citizens about the essential truths of the climate crisis, so that we can then all make informed choices as voters and consumers. We can guide and funnel our resources into genuine solutions. We can be seriously irrational, but we are also capable of being seriously rational. If we look at the previous tipping points in social thinking that litter our history, it is not unreasonable to be optimistic. If we are willing to learn from our mistakes and weaknesses, then there seem to be ways to guard the best features of democracy and to make the system more durable.

However, we also have to subject capitalism to the same level of scrutiny as our democratic systems.

The problem is that it is equally incendiary to pose questions about capitalism as it is to pose questions about the legitimacy of democracy. In fact, given the recent general lurch towards the political hard-right, it is arguably more radical to question capitalism in today's culture than it is to question democracy.

Indeed, this shift to the right can be attributed to the feedback loops that exist when democracy and capitalism grow so strongly together. We are suffering from a serious case of Truth Decay at many levels of our democratic system and this corrosion of our ability to think and act in a public way is connected to the symbiotic relationship between democracy and capitalism.[148] An honest and open discussion about the dangers of capitalism is needed.

Nothing is off the table for discussion in Philosophy. This is the lesson that Socrates and Plato bring to us. We should question the operating systems that govern our lives, even if they are widely accepted as self-evidently good. As J.S. Mill once put it, we need to be alert to the dangers of "the deep slumber of a decided opinion."

How fit-for-purpose is capitalism for the future of human civilisation? If a Marxist uprooting of the system is neither possible nor attractive, then how can capitalism be made to work in a sustainable way? It is unambiguously clear that unfettered markets are not only a direct threat to the proper functioning of a democracy, but they are also evidently capable of destroying the eco-systems that they depend upon for any economic activity at all. The track record of economic growth under capitalism cannot simply be seen from the point of view of GDP.

GDP has always been too blunt an instrument to measure human wealth. Now that we are starting to surpass the planetary boundaries that a GDP-orientated economy promotes, we are faced with a very pragmatic, emphatically not idealistic, set of problems.

What are we going to do about it? The status quo is truly perilous. There are no automatic brakes on consumption that are activated when we approach dangerous planetary boundaries. There is little to stop Bolsonaro reducing the Amazon to an industrial food plantation and eventually a

---

148 Singapore and China offer the most vivid examples of how democracy
    does not always follow as a natural consequence to more capitalism.

tropical grassland[149], but the democratic election of a myopic narcissist to the Presidency is only half the story. Bolsonaro is not just the facilitator of some basic human impulses that can quickly surge to the surface in a democracy.

There are some basic economic forces at work. The annihilation of one of the most exquisite and precious biomes is fundamentally driven by some names that few people have ever heard of. We can only sink our teeth into a burger or a steak because massive companies such as JBS, Bunge and Cargill have sunk their metal teeth into the Amazon rainforest. These companies prefer to keep a low profile, supplying international markets with beef and soy animal feed. Their products are sold to global brands that everyone has heard of: McDonald's and Burger King simply reheat their meat, Walmart, Ahold Delhaize and hundreds of other supermarket companies put their meat into their freezers and fridges.

There is nothing to stop me going into a supermarket and buying 100 beef burgers for a big party. There is nothing to stop me going to the shops to purchase 20 new TVs, or 14 hairdryers or 90 t-shirts. Imelda Marcos' crimes were related to embezzlement, but armed with the billions in her bank accounts, she could rip up the Earths' crust with impunity with her spending. In fact, not only are there no brakes on material consumption, governments frequently legislate with their foot on the accelerator for more economic growth.

Thinking about how best to manage the interventions into market forces, which will be needed to ensure that capitalism recognises external values and resources (like the atmosphere), is hugely complex and full of ambiguities. This is no place to open a discussion between Hayek and Keynes, for example. Demonising the free markets is as unhelpful as it

149 The UK, Belgium, The Netherlands (and many other nations) reduced their
     environment to grasslands much earlier in their histories.

is to demonise Karl Marx.[150] Economics is a wonderfully diverse and inquisitive discipline, and if economists themselves remain modest about the reliability of their modelling and forecasting, then those outside the specialised knowledge of the discipline must be even more modest.

The bottom line is that some basic legislation is still needed.

A football field needs some boundaries for the experts to show off their skills. Lionel Messi would be as much a magician in 7,000 sqm as he would be in 6,300 sqm. We do not allow food companies to produce toxic soup; we rightly impose stringent health and safety controls and laws on their products. Why is the concentration of CO_2 levels in the atmosphere any different? So much of human civilisation hangs on those levels. If we legislate for soup, why do we not legislate for emissions?

Again, there are many papers and books that need to be written, by those who are informed in economic theory, about the optimal way to organise the details of this legislation. Individual households and individual companies have neither the full picture, nor the mandate to implement the changes necessary. It is the singular job of a government to protect the rights of its people by limiting the greenhouse gas emissions emitted year on year to a scientifically defined level. The details can be entrusted to a balance of democratic debate[151] and market forces to work out the details.

Indeed, there has been a recent flourishing of economic enquiry into sustainability in academia, but not because it is funky or because it is a stimulating and fresh area of research; instead, it has happened because our current economic model is unsustainable – literally, we cannot go on like this. Some evidence-driven policies and laws have to be put in place to delineate the limits of the human incursion into the basic operating

---

150 This book is not arguing in favour of the inevitable red sunset of capitalism as predicted by Karl Marx. This book does not endorse the unlikely red sunrise of a communist brotherhood. Marx did have a remarkably probing understanding of the ecological sub-plot to human history, but a whole chapter rather than a footnote is the only legitimate space in which to examine his brilliant analysis of capitalism.

151 These could include laws for government incentives and disincentives, rations or bans.

systems of the bio-sphere. This is nothing to do with any political preference for the left or the right wings. It is just a brute fact.

2. Growth

For all the astonishing amount of prosperity that it has created for some, there is a fundamental problem with the capitalist ride that we are on:

It is called Growth.

Our whole economic system is predicated on growth. It is the one fundamental axis that everything in the system turns on. This would not be a problem if we inhabited some infinite landscape. However, growth is actually a problem, given that we are stranded on an isolated ball, hanging in outer space. Limitless economic growth is not possible in a closed mass system. Ask any spaceman who has visited a space station how tightly every resource is measured to sustain the human life onboard for a few months.

We live on spaceship Earth.

Every element that we are fortunate to have inside the Earth's crust was created in the intense pressure and heat of a supernova. These conditions cannot be not replicated here. Therefore, whatever lumps of gold, uranium, platinum, aluminium (and so on) that were spewed out from the guts of a supernova to form our little planet are all we have got. When we dig them up and splinter them into tiny pieces for the products that we consume they are mostly gone – because the energy and time required to lump them back together again (even by the most enthusiastic circular economy) is always heavily outweighed by the losses involved in the process. Physicists call this Entropy, the rest of us can simply call it frustrating. In the bluntest terms, "When we use it, we lose it".

Apart from the general thermal energy that arrives on Earth from the Sun, and the occasional meteorite that collides with us, we are in a closed mass system that has limited supply of precious elements[152].

The model of growth that nearly every nation of the world continues to pursue necessitates a rapacious appetite for finite planetary resources.

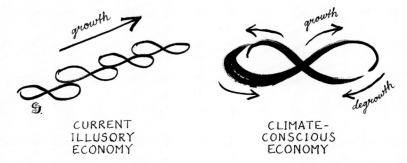

CURRENT	CLIMATE-
ILLUSORY	CONSCIOUS
ECONOMY	ECONOMY

Accelerating our resource extractions is not a tenable strategy. Yet the central assumption of growth, around which everything else rotates, is not questioned. The problem is held at a far distance from any economic planning. At best it is an abstract concern; at worst, policy makers do not even understand the problem.

The long-term problem is that we will run out of essential minerals and metals from the Earth's crust that we need (most pressingly, this can be seen in the supply of phosphorus that is used as fertiliser to sustain our food production). The short-term problem is that climate change is a direct consequence of the extraction of resources. Clearly then, if all of our government and private policies are geared towards achieving maximum material growth, then there is a fundamental problem.

Pushing for this economic growth drives extractions, that drives energy use, that drives emissions, that drives global heating. There is no way to cheat the (thermodynamic) system.

152 To be precise, there are also 382kg of moon rocks that we collected by the 12 Apollo moonwalkers between 1969 and 1972. Three robotic Soviet missions (Luna 16, 20 and 24) also returned a total of 301 grammes in the 1970s.

We have had an economy that is fundamentally based on combustion since the Industrial Revolution, and we have motored ourselves into a dangerous spot. The contradiction that we are confronted with can be summed up with the statement: "You cannot build a machine to clean up the mess you made making a machine".[153] Anybody who thinks that the solutions to climate change can be found by leveraging our growth to more advanced technologies has not understood some of the first principles of physics.[154]

Have we asked ourselves the most basic questions about economics? How long will our limited resources last to deliver our current consumption habits? How do these figures play out when we have an expanding population? How many tonnes of greenhouse gases will be emitted, simply in the process of building all the new green infrastructure that is required to sustain our current lifestyles? Will such an overhaul of our energy and transport systems bring us too close to the limit of the remaining carbon budget for 1.5°C or 2°C?

We suddenly had dashboards for the COVID crisis, so that we could meter our economic activity according to the infection rates. It was clearly in the interests of the policy makers and the citizens to make these numbers well known. When difficult decisions have to be made, keeping people informed is an important foundation to the introduction, relaxation and repeal of any laws. Why is there no dashboard for resource extractions? Why is there no dashboard for the remaining carbon budget?

There is no question that a sustainable future will demand less material consumption overall. We will simply have to live more simply. This is a reality that few are willing to look at. It is the philosopher's job to bring such uncomfortable points into view.

---

153 Again, thank you to John Doyle, a good friend in the EU Commission who is good at one-liners that are not necessarily funny.
154 More specifically, the Second Law of Thermodynamics.

	Resource Consumption			CO_2 Emissions from Consumption			
	Per capita 2018	Trend 1993–2018	Reduction for SD	Per capita 2017	Trends 1992–2017	Reduction required for	
						1.5°	2°
	Tonnes CO_2	% / yr	% / yr	Tonnes CO_2	% / yr	% / yr	% / yr
ULTRA HIGH	29	1.4%	−5%	13	0.3%	−52%	−12%
VERY HIGH	17	1.8%	−3%	8.9	0.8%	−33%	−8%
HIGH	16	4.6%	−2%	4.8	4.1%	−17%	−4%
HUMANITY	12	2.9%	−1%	4.8	1.9%	−16%	−4%
MEDIUM	4.5	3.6%	+2%	1.5	4.9%	−5%	−1%
LOW	2.3	3.0%	+6%	0.4	4.6%	−0.7%	+2%
UK	23	1.5%	−3.6%	8.5	−0.7	−28	−6.9
USA	32	1.5%	−4.5%	18	0.4%	−77%	−16%
Sweden	32	2.6%	−4.7%	7.4	−0.4%	−25%	−6.3%
Singapore	78	5.5%	−7.5%	21	1.7%	−94%	−19%
Saudi Arabia	12	−0.8%	−1.1%	19	4.2%	−91%	−19%
Russian Fed.	10	0.0%	−1.6%	9.7	−0.9%	−35%	−8.3%
Brazil	18	3.8%	−3.0%	2.5	3.0%	−8.2%	−1.9%
China	21	5.8%	−3.9%	6.2	5.1%	−22%	−5.5%
Bolivia	5.5	1.8%	+1.7%	1.8	5.1%	−6.6%	−1.3%
India	4.7	3.4%	+1.8%	1.7	4.9%	−6.2%	−1.2%
Cameroon	1.9	2.2%	+6.7%	0.5	5.6%	−1.6%	+1.2%
Chad	1.5	1.9%	+8.0%	0.1	3.8%	+2.8%	+4.7%

Just as there are known boundaries to our emissions cuts, there are also known boundaries to the amount of resources that we can extract from the crust of the Earth. It is not surprising to find that those nations that are most responsible for greenhouse gas emissions are also the nations who are responsible for the greatest levels of resource consumption. Here is a short summary of the main table of data, the full version can be found in the Appendix.

The philosopher and social critic Cornel West consistently invites his audiences to confront the hardest social realities with remarkable rhetorical power and wisdom. He insists "You've gotta start in the West with Socrates. Ooh, that's unsettling... Don't skip the moment of the Hemlock. Don't

skip the moment of the condemnation. Don't skip line, 24a of the *Apology*, where he says Athenians, fearless speech, plain speech, frank speech, unintimidated speech is the cause of my unpopularity... How you gonna domesticate him? How you gonna sanitise him? How you gonna sterilise him?"[155] Cornel West was thinking through institutional racism and trying to overturn some deeply embedded assumptions. His work is sharply relevant to the climate crisis – we have to ask the most basic questions with courage.

Do we have the moral and intellectual integrity to stand up against the system and to question the model of economic growth? Given all the existential threats we have confronted in the past this sounds like a patronising question. If we have dealt with Hitler and Stalin, then surely we should be able to confront an economic question. Moreover, the damage to the environment sustained under capitalist societies is so clear that we should not need page after page of Philosophy to point to this fact.

These are odd times, and questioning capitalism gets seriously prickly, very quickly. For the moment, 'Economic Growth' is an objective that is simply not up for discussion.[156]

155 Dr. Cornel West's lecture, 'Politics in the Humanities' at Brown University (2018)
156 Credit must be given to New Zealand for making some steps in this direction.

Humanity is running like a cartoon character off the side of a cliff, just like Wile E. Coyote. And like those Looney Tunes characters, there will come a moment when the character keeps spinning their legs, first out of habit, then out of suspended existential shock. This is where we are now. Either we do what the script writer affords to the character – a chance to defy gravity and run back onto solid ground – or we just drop. These next few years will define if we will actually overcome ourselves, be brave enough to look at the truth and make drastic plans to get back to safety. This is that precious moment of self-reflection and decision, when the character looks at the camera. We will find out how it all ends soon enough.

3. Fragmented thinking

National governments are set up into different departments, from Transport to the Treasury, from Health to the Home Office. Such an arrangement tends towards 'silo thinking'. There has to be specialisation and structure, of course, otherwise there would be an impossibly chaotic decision-making process. However, the weaknesses of such a system need to be addressed and not ignored. Climate change clearly requires policy coordination across every department; it cannot just be reduced to a single department with no leverage to direct policies drawn up in the other departments.

Indeed, a major explanation as to why we have not made progress with our greenhouse gas emissions is that our societies are not that good at holistic thinking. Fragmentary thinking seems endemic to the modern world.

A successful capitalist economy is one that is marked by the extent to which it has managed to specialise. The advantages of specialisation were most famously described by Adam Smith in "*The Wealth of Nations*" (1776) with the example of the pin factory. The creative energy of capitalism has indisputably pushed forward a huge array of technological progress. Indeed, Karl Marx was in awe of capitalism's transformative power.

However, Marx also observed the negative, alienating disadvantages of channelling the productive forces of a society into these narrow and specialised channels. He understood that the growth of capitalism would be accompanied by a corresponding growth in alienation. His analysis described how the mechanised and repetitive labour would typify an atomisation of the social order.

This lack of understanding and ownership of the product that emerges from the other end of the factory gate to the worker who helps to produce it is also symbolic of the lack of understanding and ownership that we suffer from across the whole of society. Marx anticipated that what is true for the worker and their working environment would be played out at many levels of a capitalist system. Individuals would become disconnected from each other, and society would become increasingly divorced from the natural world. Indeed, Marx (despite the carnage that Soviet states inflicted upon the natural world in his name) was a profoundly ecological thinker.[157]

Marx's diagnosis of the hardwired problems of capitalism deserves more than a fleeting glance and the vocabulary of alienation that he develops so fully is particularly rich. However, we must not stray too far from the path which is clearly marked as 'fragmentary thinking'.

At the root of his thinking, Marx, like Rousseau before him, was principally concerned with wholeness and completeness. And he saw capitalism as a deeply fragmenting period of history. Marx foresaw this fragmentation at every level, from the material realities of our daily lives to the way in which we think about the world.

This ambition to understand the underlying unity of the world and to understand how the fragmentary parts of our experience fit together was also one of the strongest impulses in Plato's thinking. Plato founded his Academy and built the curriculum with this overarching goal in mind. His graduates were to have a holistic understanding of themselves and of the world so that they could govern the state with knowledge and wisdom. After studying language and the arts, they would progress onto what today

---

157 Marx's deep ecological understanding owed much to his intense interest in soil. He studied it with a meticulous and mindful attitude that is reminiscent of the methodical scrutiny that Darwin invested in his work on barnacles before having the confidence to publish his "On the Origin of Species" (1859). Both thinkers were searching for the highly abstract governing principles of the world, and yet both were extremely attentive to the earthy, empirical details that were needed to support their theses. For an accessible and engaging analysis of Marx's green thoughts, Foster's "Marx's Ecology" (2000) is worth the investment.

we would call the Natural Sciences. Then, after a sustained period of study in Mathematics, they would complete their scholarship with Philosophy.[158]

If we compare this, the world's first university, to all of the highly specialised knowledge that characterise university courses now, then it provides a clear example of one of the major challenges that the modern world faces.

Fragmented thinking (a) – The Full Ecological Radar

This book has only had time to consider the most pressing environmental emergency – climate change. However, if our democratic ship was to look at the full Ecological radar, it would demonstrate that our situation has a fuller context.

Climate change is the most acute crisis of the Anthropocene, it rightly grabs the headlines, and it is justifiably the central concern here. However, it is not the only threat to human civilisation. Our invasive economic activities have led us to overstep numerous planetary boundaries. An examination of the radar, opposite, shows that we have sailed into some serious trouble on many sides; our unsustainable lifestyles might get pushed onto the rocks by other breakdowns in the biosphere. This radar provides a much bigger picture of the climate crisis.

In this acclaimed research, compiled by Professor Johan Rockström[159] from the 'Stockholm Resilience Centre', the dashed border drawn around the planet represents the boundary lines for different aspects of our environmental situation. This 'radar' summary chart represents thousands of scientific papers. Any summary would require references to the original sources to justify the conclusions; however, it remains a valid move to provide an overview of the current science with a wider zoom lens. Summaries serve an important role in making the main conclusions clear,

---

158 The details and the justifications for structuring the syllabus of the Academy like this can be found in the pages of The '*Republic*' in the 'Simile of the Divided Line'.

159 Steffen et al. 2015. "*Planetary Boundaries: Guiding human development on a changing planet*". Science Vol. 347 no. 6223.

which might otherwise be lost in the squall of details that the science necessarily has to provide.

Most of the segments of the radar in the chart are just basic to the entire ecological system. The important consequence of this is that if the level of disturbance in any one segment was to go beyond scientifically understood limits, it could cause everything else to collapse.

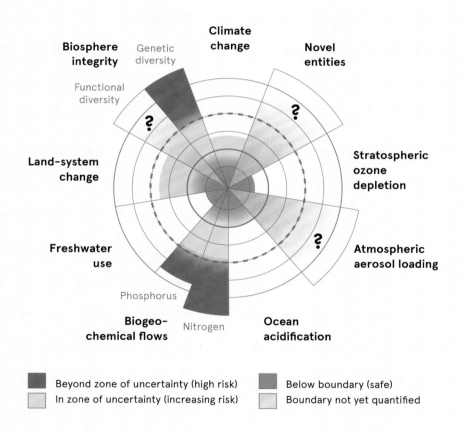

Image 34.- Steffen et al. "Planetary Boundaries", (2015)

Beyond zone of uncertainty (high risk)
In zone of uncertainty (increasing risk)
Below boundary (safe)
Boundary not yet quantified

Estimates of how the different control variables for seven planetary boundaries have changed from 1950 to present. The green shaded polygon represents the safe operating space.

Steffen et al. 2015. "Planetary Boundaries: Guiding human development on a changing planet". Science Vol. 347 no. 6223

Biodiversity is a clear example of this. Humans are ripping into their habitat with a savage energy in the absence of a rational framework for our economic development. The "Great Acceleration" has wiped out an epic proportion of the Earth's biodiversity. The planet's sixth mass extinction event is now extensively documented, but although the UN has published a landmark report[160] (Intergovernmental Science Policy Platform on Biodiversity and Ecosystem Services (IPBES), May 6th, 2019) on the monumental depth and speed of this loss, we have only offered tentative and fragmentary responses to the crisis.

The former Chair of the IPBES, Sir Robert Watson, notes that:

"The overwhelming evidence of the IPBES Global Assessment, from a wide range of different fields of knowledge, presents an ominous picture. The health of ecosystems on which we and all other species depend is deteriorating more rapidly than ever. We are eroding the very foundations of our economies, livelihoods, food security, health and quality of life worldwide."[161]

Image 35. - Jenga Bricks

It is rather like we are playing a game of Jenga with the natural world: Bio-Jenga.

Pulling out key blocks of the architecture of the biosphere, and at the same time placing more demands on it, is not a clever strategy for building a civilisation. Each time a brick is removed and then replaced at the top of the system as another weight, the more the tower becomes destabilised. The natural world used to be so immense and diverse, compared to the homo sapiens within it, that this wide base looked invulnerable to our ambitions.

160 https://www.un.org/sustainabledevelopment/blog/2019/05/nature-decline-unprecedented-report.
161 https://www.ipbes.net/news/Media-Release-Global-Assessment.

However, such are the current pressures of increasing population and resource extraction that the biosphere has now been reduced to a very narrow base.

It is not possible to identify the one key brick that would cause everything to topple – but when the towering ambitions of our lifestyle are compared with the limited resources of the planet, the whole system looks at great risk to those who have the expertise to see the big picture with the data.

Returning to the central concern of climate change, Chapters 8 and 9 explain how the solutions boil down to a particular percentage of each nation's emissions reductions. Yet, these abstract percentages are rooted in different aspects of our economy. This means that reducing our emissions will involve a complex interplay of factors. However, the upside is that by being attentive to one singular target and showing determination to follow through with realistic solutions will also drag forward all of the other embedded problems associated with it. For example, reducing the number of cars will also reduce pollution, which will also reduce respiratory diseases. Finding solutions to climate change will have a positive effect on so many of these wider aspects to our ecological crisis.

One Bio-Jenga Brick

One notable brick in the precarious standing of our global economy is the urgent need to address our agricultural practices.

Our agricultural yields currently depend on the artificial boost of adding phosphates to the crops – a very limited resource. If the global agricultural industry does not back away from hitting this brick-wall, then there will be catastrophic consequences for our food supply. Industrial farming is also a major cause of greenhouse gases in the atmosphere.

Deep reforms of agriculture, away from huge industrialised practices, will not only reduce emissions but would restore biodiversity too. Indeed, the recent bio-technology breakthrough by the Finnish company, "Solar Foods" which can produce food from water in astonishingly dense quantities (using hydrogen energy and bacteria) demonstrates the ingenuity of human beings to discover solutions in seemingly impossible situations. George Monbiot's documentary, "Apocalypse Cow" provides a chance to chew the cud on the details.

Framing our flexible economic ambitions inside the absolute boundaries of the planet requires understanding and the skilful management of limited resources. It does not require us to abolish democratic rule, but it does require that we are prepared to undertake a root-and-branch rethink of our economies.

Fragmented thinking (b) – The Cartesian Split

Since the time of Descartes (d. 1650, see *Descartes Tackles Climate Change*), it has been possible to divide up our thinking about existence. His work chopped the world into two distinct realities: the mental and the physical. Serviced by this dualism of mind and body, the spiritual and the material, we have been able to pretend that our economic planning somehow has nothing to do with our morals.

In some respects, Descartes' work caused a split that was healthy and constructive. There was an unhealthy interference by the Church in matters of science that the Cartesian split between mind and body solved. Ask Galileo about it. However, there have been some negative consequences in how his binary division of the world has played out over the centuries of human development since he wrote about this duality.

Now that we are right up against planetary boundaries, this compartmentalisation of our thinking is not adequate at all. We cannot treat the planet as an entirely external machine that is open to any level of exploitation. The Cartesian model of the world had its use, but it is now too simplistic, mechanistic, and unhelpful. It is a kind of thinking that we can no longer afford.

The economy has never been a neutral space; it has never been just an external concern. It has been a convenient myth promoted by some to pretend that it was. Those who have the power and means to profit from the planet have a lot to gain by keeping the physical and the mental, the material and the moral, realms apart. It is useful for those who profit from the status quo to sustain the idea that values are merely something subjective and internal, as it makes it seem as if the material world is just an object without any moral significance.

Yet this myth gets busted in a time of war. A crisis, like war, necessitates that we think holistically about our societies. The division between what is a material concern and what is a moral concern becomes far more conflated. Civilian factories are weaponised, and people are drafted into strategically important roles. Restrictions on certain resources are implemented and the government takes a leading role in communicating significant information to its citizens. In addition to the enforcement of certain laws by the government, a war dominates so much of civic life that people then see everything in that context. During World War II in the UK, there were vast voluntary harvests of saucepans that were transformed into the wings of RAF bombers. Everything in a wartime society became an asset to be measured inside the context of a victory against the enemy.

Getting to see reality in this wholly different frame sometimes requires a shock as brutal as war. In times of profound crisis everything has a sharp consequence to the bigger picture, nothing remains banal. As Sartre famously commented about the French under Nazi occupation, "every one of our gestures had the weight of a solemn commitment."[162] Climate change is not yet close to being this overriding storyline to every sector of our society. It is not the cross-sector plotline to major infrastructure planning, banking investments, taxation, education and so on. There have been numerous climate emergencies declared by cities and there are some fragmentary pieces of systemic thinking, but these have not yet coalesced into a genuinely holistic approach to the crisis.

162 J. P. Sartre, *"The Republic of Silence"*, pp498-500 (ed. A.J. Liebling).
   New York, Harcourt, Brace & Co. (1947).

We need a rethink of our economies and lifestyles. It needs to be done with all the cards clearly on the table. If we do not want to get rid of cars, then what will we give up? If we don't want to stop flying or eating meat, then what else will take up that gap in the emissions? If we must adopt a policy of degrowth to get the emissions down to an acceptable level, then how and where will we allow the economy to drop back? If companies are forced to make more durable and replaceable goods, how much help will different sectors get to adapt to those requirements? Will governments have to require the media to be involved in educational programmes about the crisis? In wartime, important information was communicated at cinemas, but will a government point out the serious consequences of eating beef, having an excessive number of cars[163] or the high turnover of mobile phones?

Once binding laws for national emissions are in place – the difficult but necessary job of reducing emissions in a democratic way can take place. Each piece of the jigsaw can be assessed against each other and measured against the target.

The climate crisis pushes us into these deeply moral and demanding choices with major impacts at every sector of society, some positive, some negative. But until we square up to the planet's limits, we should not pretend that the tinkering that we are doing with recycling and efficiency savings have any moral depth. We do not expect to be morally congratulated for putting an empty crisp packet in the bin; that is just the most mundane civic act. The choices we have to make about climate change are far more significant than anything that is currently debated in a parliament or a radio show. Since Greta Thunberg, there has been a radical shift in the vocabulary used to describe our situation, but the Overton Window[164] has not yet shifted to an appropriate place to discuss our responses.

---

163 Any car, electric or not, has a significant carbon footprint.
164 Explained in *"No Common Sense – Nietzsche"*.

Plato was always committed to understanding the world as a whole. It is true that the '*Republic*' divides the polis into three parts – the rational, the spirited and the appetitive. The reason that he did this was precisely to insist on the fact that the rational looks at everything from the top, to enable it to consider the whole. His economic thinking cannot be separated from his political, moral or epistemological thinking.

It is disingenuous to pretend that our private interests and our material ambitions are somehow value-neutral. There is a context to every choice. Plato was a systems thinker and he provides us with a helpful reminder that on board our democratic ship everything counts, everything is part of the whole.

Fragmented thinking (c) – A limited perspective

Our fragmented thinking also arises from the simple fact that we are limited to our own little blocks of time and space that move around with us. We are all trapped in our own perspectives. Each of us has a different background and an array of interests that lead us to a wide range of vantage points of the problem. We only have a limited time to invest of ourselves in understanding the climate crisis and acting to help solve it. It is, therefore, very demanding to keep the full picture of what is going on before our mind's eye – the science, the politics and the social reactions.

In short, we are human, not gods.

However, the reason why Philosophy is a compulsory subject in nations such as Italy and France[165] is that it provides a brief moment when we get to look at the whole of reality from a higher perspective.

---

165 It is also compulsory in the European School system, and the International Baccalaureate where it features as the compulsory core module, the 'Theory of Knowledge' (TOK).

A bird's eye view

The picture (below) is of a fire at a Petrol station in the town on Bodega Bay, California. This town has been suffering from a sudden and disturbing series of attacks – from "*The Birds*" (1963). In Hitchcock's film, there is a frenetic sequence of close-up details as an unfortunate man accidentally ignites a petrol leak. The camera jumps between the unfolding disaster of the spreading flames and the shock of the people in a nearby restaurant who can only observe and helplessly shout in horror. The camera is particularly interested in the face of one restaurant diner, Melanie Daniels, whose arrival in the town seems to have triggered the weird events.[166]

Image 36. – "The Birds", Hitchcock (1963)

But then, the camera suddenly cuts to this high vantage point, well above the city, where we can see the entire town. Slavoj Zizek takes this important scene from the movie and explains: "We automatically take this shot to be the standard establishing shot. So that after details, which perplex you, which prevent you from getting a clear orientation, you need a shot that enables you to get some sort of cognitive map, so that you know what is going on."[167]

---

166 Hitchcock himself had an obsessive interest in Tippi Hedren, the actress who played Melanie Daniels (See Donald Spoto, *The Dark Side of Genius: The Life of Alfred Hitchcock* (1983), Little, Brown & Co. for the details of Hedren's account).

167 Slavoj Zizek, "*The Pervert's Guide to Cinema*" (dir. Sophie Fiennes) (2006).

This image from a divine vantage point is the sort of view that Philosophy provides of any issue. It helps us take in the whole, it helps us see connections between details and to measure the relative importance of things. As Zizek comments: "Great cinematographers enable us to think in visual terms."

However, there is a twist.

This is not a God's eye view of things. This position actually turns out to be a bird's eye view of things – the view of "*The Birds*" in fact; the sinister, mysterious birds.

After a few moments of silence from this higher perspective, the ominous sound of the birds is heard; then, one by one, they menacingly enter the frame. We are now no longer in a neutral position and the objective view is suddenly undermined. Hitchcock puts us into the perspective of the birds themselves as they attack. As Zizek puts it, we are thrown "into an evil gaze". With his artful dexterity as the director, Hitchcock flips the meaning of the scene from reliable, passive observer into unreliable, implicated subject.[168]

Indeed, the history of Philosophy has a similarly important hinge. From Plato through to Descartes and into the modern world, Philosophy has celebrated and explored the power of reason to lift humans to an almost divine standpoint on our affairs. This ambition to achieve an objective and reliable view of the world reached its highest point in the Enlightenment, to the extent that some have reasoned that their map of reality was so complete that God had been displaced (from his loftiest of positions).

168 This switch from objective to subjective view happens at several moments in Hitchcock's films. Most notably the scene in "Psycho", when the camera observes the detective Arbogast cautiously walking up the stairs of Norman Bates' house, towards the room where "Mother" is Then from a geometrically attentive bird's eye view we see "Mother" attack the detective on the landing. The eye of the camera then suddenly flips, and we see everything as if we were Norman. We are put into the place of the murderer, repeatedly stabbing Arbogast, as the action falls down the stairs.

As Laplace famously commented, in a conversation with Napoleon in a discussion about the existence of God, "I have no need for that hypothesis."[169]

Following Kant, and especially since Hegel, the gaze of the philosophical eye turned inward upon itself. Eventually, in thinkers such as Nietzsche and Freud, human beings really got a sense of vertigo as they realised that their wide vision of reality might not have been as objective as was first thought Philosophy realised that previously unobserved forces might actually be decisively influential in how we see the world. Some of these forces are deeply irrational.

Therefore, pulling these two capacities together, Philosophy does not just allow us to get a decent cognitive map of a situation from a higher perspective, it also enables us to ask ourselves deep, internal questions about our own role in the state we are in. It is a precious viewpoint. For the moment, the media coverage of the climate crisis is strikingly poor. The climate science is either badly distorted or diluted, and the depth of questioning about our responses to it are maddeningly limited. There is little hunger to see the bigger picture and little intellectual courage to probe the causes of the crisis.

In our modernity of overwhelming information and specialised knowledge it is hard to reach a reliable understanding of an issue. In a society where the commercial interests are so powerful and genuine civic space is limited, Philosophy affords us a valuable place to think.

Having a full map of where we are, and making it accessible, has never been more important.

169 The details are a little bit unclear, but the basics of the conversation are well-documented. (For example, cf. p. 282, *Mémoires du docteur F. Antommarchi, ou les derniers moments de Napoléon*, vol. 1, 1825, Paris: Barrois L'Aîné).

Chapter Seven

The Key Solutions

Turning problems into solutions

Those who have seen the big picture do not want to just remain as observers. After the understanding comes the action. This is especially true for the young people whose future is most impacted by what they see. They rightly want to shape the world around them. Moved by a genuine sense of injustice, or a clear mindedness about the dangers ahead, it is only reasonable for them to put some energy into making a change for the better. In his Seventh Letter, Plato looks back on these times in his own life, **"When I was a young man, I felt as yet many young men do. I felt at the very moment I attained my majority I should engage in public affairs... (324c)"**

This youthful spark can hit at any age of course.

It can be provoked by a poignant personal experience or the force of a major global event. The realities of climate change have awoken millions of us to engage in social and moral issues – from veganism and buying local food, to a no-fly life or a push for fossil fuel divestments. Each one of them is utterly worthy and important. All of the efforts to transform our society towards a low greenhouse gas emitting future are important.

It is vital that each area has its own committed advocates with their own detailed understanding and moral energy to fight for that cause, given that there are so many different parts to our economy. The puzzle of getting our economies down to a safe emitting level requires that every sector transforms itself, every bit of it is part of the solution.

Indeed, a walk inside a climate protest march is a wonderful illustration of the astonishing plurality of people that are determined to struggle for justice. Aside from the sheer variety of human characters and backgrounds, there is a beautiful range of ecological concerns in the chants and the banners. A youngster, shaped by a matrix of influences, sees veganism as the key to radical change. An older youth can see the importance of banks, who need to divest billions of dollars from fossil fuels and into green infrastructure. Amongst all the distress signals about our invasion into the biosphere, there are those who stress the importance of hope and the rewilding of nature.

The scope of interests is vast, yet all of these fears and dreams interlock. The good news is that they could be united into a formidable force. Indeed, climate change even has the capacity for both the left and the right sides of the political spectrum to find common cause. For the left it represents a monumental issue of justice and equality under the one atmosphere, for the right it represents a threat to the fundamentals of society: life, property, security and family.

If Socrates were to walk amongst a crowd of climate protesters and ask questions about why they were there, behind all of the details of each cause and each individual, he would be able to identify their one central concern. In short, their desire is to stabilise greenhouse gas concentrations in the atmosphere to a safe level for human civilisation. This is what it all comes down to.

However, if people have taken up a position on one of the issues, it does not take long to realise that so much of the problem is out of an individual's control. Anyone who takes up a cause on the merry-go-round of political and economic affairs, immediately understands that their particular concern is screwed into a much bigger object of machinery. It can easily feel very disempowering to kick and pull at one part of the system when it seems so heavily bolted to economic and political cycles that drive everything from the middle.

The "dizziness" that Plato felt when he looked back on his early life, which was marked by political turmoil, is familiar to those who are engaged in the struggle for modern climate justice. Those fighting to stave off the worst effects of global heating are keenly aware of the major forces that reside at the centre of the system. Indeed, it often feels like stepping onto some kitsch merry-go-round roundabout that churns out the same old Looney Tunes. The solutions to climate change need to get to the hub of the problem. What is required is a level of control at the centre of the system.

Image 37. - Merry-go-round

In any society, the only way to get a systemic handle on a situation is through legislation. Climate change cannot be managed by piecemeal initiatives; instead, it needs one singular core legislation that sets the speed for a nation's overall emissions. A law that is based on science and fair *per capita* responsibility.

It is around this that everything else can turn. With such a law, all of the diverse interests for climate action would be empowered. Without this central act of common sense, all of the other efforts will be fighting against an impossibly strong force.

There has been a repeated emphasis on the importance of laws at different points throughout this book, and an accent has also been placed on the need for Western society to re-examine its values. These two fundamental lines of argument should be put on display in their own right and for one last, concluding time:

1. The central solution – Rational Laws

For the moment, this kaleidoscope of interests do not yet have a regular and settled core demand. It is easy to get carried away by the sentiments and energy that have filled so many city centres with climate protests marches – but, in and of themselves, they do not accomplish anything. In fact, around 50 years ago there was an Earth Day March on April 22nd, 1970. It mobilised 20 million grassroots people to the streets – this comprised a remarkable 10% of the US population. It still stands as the largest ever public demonstration in US history. It momentarily raised awareness, but it only achieved relatively limited legislative success, with the Clean Air Act, the Clean Water Act, plus the founding of the EPA. At the time, these were important steps, but they would never be enough to safely contain the surging impacts on the environment of a booming population and consumer culture. For example, the Clean Air Act did not include CO_2, and the Clean Water Act did not include oceans.

Likewise, there is no doubt that the recent social movements have indirectly achieved some progress. It is hard to imagine that the EU would have committed to their Climate Change Law in 2020 without the strong mandate that came from the streets. Yet, this 'world leading' commitment to tackling climate change still falls short by a long way. Carbon neutrality by 2050 is far too slow and light for any scientific scenario that keeps average temperature rises at 2°C, and (unsurprisingly for such a weak target) the EU does not commit itself to basing the climate law on science until 2030.

There has to be a standard way to hold governments to account in response to both the good news and the bad news about climate change. Raising awareness is one thing, reducing emissions in line with the science is another.

As Greta commented at the end of 2019 with her usual clear mindedness: "the strikes have achieved nothing." Many would like to praise her for making such a difference in awareness, but the bald truth is that in 2019, annual global emissions climbed by 2%. Greta was right. Certainly, raising awareness and building momentum in climate actions are always the first steps to real change. We must never get distracted from where the real action is, or is not, taking place.

Greta mobilised millions onto the streets with incisive and clear minded words; now these diverse calls for action need a solid, empirical base to plug into. Beyond the adjectives, the numbers are needed; and these numbers need to be embedded into laws.

Without a science-based national requirement, the protests have been easily side-lined and deflected. Many governments have waved a bundle of initiatives at the media, presented some fragmentary statistics, proudly claimed to be 'doing its bit' and applauded the strikers for their commitment. Meanwhile, emissions have continued to climb. For the moment, the change demanded by the protesters has remained elusive.

Having national legislation rooted explicitly in the latest science and basic notions of equity (outlined in Chapters 8 and 9 and the appendix) is essential for many other important reasons. First, it empowers the press and parliaments to scrutinise a government's commitments. Second, it flips the perverse perception of the climate strikes that the pragmatists are in government, and that the radicals are the ones on the streets. An explicit commitment to the science and basic fairness (such as consumption based and *per capita* requirements) demonstrates that those who are demanding reform are the ones acting with common sense, and it is the dogmatists who are trying to hold onto the status quo. Third, it would reduce the possibility of a psychological burnout in the protest movement as it would provide an objective finish line for a nation.

Above all else, though, it is the only systemic solution to a systemic problem.

Looking over our shoulder at one of the most successful social movements of modern times, much can be learnt from The Civil Rights Movement in the USA. It was not only a protest movement, it also had a legal backbone – the NAACP.[170] Indeed, the legal fight was just as visceral as the other aspects of the Civil Rights movement.

Martin Luther King is rightly honoured and remembered for his absolute commitment, but far fewer know about the equally astonishing sacrifice of Medgar Evers (see textbox). The work of all those in the NAACP was the invaluable, quieter subplot to the movement's success.[171]

Throughout his leadership of the Civil Rights Movement, Martin Luther King would never accept small political victories or concessions as something that he was supposed to be grateful for. He refused to accept that the status quo was reasonable, and that any progress was some sort of gift.

---

170 The NAACP was also heavily involved in developing important networks and co-organising various marches, such as the March on Washington for Jobs and Freedom.

171 As well as the major breakthroughs in both 1964 and 1965, they also put together and fought the Brown v Board of Education of Topeka in 1954, successfully argued by the black lawyer Thurgood Marshall.

He was intolerant of each incomplete gesture towards the systemic problems faced by non-white people in America, even if they were positive steps forward. He understood that the only proper response to their demands for justice was full equality before the law[172].

Binding national laws[173] for total greenhouse gas emissions would be the most rational way to embody all of the diverse interests of a country into a singular, clear requirement.

At the time of writing, to likely keep the warming to 2°C would require the UK to cut its emissions 6.9% per year, starting from today.[174] Holding the focus at a national level, with its own individual percentage as

---

172 Moreover, once the law was put in place through the Civil Rights Act of 1964, Martin Luther King was committed to delivering all of its consequences through the system.

173 The case of EU countries is a little more complicated. The EU, as an umbrella organisation, has a collective target for all of its Member States – principally, carbon neutrality by 2050 – but with intermediate targets to get there. This collective agreement allows some Member States to go slower (mainly Eastern European states), whereas other more advanced economies fill in the emissions gap. In this arrangement, the average emissions reductions would be 7% per year starting from now (for 2°C) or 25% per year starting from now (for 1.5°C). These are figures that were correct in 2020, but which will rise with inaction. This particular detail about EU countries has some consequences for making a national demand, but given that most people's political consciousness grips at a national level, it makes sense that the protests and the laws should centre on their own national *per capita* responsibility. The calibrations for the EU, as a whole, could be examined once the basics are established.

174 See Annex for full table of the emissions reductions required, nation by nation.

a central hub, allows a nation to keep the overall requirement of the science squarely in view. It also enables a nation to make the adjustments with an understanding of their own particular economy, and within the boundaries of their own democratic borders. A democratic solution appears feasible with a properly informed electorate, a wealth of climate data and the advanced processing power of computers that can calculate the interconnected effects of policy changes.

Every successful campaign, from the cause of female suffrage to the Civil Rights movement, has held a change in the law as the ultimate measure of success. Given the sheer range of interests that climate change inspires, where there is no natural centre of gravity, the case for national climate law seems to be even more essential.

In 2019, the Dutch Supreme Court ruled in favour of "**Urgenda**" – a ground-breaking decision in the legal fight for climate justice. The judgement requires the Dutch government to reduce its greenhouse gas emissions in line with its Human Rights obligations.

In 2020, the Danish Parliament voted through an even more stringent and binding law. Both laws are a major advance in the fight to get a proper grip on emissions. Most notably the Dutch law, as it is rooted in Human Rights and could act as a precedent for other nations to follow.

Neither the Dutch nor the Danish case formulated their demands by a *per capita* division of the remaining global carbon budget for 1.5°C or 2°C heating, the targets were unhelpfully framed with the usual formulation of x% reductions by x date, based on 1990 levels. However, both laws are major steps forward for humanity and both nations can ratchet up their commitments to be more transparent and equitable in the near future.

The end game of all of the diverse interests has to be legal, either by court action, such as the Urgenda case, or through the public will and parliaments. This is the central conclusion not only of a chapter on Plato, with his demand for a rational framework for a society, but also for the whole series of books in "No Common Sense".

All the science, all the psychology, all the social forces will be judged in time against the concentrations of CO_2 in the atmosphere. The only proper handle that gives us a comprehensive view and control of those levels of CO_2 is a legally binding commitment to the mainstream science.

Why is the central goal missing?

As it stands, science-based climate legislation is simply not the central issue in the public discourse about the crisis. It is not a pivotal issue for the media, not least because it is not pivotal for all of those engaged in climate action. Indeed, it is a very marginal concern. Why?

Leaving aside the billions spent by the fossil fuel industry to deflect and distract the social narrative away from where it would hurt them the most, there are other plausible reasons why we do not yet have this simple ambition established as the hub to our demands for climate justice. Perhaps the most obvious explanation would be that a law is abstract, whereas planting trees or going vegan is more tactile and immediate. Perhaps it is due to the fact that we have all arrived at the global threat of climate change from a huge range of particular concerns or commitments that naturally stick with us.[175] Perhaps the current lack of focus is just part of the normal evolution of how social movements develop, from fragmentary concerns to a unified goal.

It could be argued that it is a consequence of the 'superstructure' of a society that leans heavily towards individualism. Many social theorists would point to the tendency of capitalism to encourage us to think about

---

175 A good friend Shannon Jackson, originally from the small town of Todmorden (UK), in 2018 worked with a team of ambitious young people to mobilise thousands to strike in the streets of neighbouring Leeds about the climate crisis. Her drive and concern for climate justice was triggered by the contrasting injustice seen during the time she spent on the UK-French border, at the height of the refugee crisis in 2016. Motivated to prevent more brutality against those forced to move as a result of climate related disasters, her story is part of a remarkable kaleidoscope of the millions of people that make up this movement's demand for something better.

self-development and self-maximisation at the expense of developing shared ambitions. A concern for the self does not exclude a concern for common goals, but a capitalist society exerts a strong pull on our energy for transformation and development inwards, and away from the social space.

It could be argued that an example of this can be seen in the shape of our social media. The fact that top social media 'influencers' earn millions[176] through their Instagram followers is indicative of how we most frequently frame our 'social' thinking in personal terms. It is, therefore, not surprising to find that our thinking about major social issues is neither holistic nor coherent.

This personalisation of our thinking is not wrong in itself, of course. If litigation became a key demand of the fight for climate justice, then this trend could actually be very useful, given that having a personal connection to critical social issues seems indispensable. Protesting on the streets for our government to implement a climate law might seem too abstract until it is also coupled with an issue that hits close to home, or with a particular cause that we have genuine ownership of.

The strength of modern identity politics, and its wide range of concerns, provides a good example of how we can establish common causes through a common sense of injustice. Powerful traction and energy has been generated through each cause, as they are rooted in profoundly personal experiences. Being deprived of some fundamental rights on an issue that is wired into the colour of your skin, gender or sexuality has a visceral power. And such is the grip of systemically entrenched injustice that it requires a seriously powerful energy to break free of it.

For example, vicious slavery has scarred the lives of black people in America for centuries. Racial segregation and inequality seemed permanent. Martin Luther King managed an extraordinary double act: he harnessed the raw, instinctive sense of injustice to a movement that was profoundly committed

---

176 For example, Christiano Ronaldo earnt a reported $47.8m in 2019, ahead of Kendall Jenner ($15.7m) and Selena Gomez who was paid $8m for posting nine sponsored pictures and Tyler Oakley, an LGBTQ activist, commands an estimated $6m per year.

to love and peace and he sustained a campaign that focused all its energy on the establishment of an abstract law.

The deep historical well of personal suffering that he tapped into contrasts markedly with all of the graphs of climate data. Looking at an image of Representation Concentration Pathway 8.5 (RCP8.5) climbing over 4°C heating by 2100 is truly disturbing, but it does not have the same impact as witnessing a racist lynching. The energy of identity politics is simply not available to the cause of climate change. Is it just not sensorial enough?

Establishing a Common Sense of Climate Change

However, that might all be about to change. A reading of 416.39 ppm in June 2020 from the Mona Loa observatory[177] signalled a truly dangerous territory for the climate system. Our senses from here on in should brace themselves for a shock.

For example, the sheer scope and primal threat of the wildfires in Australia are the sort of tactile menace that could provoke that type of existential reaction that is needed. Repeated shocks like this could push us to seek the shelter of the law. Thousands of people were  cornered onto the beaches of Mallacoota (Victoria) on New Year's Eve 2019 as a final place of refuge, from the unpredictable tracks of the savage heat. Certainly, having one of the world's most highly developed nations being scorched to char and choked in thick orange fog provided the global consciousness with stunning dystopic images.

Image 38. - Wildfires, Australia 2019

The rising heat of the atmosphere must unleash its energy somewhere, so it is only right to brace ourselves for similar invasions into our civilisation. These incursions will surely wake us up in the end.

177 https://www.esrl.noaa.gov/gmd/ccgg/trends/

Strong leadership

However, when we are properly awake, we will need strong leadership to guide our responses. Again, MLK provides a remarkable role model here. He unapologetically upheld the values and the vision that were needed to sustain an effective response. He managed to billow the sails of the Civil Rights Movement with formidable strength.

He never lost sight of the reason for all of the protests and activism: civil rights had to be enshrined into law. Anything else was patronising and empty.

Image 39. - MLK, Washington DC, Aug 28th, 1963

In 1963, in the middle of a speech at the Lincoln Memorial, Washington, Mahalia Jackson shouted out: "Tell us about the dream, Martin!" – and he set off on a rhetorical riff that gave the speech its name and its celebrated place in history. These lines about dreams provided the headlines, however, before the request by Mahalia Jackson, MLK was delivering some major points too.

It is helpful to read this lesser known section of his speech with the context of the climate emergency and the protests of 2019 borne in mind:

"We have also come to this hallowed spot to remind America of the fierce urgency of now. This is no time to engage in the luxury of cooling off or to take the tranquilizing drug of gradualism. Now is the time to make real the promises of democracy. Now is the time to rise from the dark and desolate valley of segregation to the sunlit path of racial justice. Now is the time to lift our nation from the quicksands of racial injustice to the solid rock of brotherhood. Now is the time to make justice a reality for all of God's children.

It would be fatal for the nation to overlook the urgency of the moment. This sweltering summer of the Negro's legitimate discontent will not pass until there is an invigorating autumn of freedom and equality. 1963 is not an end, but a beginning. And those who hope that the Negro needed to blow off steam and will now be content will have a rude awakening if the nation returns to business as usual. There will be neither rest nor tranquility in America until the Negro is granted his citizenship rights. The whirlwinds of revolt will continue to shake the foundations of our nation until the bright day of justice emerges."[178]

A social tipping point had been caused in 1954 by the appalling image of Emmett Till in his open coffin.[179] A tremendous momentum had gathered through the boycotts, the sit-ins and marches and all of the NAACP's grafting work. His speech to the crowds in Washington 1963 carried such power because it took place in a year that was loaded with a focused determination for systemic change. Indeed, within 12 months of that speech, the legislative breakthrough for citizenship rights that MLK was demanding was finally achieved as President Lyndon B. Johnson signed the Civil Rights Act.

Martin Luther King would have never settled for equal rights limited to a small part of Selma, or a law that was limited only to the State of South Carolina. He would not have accepted that black people could have equality in shoe shops, but not in schools. Racial equality was nothing to do with making more black people feel welcome. When MLK continuously reminded everyone to keep their "eyes on the prize", it was legal, actual equality. Equal rights had to encompass everything. The climate action movement needs the sort of noble intolerance and full-mindedness that Martin Luther King sustained. We all live under one atmosphere and we all have an equal right to the life that it secures.

178 Martin Luther King, "*March on Washington for Jobs and Freedom*" (August 28th, 1963). Extract from his address made at the Lincoln Memorial, now known as the "I have a Dream" speech. (Italics and bold added)
179 See "*No Common Sense - Nietzsche*".

Every measure of climate action is an important part of the move towards justice. However, we should suspend our applause for a successful campaign about tree planting and transport systems, single use plastic or veganism, divestments and decarbonised industries, Blue and Circular Economy advances and any segment of society until they are part of a legal imperative that ensures that it all adds up to what the science demands.

A national law for the climate could be an equivalent to the Civil Rights Act of 1964. The law would stipulate the annual percentage emission reductions required for that nation, starting from the year in which the legislation was passed. A full table of the national reductions required, along with a full explanation of how those figures are calculated, can be found at www. Cut11Percent.org.

Yet, it is important to note that it would be naïve to think that this one central legal measure would be sufficient in itself. There will need to be laws that follow-up on this basic ground rule. Martin Luther King took his Civil Rights Movement to Selma in 1965 because the abstract law to vote in so many cities across the South was not being carried out in practice. The Voting Rights Act of 1965 was a hard-won victory too and was perhaps Martin Luther King's greatest achievement.

It will take some time to roll out all of the legal work for the climate – but the first step must be the essential central act of binding a nation to a responsible level of reductions overall. It is around this central legal hub that all of the other laws and actions can spin out from.

2. The deeper solution – The Virtues

The external and internal laws

Having these rational laws as the basic mainframe to our society is not just good for the city, Plato would argue that they are also typical of what is good for the soul. The symmetry pointed out earlier (in Chapter 3)[180], between the happy city and the happy soul, now provides the angle to get deeper to the heart of the '*Republic*': the virtues.

This symmetry that Plato sets up between the external and the internal laws might seem a bit odd to modern minds, given that the modern polis has largely detached political thinking from private thinking. Once the importance of the virtues in his Philosophy is understood, this symmetry will start to make good sense.

Indeed, it is probably not surprising that the commitments that governments need to make for the state will be reflected in the types of decision-making that we need to make as individuals. Plato argues in the '*Republic*' that the holistic thinking that is required to implement just laws in society 'without', would best be mirrored in the citizens who are trying to cultivate a similar wisdom to govern their psyche 'within'.

In this mode of thinking, an external law on emissions is not simply there to protect our basic human rights; it also functions to illuminate what sort of shape our inner psyche should hold. This rudimentary act of a government should provoke an examination of the internal laws that govern us as citizens. If the external law is totally in conflict with our inner priorities, if there is a serious tension between the laws of the state and the ruling voices of the soul, then Plato would diagnose that something is amiss.

180 Page 60

A state cannot function properly if it is divided against itself.
Neither can a person.

The Platonic Virtues

The just city should be in harmony with the just soul. The virtues required for both are going to be informative about how we can not only achieve an external barrier to our own self-destruction as a civilisation, but how we can be a more balanced and happier people.

Indeed, solving the climate crisis will require us to step into the social space with a full set of virtues. We will need to use our intelligence (*nous*) with wisdom, our spiritedness (*thumos*) with courage and our desires (*epithumia*) will have to be moderated.

The just soul and the just city

Wisdom, courage and moderation – three of the four Platonic virtues. And when they all come together, it generates the fourth: Justice (Δικαιοσύνη, *dikaiosyne*).

Justice for the soul and justice for the city.

The virtues lie at the hub of Plato's thinking and they provide us with a powerful set of concepts for us to move ahead with in the struggle for climate justice – not just at a surface level, but also at a deeper and fully sustainable level.

The virtue that will fill the conclusion of this chapter will be the virtue of courage. This is because the spirited part of our psyche is that which gets us off the sofa and jolts us into action. It is one thing to understand what is going on, it is quite another to act. The *thumos* will hold our attention because it is the place within us that is triggered by climate change.

Our *thumos* is that part of us that is disturbed when we think through some of the astonishing consequences of the climate crisis. It is utterly offended that we would sink entire ancient cultures into saltwater for the sake of keeping a banal consumer culture alive. Our *thumos* is deeply rattled when both the extraordinary wealth of a tiny few is further inflated at the expense of the most basic rights of so many millions. When we are confronted with the massive scale of the political and economic powers, it is the *thumos* that shouts: "OK, but I count for something"[181].

It is the *thumos* that galvanizes a steely determination to fight a system, because it is locked onto a disastrous pathway to collapse. When the odds seem piled up against a solution, it is the *thumos* that either provides the gritty resolve to follow through on personal commitment or the energy to continually throw itself at the injustices of the status quo.

But our *thumos* also makes the struggle for justice a positive one. The *thumos* insists that we can restore the natural world to some of its former beauty and diversity. It also enjoys trying to restore our social space to recognise the worth of all the people in it.

In a consumer culture that has become nervous and tentative about values and commitments, Plato provides us with a powerful reminder of how reasonable and transformative they are. His '*Republic*' shows us how we can awaken our passions from the listless banality of a careless culture, without rousing them into a blind bombastic anger that has no dignity. He shows how the limp media coverage of the climate crisis could be reinvigorated by a conviction about injustice and human rights, without it hyperventilating into a xenophobic blame game.

However, for the sake of a clear narrative about the virtues, it is helpful to just block out our '*thumos*' for a moment and concentrate on the other

181 And, most recently, our *Thumos* rightly assert "#metoo".

two parts of the psyche: Reason and Desire.

In other words, we will be looking into our Sense and Sensibility, the two poles of our human condition.

Reason first

Without understanding the role played by all of the virtues in Plato's writing, his proposal for the best structure of the state might look rather punitive. This is especially true if the '*thumos*' is blocked out, given that it leaves abstract reasoning on top of the stack and desires at the bottom. However, this starting point helps to clarify some important basics.

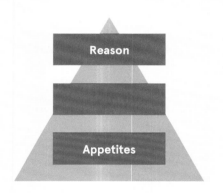

The just soul and the just city

A casual reading of Plato might infer that he was a rather ascetic man, preaching a totalitarianism of rationality or a thinker who endorsed a dictatorship of stingy control and constraint. His '*Republic*' might look like a state in which the law givers are the spoilers, as they castrate and suppress the desires.[182]

Indeed, a parallel to this casual and negative view of Plato can be observed in many people's attitudes towards climate laws. Those opposed to limits on emissions often swipe at them as if they were a threat to civil freedoms. As Trump stated in Davos 2020: "These alarmists always demand the same thing – absolute power to dominate, transform and control every aspect of our lives. We will never let radical socialists destroy our economy, wreck

---

182 Those familiar with Freud's threefold division of the self would not be wrong to observe the fundamental conflict between reason and the appetites as a parallel to the conflict between the Super Ego and the Id.

our country or eradicate our liberty." Such a cartoonish understanding of the demand for climate laws is the one most often peddled by libertarian activists. It is part of their strategy to present environmentalists as 'Watermelons' (thin green on the outside, deep communist red in the middle). This is an association that brings to mind stagnant economies, harsh environmental damage and the dangers of an invasive central state.

Indeed, those opposed to climate regulations often battle against them as if they were the snide ambition of some Calvinist-minded bureaucrats who (twitching at their desks) discharge their repressed desires and anger by zealously pushing through regulations to strangle the economy, down to its slowest pulse.

But the truth about the priority of reason has nothing to do with some grumpy attitude towards human desires for Plato. In the '*Republic*', reason is primary simply because that is the best place for it in a well-ordered state.

Having desires in charge is not wise. The brunt of Plato's attack on democracies, which has been sustained through this chapter, must be understood as an attack on a lifestyle that reduces reason to a slave of the desires. Plato argues that having reason pushed around in the service of basic pleasures is a characteristic of a democracy and is typical of an individual whose life is unhappily chaotic. To be overwhelmed by the competing desires of the body is both disorientating and unfulfilling.

By contrast, Plato thinks that a well-ordered state, with the three parts of the city in the right order, is a genuinely happy one; it is a situation that is mirrored in the happy individual. I do not mean happy in the superficial, momentary sense, like the pleasures given by leisure or wealth, but instead, happy in the fullest sense, because it is balanced and well-orientated.

Having everything in its proper place is the first step towards achieving virtue. Plato argues that only the virtuous city and the virtuous person can truly be happy. The most common error that people make in a democratic society is to get things upside down, by placing desires at the top and reason at the bottom.

The Ring of Gyges

These concerns about the power of the appetites, to swamp our thinking and throw our system out of balance, come most clearly to the surface in a passage at the start of Book 2 of the 'Republic'. In one of Plato's most muscular moments in the 'Republic', he deepens the reflection on why a simple pursuit of pleasure is an impoverished life and why a good life needs to be attentive to the fuller picture that reason provides.

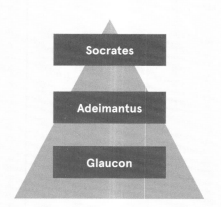

The just soul and the just city

In the passage, a new trio of characters take over the dialogue; unsurprisingly, they fit into the now familiar structure of Plato's thinking. Glaucon represents the desires, Adeimantus the spirit, and Socrates represents the voice of reason. It is, therefore, Glaucon who poses a challenge about the desires to Socrates by introducing the myth of The Ring of Gyges (2:359a-2:360d).

It is a magical ring that gives its wearer the power of invisibility and, therefore, impunity. Glaucon claims that anyone who puts the ring on would binge on their desires with no regard for others and with no respect for social or legal norms. This a fantasy that Aristophanes had already put into rather graphic language in his play, "*The Birds*"[183] (a fantasy that included the pleasures of adultery and farting with impunity[184]).

" ONE RING TO FOOL THEM ALL ."

Glaucon states: "For all men believe in their hearts that injustice is far more profitable to the individual than justice... If you could imagine anyone obtaining this power of becoming invisible, and never doing any wrong or touching what was another's, he would be thought by the on-lookers to be a most wretched idiot."

Anyone who thinks that some actions are intrinsically good or bad, need to test their beliefs by imagining what they would do if they obtained the Ring of Gyges. Anyone who thinks that they are a good person needs to imagine how they would act if they had absolute impunity. Glaucon suspects that if the ring of Gyges was given to a 'just' man and an 'unjust' man, they would both behave the same – 'unjustly'. By taking away the social constraints that limit our behaviour, he thinks that he has exposed justice for what it really is: a mere social convenience.

Glaucon thinks that the reason that we have laws in society is simply because we need some way to protect ourselves from each other. He argues that there is no value in the laws of a state beyond the pragmatic need to create a liveable space. It is a sharply modern and cynical view about the

183 "Some Patroclides, needing to take a crap, would not have to spill it out on his cloak, but could fly off, satisfy his requirements, let a few farts out and, having recovered his breath, return. If one of you, it matters not who, had adulterous relations and saw the husband of his mistress in the seats of the senators, he might stretch his wings, fly to her, and, having laid her, resume his place. Is it not the most priceless gift of all, to be winged?" Aristophanes, "*The Birds*", 795. (The Complete Greek Drama, vol. 2. Eugene O'Neill, Jr. New York. Random House. 1938).

184 In his comedy "*Archarnians*" (425 BCE), Aristophanes has the fantasy of a man (Dikaiopolis, note the name) observing the folly of his fellow Athenians, who seem to have no interest in making peace with Sparta. So Dikaiopolis makes his own private peace - so he can act just as he likes, as if the war had never started.

true nature of laws.[185] In a dog-eat-dog world, the laws of a state simply stop us from imploding as a social unit. In Glaucon's reductivist view of the laws, his imagination is limited to the practical consequences only.

Likewise, the reasoning for the climate change laws put forward in this book have often insisted on this simple, rather negative justification. This has been oddly necessary, because this basic pragmatic thinking is almost entirely absent from the climate change discourse. The framing of our societies with effective climate change laws is a rather rudimentary act of common sense.

Going beyond "Reason versus Desires"

However, just as Glaucon provides Socrates with a chance to affirm the fuller value of the 'well-ordered soul', he also provides this conclusion with a hinge that can lead to a consideration of the broader values of recalibrating our societies to a different set of fundamentals. Legislating for the climate could also be the first step in a wider regeneration of both nature and the public space.

> *Eudaimonia*
> Literally, "good (*eu*) spirit (*daimon*)".
> It is most often translated as 'happiness' or 'welfare', but the closest and most fitting word is probably 'flourishing'.
>
> An ancient dictionary, probably written by the earliest members of Plato's Academy, describes it as the "good composed of all goods".

Affirming the importance of climate laws will lead to a broader discussion of what really matters to us. The difficult decisions that will have to be made to fit our economic and social ambitions to the limits of what the laws of nature allow could turn out to be deeply good for us. We will need to reflect on what it is to be a human.

---

185 He has taken over this reductivist view of morality from Thrasymachus who voiced them in Book One.

We will need to think about what 'eudaimonia' looks like.

The rather rudimentary contrast of reason versus desires is very pervasive in the modern Western world. It frames so many adverts and so much media output, it shapes many political debates and many of our own inner dialogues when we are faced with key decisions. Plato's work on how best to set up the inner structure of a state, and the inner structure of the self takes us well beyond this unhelpful binary choice. By following Plato to a fuller understanding of the self, we can not only see that climate laws are a rational necessity, we can also even appreciate that such legislation would be symptomatic of a society that was genuinely happier – a society that enjoyed 'eudaimonia'.

The Simile of the Charioteer

The 3-fold division of the psyche

It is now pertinent to note that it is in the '*Republic*' that Plato goes beyond the binary opposition of the desires versus reason in his works for the first time.[186] This is the moment to bring '*thumos*' back in.

The introduction of '*thumos*' is an important landmark for a couple of reasons. Firstly, the threefold division of the psyche structures the entire '*Republic*' – most obviously in the clusters of people who enter into dialogue with Socrates. Secondly, '*thumos*' both makes Plato's analysis of the human condition that much richer and it provides a whole range of extra vocabulary. This richness is especially useful to Plato as he explores the importance of the virtues.

---

186 There is much scholarly debate about the order of Plato's works. However, it is a safe bet that the "Phaedrus" was written after the '*Republic*'. As noted in "Concerning the date of Plato's *Phaedrus*", Anna Usacheva, 'Hermathena' No. 189 (Winter 2010), pp. 53-70.

In order to understand the investment that he makes in opening up a 3-fold division of the psyche, however, it is best to step outside of the 'Republic' and into a later work, the "Phaedrus". It is in this more mature work that he describes the structure of the psyche with the sharpest detail; he presents his thinking in the Simile of the Charioteer.[187]

So far in this chapter, the three parts of the soul have been visualised in a vertical order of power: with reason above the spirit, followed by the spirit above the appetites.[188] This format has been employed until this point in order to establish the basics, and to reflect the whole setup of The 'Republic'.

However, like Plato does in his book "Phaedrus", it is actually more helpful to push the pyramid onto its side. Now this configuration forms the shape of the charioteer and his two horses.

In this vivid allegory ("Phaedrus", 245c-249d), Plato helps us to think through the importance of establishing the right priorities and the right balance for the state and the individual. The metaphor describes the

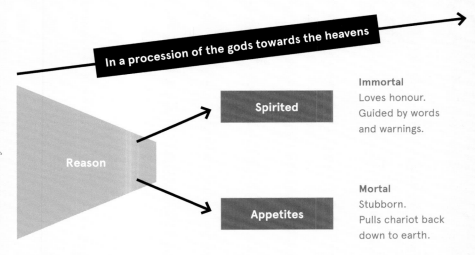

The "Simile of the Charioteer"

In a procession of the gods towards the heavens

Reason

Spirited

Immortal
Loves honour.
Guided by words
and warnings.

Appetites

Mortal
Stubborn.
Pulls chariot back
down to earth.

187 Briefly noted on p28.

188 The reason for illustrating it with a triangular shape was simply to reflect the different numbers of citizens in each different body part of the 'Republic'. The small elite community of the golden-souled philosophers at the top would be supported by the populous bronze souled workers at the bottom, with the army being somewhere in between.

charioteer (reason) and his winged horses (spiritedness and desires) who have joined in a procession towards the heavens with the gods.

The charioteer understands what the noble plan is and how best to get there; however, he cannot get anywhere without the energy of his horses. However, these horses are very different and although their powerful energy is indispensable to the rational charioteer, controlling and guiding them is highly problematic. As Plato writes in the Phaedrus: "the task of the charioteer is necessarily a difficult and unpleasant business".

All three parts of the psyche have their value, the challenge is to get them to work together towards a noble goal.

a) The black horse

The ignoble black horse represents the appetites. It is stubborn and incapable of being persuaded. It only wants to head down to earth. The nagging pull of the desires, which wants to undermine the rational part of the psyche, should be familiar to everyone. It speaks loudly to us when we are on a diet and open the fridge door to get something sensible to eat, only to then notice something rather seductive. It moans soporifically at the mind for another minute in bed, when the clock coldly informs us that we must push off the sheets and get up.

Plato writes that the black horse is a "crooked lumbering animal, put together anyhow...of a dark colour, with grey eyes and blood-red complexion; the mate of insolence and pride, shag-eared and deaf, hardly yielding to whip and spur."

A clear image of this tension between reason and the desires could have been observed at my daughter's seventh birthday party: It seemed like a good idea to rent nine dwarf ponies from the local stables and to go for a leisurely ride. Maybe we had picked a bad time of the day, or maybe the ponies were either particularly stubborn or habitually over-indulged. Whatever the reason, instead of a relaxed, social event with the children and their parents walking along the paths in the nearby fields, the party turned into an absurdly comic standstill as soon as we got to a path sided with grass. The children belly-laughed watching their parents lean almost horizontally on the reins in front of the ponies, whilst digging into the path with their heels for some grip. There were moments in this new equine sports-event when our four-legged friends did move forward – only to return to another gridlock a couple of metres later. Despite encouraging pats and words from the adults, and enthusiastic rocking horse movements from the children, we lost the tug of war 9-0.

The Platonic lesson that can be learnt from this experience is that reason, in itself, is too puny to control the desires.

We have known about the planetary boundaries to our economic activities for about half a century. But our brains have not taken enough control of our desires yet to rein them in. The black horse is pulling us down to Earth, and reason seems powerless to stop it. Our chariot appears to be out of control.

George Monbiot's description of capitalism as a cancer to the planet's living systems is shocking. But is it wrong? He explains: "Every human being grows. We grow through childhood and then when we reach adulthood, we reach a plateau. Our body has a regulating system which stops growth beyond a certain point. Occasionally that system breaks down and a cell begins to multiply and grow without regulation. And we call that cancer. Cancer is basically infinite growth within a finite living system, which is the human body. That is what is exactly what is happening with capitalism. Capitalism is dependent on infinite growth within a finite living system which is the planet. Capitalism is the planet's cancer."[189]

---

189 George Monbiot, *"Capitalism is the Planet's Cancer: Operate Before it's too Late"*. Double Down News, January 30th 2020.

Our crash course in consumerism can be visualised as a colour bar code. These "warming stripes"[190] illustrate the changing temperatures year on year from 1850-2019. They also illustrate how impotent our intellect has been so far in mobilising our societies to implement the necessary changes. Reason might be able to see with clarity that the trajectory we are on is awfully dangerous, but it has not been able to persuade the black horse out of its nosedive.

But this binary opposition of reason and desires can be fixed by the addition of another horse: A white horse.

b) The white horse

The white horse represents *thumos*.

In contrast to the black horse, the noble white horse is biddable. It can listen to reason and it is drawn to higher things. In Plato's words, it wants to "ascend towards the ridge of heaven", and so the charioteer must work hard with the white horse to guide them all upwards on "the great circuit".

190 Ed Hawkings, 'showyourstripes.info'.

Thumos has denoted 'spiritedness' throughout this chapter; in truth, it is a word that is very tricky to translate into English because it covers such a wide range of ideas. The Greek "*thumos*" (θυμός) can mean "spirit", "breath" or in some cases "soul",[191] and the influential pre-Socratic thinker Empedocles describes it as "the seat of life."[192] *Thumos* stirs us to feel joy and hope, pain and fear. It is at work both when we love and when we grieve. It can seethe with anger at the external world, or the internal self. *Thumos* can take deep satisfaction from a job well done and become bitter with failure.

Thumos is an immensely rich and complex word that continually morphs throughout Greek literature, both before and after Plato. However, the notion of honour always remains integral to an understanding of it. For example, in Aeschylus' tragedy, "*Seven Against Thebes*", the word is used to describe the men on the battlefield with "iron-lunged *thumos*, blazing with valour, breathed out as if from lions glaring with the war-god's might".[193] And in the '*Republic*' itself, Plato describes the military class, who embody *thumos*, as men striving for "control, victory and high repute" (414b, 415a).

Indeed, the centre of gravity with *thumos* lies with the emotional energy that comes from our urge for recognition. It is the part of us that is reflective enough to be wired into the higher values, such as justice and status; at the same time, though, it is rooted into our bodies at a visceral level. For example, injustice needs the mind to recognise the problem, but it is something that causes a reaction in the guts too.

---

191 Noel W Smith, "*Greek and Interbehavioral Psychology*", p66. American University Press, 1993.
192 Empedocles pioneered the division of reality into the 4 'roots' 'air, water, wind and fire' in his poem "Purifications" – a division that shaped our understanding of Nature so much in early science. In it, *thumos* appears twice as "the seat of life": B 128:10, B 137:6.
193 *Ibid.* p8. (Angela Hobbs).

Harnessing the Homeric *thumos*

What Plato does in the '*Republic*' is to take this indomitable and courageous heart of the word and to emphasise its reflective capacity. He is aware that he needs the raw drive of the *thumos* to do the work of defending the city against its enemies. At this macro level, the *thumos* is embodied in the army. At a micro level, a strong *thumos* provides the spirit and energy needed for a person to stand up for themselves. However, Plato is conscious of the fact that he has inherited an understanding of *thumos* from a Homeric culture, one that is heavily embedded in masculine notions of courage ('*andreia*').[194] These readings of *thumos* do not necessarily mean that either intelligence or wisdom are involved.

Combative strength and boldness might enable us to fight for what is important, but jumping headlong into a battle with guts, but with our eyes closed, is reckless. Plato can clearly see the dangers of a blind *thumos*. One classic example of when the *thumos* can override reason comes from Homer. In fact, the very first word of Homer's "Iliad" is "μῆνιν" (from '*menis*' – meaning "rage", "wrath" or "fury"). The whole epic poem is driven by the war hero Achilles' pride and rage and who is the embodiment of *thumos* in the plot. His honour has been attacked by King Agamemnon and his offended pride propels him through a whole sequence of events that also pulls and condemns so many others to their tragic fate.

Image 41. - Achilles

194 Indeed, Sophocles' tragic play '*Electra*' shows how embedded masculinity was in the Greek words for courage. When Electra's father Agamemnon is killed, she is warned by her sister that to exact revenge on the killer would not be a fitting act for a woman. Writing before Plato, Sophocles did not have much choice in the passage when Electra expresses her bold intentions to fight back but to use the word '*andreia*' ('manliness') for courage.

There is a definite sense that Plato is entering into dialogue with both Homer and Achilles in the '*Republic*'. Plato wants to expand the discussion about courage and pride to something much wider than the battlefield. The '*Republic*' enlarges the role played by our *thumos* to the full civic space. He endorses the idea that *thumos* does not have to pull everything else around it into a tragic ending. Courage does not require us to sacrifice everything to it.

It should be noted that the Homeric tradition that Plato inherits does not have a view of the *thumos* that is entirely deaf to reason.[195] However, Plato is making a bold move in recasting the values of his world by inserting '*thumos*' into the heart of the psyche, but still close to reason, by putting it into the middle of the polis as the Auxiliary soldiers, but close to the ruling Guardian Philosophers. He is drawing out an important reflective feature from the dominant masculine and muscular character of the Homeric *thumos*. By putting *thumos* very squarely as the distinct middle component of his threefold structure, he is taking the Homeric tradition to a new level.

Much of this important work with '*thumos*' is done by Plato in Books 2 and 3 of the '*Republic*' when he is describing the education of the military class of his ideal polis. These silver souled soldiers of the polis are trained with the usual Greek military techniques, and develop their physical power and endurance; however, Plato also proposes a cultural education (musikē)[196] that cultivates their wider skills too. By Book 4, Plato is able to put forward his understanding of what being a real man is and what real courage is

---

195 For example, in Book 8 of the "*Iliad*" after observing the slaughter of the Trojan War from the vantage point of Mount Olympus Zeus announces: "Hear me, gods and goddesses, while I say what my heart (*thumos*) prompts..." (8:5). In Book 24 Hermes considers in his *thumos* how to get King Priam out of Achilles' military camp.

196 *Musikē* includes music, but it is certainly not limited to that.

(ανδρεία, *andreia* [197]). The true Platonic man harnesses his *thumos* as he "holds fast to the orders of reason about what he ought or ought not to fear, in spite of pleasure and pain". (*'Republic'*, 4.442c). As Angela Hobbs has helpfully summarised: "courage involves both emotional commitment and evaluative belief, an intellectual and emotional appreciation of what things are worth taking risks for and in what circumstances."

Plato called the skill required to handle our *thumos* with this informed balance "courage".

Courage is the central virtue of the psyche, guided by the virtue of wisdom from above and secured by the virtue of moderation from below.[198] With the passions well ordered, Plato understands that it provides a moral resilience for every aspect of a good life: military and municipal, political and private.

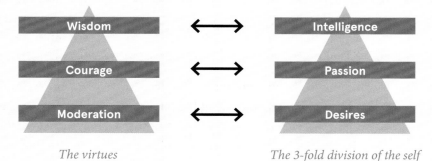

The virtues   *The 3-fold division of the self*

---

197 Ανδρεία can best be translated as 'manly spirit'. It is closely related to the Greek word for man, '*andro*', which was later translated into the Latin as '*vir*' – from which we get the words virile, and of course, virtue. Indeed, Socrates was quite radical in his assertion that women were just as capable as men of showing bravery.

198 It is informative to see what Aristotle understood about courage. He expanded his teachers' work on the virtues and built a complete system. For Aristotle, courage (*andreia*) requires us to navigate a course between rashness (*thrasos*) and cowardliness (*delios*). In fact, Aristotle's ethics of Virtue are rooted in the notion of balance between two extremes – a principle known as the 'The Golden Mean', or 'The Golden Middle'.

Harnessing the modern *"thumos"*

We are rightly accustomed to being alert to the dangers of societies that are driven to collapse by a blind rage or zealous fever. An overdose of *thumos*[199] can be lethal. It is true that we no longer move towards our enemies in a hoplite phalanx, holding an aspis and a xiphos.[200] After the rampant *thumos* of both World Wars, we are now most often seen carrying a plastic credit card into combat in our struggle for recognition. Yet, although the scenery and weaponry have changed, the power of *thumos* to flood our thinking remains undiluted.

Furthermore, the problem with our modern situation is that although the tragedy is of epic proportions, the drama is neither confined to the lives of a few heroic men, nor is it confined to the territory of a battlefield. The Anthropocene could get universally ugly.

It is nevertheless important to underline that the 'civilising' of the Homeric *thumos* by Plato should not and must not diminish its power and energy. The strength of the spirited voice within us should remain strong, sometimes formidably strong. Indeed, aligning the climate emergency with the language and concepts of war and struggle is not unhelpful, given that there are dangers at the other extreme of an unbalanced *thumos*.

A *thumos* that is too slack is very hazardous. Life in a superficial culture can be perilous. A society that has been hollowed out and placated into a crowd of dopey consumers, with no lust or love to get things right, is vulnerable to a host of dangers. We have been caught napping by the mundane facts about the chemistry of the atmosphere. The work of Hannah Arendt on the banality of evil (explored in *"Arendt Tackles Climate Change"*) demonstrates how deeply into trouble a shallow mind can get.

---

199 In Homeric terms this rage is best captured in the moment when Achilles
      ignores the pleading of Hector for mercy at the end of the Iliad. "
200 An ancient Greek shield and sword respectively.

Indeed, those who have tracked the accelerating assault of the Anthropocene into the biosphere will have experienced moments of raw anxiety and anger. Plato would not want to mollify this energy. We need the *thumos* as it does not back away from confronting injustice. It is the drive behind social transformation, or as McKay puts it the *thumos* is that "energetic thinking that leads to action."[201] We need to harness the power of the white horse. We have to engage with that "visceral thinking"[202] which is indignant about the shambolic situation we are in.

It is easy to be cynical about the values that we share.

Reading Plato helps us to be more resilient. The *thumos*, a noble horse, is inspired by the realisation of how much better things could be. In the Allegory of the Charioteer, as the chariot reaches the heavens, the eye of the soul catches a glimpse of something that "no poet could ever put into words" (247c), "absolute justice, temperance and knowledge" (247d). It pulls us upwards. Anybody who has wrestled with systemic power, or who has been flattened by it, knows that there must be something stronger than reason that pulls them back onto their feet to fight again.

This is an odd part of the human condition, but the boldness with which Plato puts forward his vision of the Forms of justice and goodness enables us to remember what it looks and feels like.

---

201 A *Man's Life, On Manhood, On Virtue*, Personal Development, Philosophy. Brett & Kate McKay, March 11, 2013, Last updated: November 11, 2018.

202 Barnouw, J., "*Odysseus, Hero of Practical Intelligence: Deliberation and Signs in Homer's Odyssey*", p100. University Press of America, 2004.

c) The wise charioteer

There are two respects in which our *thumos* needs to be mindfully calibrated. The guiding hand of wisdom is needed.

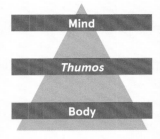

The 3-fold division of the self

It is no use if our spirited energy carries us into the fight for climate justice without a strategy. Activism has to be smart, aware of the risks involved and not just blindly, bluntly assertive. We need to be attentive to policies and the updates of the scientists, and our demands for legislative change need to be crystal clear.

Reason is crucial.

However, our spirited engagement with the climate crisis must not be sucked up into a merely mental world. It is no use if we only watch nature documentaries, click 'Like' on Facebook posts that appeal to us and shake our heads about what is going on around us. We also need to occupy the civil space with our bodies and our actions.

Activism must smart with the desires too. The *thumos* has to pull the black horse upwards and towards the rational goal. It cannot be allowed to just pull us down into some tactile individual projects about consumption. It has to remain fully unaware of their impacts on the bigger picture. The determination to put the world to right is far less effective if we turn our sense of injustice inwards and retreat from the social sphere into isolated green communities that have little to do with the whole, unjust system. Walking, planting a tree, restoring a wildlife system, reducing meat and flights are all meaningful and important acts, but they must be part of an overall strategy that will actually take the concentrations of CO_2 in the atmosphere to a sustainable level.

Any meaningful breakthrough in climate action will remain highly improbable without this balanced understanding of what we are doing. Millions of people are desperately anxious about the collapse of human civilisation, the imperative to exert greater effort becomes stronger with every tightening of the scientific scenarios. It is then easy for our psyche to be overwhelmed by the insignificance of our individual actions, precisely because they are insignificant. Our efforts to be wise, courageous and moderate have to be matched by actions that will ensure that a parallel balance is achieved at a national level in the end game of these last couple of decades in which we can actually control our own destiny.

The systems we live in must be more rational, and this systemic thinking has to start at the top with nationally binding laws that will frame everything else[203]. This type of thinking still feels uncomfortable because we are conditioned to perceiving climate legislation as an action that will reduce our lives, rather than enhance them. Without the affirmative language of values and without an imagination that is encouraged to remember the teeming beauty of the natural world, the fight for basic legislation will be an uphill struggle.

It is notable that both the Civil Rights Movement and the Women's Suffrage Movement won rights and deployed the language of victory and success. Likewise, the Climate Movement must also put the fight for legislation inside a context of well-being. Climate laws will almost certainly require a managed recession, a truly odd goal for policy makers to consider[204]. But in the long-term, it is all about claiming the right for a safe and liveable future with an economy that is rooted in skills, activities and healthy communities. Climate justice is not about constricting our freedom, but about deepening it. It is an advance, not a step back.

---

203 See www.Cut11Percent.org
204 Although COVID-19 did open up many examples of how we need to recalibrate our ambitions
    when we are confronted with a threat from nature.

Plato saw reason as the divine spark that could get us to look beyond the surface of things and which could help us to get things in their proper place and proportion. He was not a tragic, despondent thinker.

The just soul is a happy one because each part does what it is suited for. It is intrinsically desirable and it is much better to have the parts in harmony, not at war with themselves.

"The unexamined life is not worth living"

Socrates was faced with a choice between exile and death at the conclusion of his trial.

He could have shuffled off to some quiet retirement, far away from Athens. He could have allowed the Athenians to just get on with their lives – fulfilling their duties and satisfying their desires, more or less. The Athenians had their settled ideas about both what a good state was and what a good life was. After fighting for so long to drag them outside of their conventional thinking, Socrates could have just dusted his coat off and walked away.

A truce would have given both sides a calmer life, but he stayed, and he chose the hemlock.

Cynics can read his death as a stubborn, exhibitionist or self-indulgent act, but this overlooks the fundamental importance of the virtues to Socrates, and by consequence, to Plato.

Just as the Ring of Gyges offers its wearer the possibility of acting without any concern for what is truly right or wrong, so Socrates was offered the chance to walk away from the consequences of his behaviour. The fact that Socrates stayed and was executed in 399 BCE is a striking level of commitment to a set of values. To have walked into exile would have been a negation of the whole system of his thinking.

He chose to be true to his city and to his virtues, not just his own virtues, but also the city's virtues. He understood that his life was part of 'social contract' and that the two were inseparable.

In explaining his choice, he comments that: "the unexamined life is not worth living" (*Apology* 38a).

This sentence is now one of the most famous lines in all of Philosophy, and it is often taken to be some sort of elitist swipe at an uncultured life, as if a night at the opera were better than a night in a football stadium. But this is to miss the point. In this line, Plato is affirming the deep value of a life in which there is balance and harmony. Philosophy is an invitation for us to become more fully ourselves and part of that requires that we take up our space in the civic space, to make it wiser too.

The virtues of the Civil Rights Movement

Returning one last time to Martin Luther King, and to all those engaged in the Civil Rights Movement, they provide a salient illustration of what Plato would like to communicate in the '*Republic*': they resolutely demonstrated the importance of the virtues. They also did so with all of the fierce boldness that is needed on the battlefield, but they transposed it into a non-violent, civic fight.

The activists had to show tremendous courage at two levels to achieve what they achieved. Their tenacious fight for justice with the external laws was matched by the fierce internal struggle to keep their movement a peaceful and focused one.

Their external fight was for legal equality. From the outside, they were faced with lynching, church bombings, jail beatings and mass arrests. They were confronted by white supremacists (both by those in uniforms and those in jeans) who ran at them with barbed batons during the freedom marches. There were water cannons and dogs deployed to push the marches off the streets. There was a constant flow of death threats and hate. Indeed, everything was designed to crush the spirits of those who were committed to a change in the law, and every effort was made to blow it off-course. The powers that wanted to keep the status quo carried out a siege of violence on the bodies of the activists.

Yet the external force of the racists also wanted to invade the internal space of the activists. To protect the racist system of segregation, those calling for change needed to be kept in their place. So alongside the sheer inertia of the status quo, repeated and vicious attacks were carried out to strangle their inner spirit.

Our inner space matters.

Those opposed to the Civil Rights Movement took aim at the activists' *thumos*. They wanted to destabilise and undermine the drive that was powering their actions and their demands. They wanted to crush their pride and suppress their identity by insisting that the status quo was too heavy to change. They wanted to siphon their energy away from their central demands by offering token concessions. They might have hoped that the protests would boil over into a burst of violence that could then be extinguished by overwhelming force.

Image 43. - Bedford (US), 1964

The monstrous stress on the inner worlds of all of those involved made it so difficult for them to maintain their values and to hold their shape. There was a war without, and a war within. To win in their fight for justice, they had to show deep courage – remaining true to their demands for an external system change and remaining true to their inner virtues. It needed the courage of Martin Luther King to consistently model that thinking and their actions.

This powerful and successful civil movement provides a formidable example of how we need to tackle climate change.

The final viewpoint

Climate change can no longer be treated as an afterthought to our societies. We cannot busy ourselves with getting on with our usual business, only making a gesture towards it as it goes by. We have done this for more than 30 years and mainstream science now affirms the fact that we are now entering into the end game. Climate laws must be the first ordering principle for how we think about all of our other economic and social ambitions. We need a complete understanding of the problem and a systematic response to it.

The 'Kallipolis' – The beautiful city.

Plato was compelled to contemplate a new social order because the politics of his time demanded it. He wanted to understand what went wrong around him and he wanted to think through how society could be set up in a balanced, coherent and sustainable way.

Plato's 41 works provide a place for Western civilisation to continually revisit. They offer us a space to think that is both helpfully unsettling and settling. His Philosophy is like a major conurbation of ideas.

The major construction that stands taller than all of the others is the *'Republic'*; it is both imposing and beautifully constructed. From it, many major roads fan out to the other areas of his sprawling city. Crisscrossing this polis of ideas, there are hundreds of streets and paths that link all the hubs of his thought together. Like with any city, it was not certain at the start how things would develop; it is not always clear how you might get from one place to another, even though there are dozens of wonderfully finished areas. Indeed, some buildings are not really finished. These features of the city are charming to some visitors and just frustrating for others.

There is a hubbub of talk throughout the city, as the inhabitants mill around. It is easy to eavesdrop on these conversations by walking around the streets. Some clusters of people are loudly debating with irony and laughter, others are being simple and direct. There are dialogues confessing lust, discussions about geometry, and many exchanges about the more mundane details of everyday life. Some of the conversations are taking place at a dinner party, others outside a courtroom, some in the bustle of the marketplace and others still under the shade of a tree.

In this city, there is a vibrant but edgy atmosphere down in the harbour area. Here, most people are too busy to really pay proper attention to each other. As they hustle around, much of the talk is about business or people are reliving a proud moment from their travels. By the water's edge, there is an old, unkempt man who is engaged in conversation with a group.

As the group walks away from the boats and the noise, towards the house of Cephalus, the old pug-faced man occupies the centre of attention.

It is worth holding a sustained dialogue with him. His name, of course, is Socrates.

He was the wisest man in the whole city because he knew how little he knew. He is the person that can get us to question our common sense and to move far beyond it.

Plato, the artful scriptwriter to these conversations, is the person who can help us to piece our common sense back together again.

Behind the modern boom in both consumption and population we have set ourselves up for a monumental bust. We urgently need to stop hyperventilating on the present and to take in some deeper, slower breaths from the past. A full understanding of the state we are in, and even a full understanding of ourselves, can provide us with the wisdom and the courage that we need to enact the systemic solutions to the climate crisis.

Philosophy is not a luxury and it is not an irrelevant artefact from the past. It is basic to what it is to be a human being and it is of fundamental importance for our plans for the future.

The Academy

Where might the virtues and the respect for reason arise from to enable us to find the safe exit from the climate crisis? If we were to ask Plato this question, the answer would be clear: education.

Plato founded the first university - the Academy. He understood the power of education.

Indeed, a school can be such a powerfully transformative place. A school is in the business of truth and the development of the whole child. Yet, education on sustainability remains marginal, timid and limp. Since 2011, I must have chewed through about a dozen desks a year in frustration. After the impact of Greta Thunberg, I have managed to get the number down to about 10 a year.

It is not good enough.

We should not dare to call it modern.

The hard questions

Year on year, the ambition of each teacher is to advance our students to higher levels of skills and understanding. In every subject we celebrate progress in the depth of their knowledge and we rightly applaud them as they develop a more complex and nuanced grasp of the world and themselves. But what is the general level of expectation for their environmental knowledge? How far beyond a diagram of planet Earth with an atmospheric thermal blanket do we get? What happens once the basic mechanics of global heating are explained?

After teaching about extreme weather events, do we push on to explain the danger of collapsing ecosystems? After endorsing the advantages of solar panels and wind turbines, do we ask if there are enough resources to build them all? In the compromises needed to stay "well below 2°C" heating, would we give up cars or cows first? What are we prepared to give up? How do we live a full life without massive material consumption?

When solutions to climate change are discussed how many of them are individual actions (fly less, recycle more, etc)? How many teachers underline the fundamental importance of overhauling the infrastructure of our societies? Are we brave enough to ask the hard questions of capitalism? How many textbooks have images of Chinese coal power stations to illustrate the problem, and how many have pictures of a hyper-consumptive lifestyle?

These are the type of questions that have to be planted into the middle of our classrooms – and if they are asked with purpose and clarity, they might well end up being planted into the conversations our students have with their families and friends.

Growing up

It would be absurd to congratulate an able student of 17 years of age on a stage for successfully doing some single digit addition. We do not hand out certificates for young people who have managed to be polite for a week. The question is, how demanding are we when we celebrate achievement in response to sustainability and climate change? Should we loudly applaud older students who do manage to do more recycling? The fact this would not be very embarrassing says a lot about how little we understand the depth of the crisis we are in.

Of course, it is unquestionably right to support every gesture made towards a sustainable planet. However, there are so many secondary schools and staffrooms that are entrenched in such a limited range of ambition, imagination and understanding of the climate emergency. Unfortunately, for the moment, parents and staff generally only feel comfortable endorsing recycling projects, allotment projects, vegan days, woolly jumper days, and a reduction of single use plastic. For younger children these are entirely appropriate; they should not be burdened with the stress and weight of the bigger crisis. But we should not patronise our older students with such limited responses to problems that are so profoundly systemic.

If our road safety education for children just encouraged them to wear a woolly jumper as a decent level of protection for an oncoming bus, we would be rightly taken to court. Why do we strive for academic excellence in physics and chemistry, history and economics, but we are somehow untroubled that their understanding of the environment never gets beyond a primary school level? Why should the depth of their interests and knowledge in school not be sustained to enter a proper dialogue with the climate crisis? What are we fearful of?

They deserve better, they often demand better, and we should be the adults that stand with them in achieving a proper system change in education. Urgently.

There are heroic teachers out there who are giving it all they have got. However, when their efforts in a school are diluted by a wider apathy or timidity it is hard for such important people to not look like dangerous, unhinged radicals. Surely in places of learning we don't have any more Flat-Earthers' in our staffrooms who would deny the severity of the problem? But these whackos are not the really the problem. The problem is that national education systems do so many things right that it is hard to spot the one thing that is fundamentally and critically wrong. All those secondary schools that are comfortably leaving the hard questions to the side must do what every sector of society is required to do: system change.

Our education systems were conceived in the industrial revolution.

It is time they were reborn to meet the demands of the 21st century.

2011

I started my Climate Academy in 2011.

Michael Wadleigh (Oscar Winner, 'Woodstock', 1970) and Birgit van Munster (expert in sustainability and IPCC expert reviewer) have worked tirelessly with me since then to close the gap between the science of the crisis and the social reality. As I am a Philosophy teacher, it seemed wise that their work with me should follow the lead of Plato: establish an Academy.

In 2011 it did not look remotely possible that nations could wake up in time to establish the necessary climate laws through the parliamentary process. It was a time when even the language of an ecological 'crisis' or 'emergency' would trigger a shut down in people's hearts and minds. Likewise, as one teacher in one school in one educational system, it was impossible to consider working on a wide scale. Therefore, if I was going to break through heavy cultural expectations and work with the depth required to sustain a meaningful project, I needed to start with a small group.

"Education" literally means "to lead out" (from the Latin, "educere"). The Philosopher Kings and Queens in Plato's 'Republic' were taken out of everyday society to be educated. Plato envisaged decades of intense training in knowledge and virtues; we had a lunchtime slot and whatever else we could manage. However, the goal was the same: a small community dedicated to wrestling with the truth and committed to achieving justice.

Understanding the reality of the sustainability crisis can be a shuddering shock to a young adult; it can feel utterly disempowering. Therefore, the Academy had two founding principles. Firstly, it had to be embedded in the most secure knowledge of the science as a bedrock to everything. Secondly, it had to equip the students with courage and wisdom about which actions would have the most meaningful impact. With guidance from all the teachers in the school, 12 students with the right capacity of heart and mind started to build the Climate Academy.

The essays printed here in Chapter Ten, nine years later, are a snapshot of what the Academy does.

As Ficino (d. 1499 CE), the great advocate and translator of Plato in the last major Renaissance understood, deep dialogue with the self, the world and the truth, can foster talents in an Academy which can go on in life to have a major impact in the world. His Platonic Academy had no building, the power of autonomous thinking and acting has no need of it.

The first major climate strike in Belgium was organized by the Climate Academy on UN Universal Children's Day, November 20th, 2018. The powerful video below captures the strength and understanding of the group. The cartoonist for this book, Carl Jonsson (22) graduated from the Academy back in 2016. Over the years, the students have met with world authorities of climate science, gone toe-to-toe with politicians, and as social entrepreneurs they have designed and implemented their own projects such as www.Cut11Percent.org.

This book on Plato, made possible by the generosity of Hans Leewens, opens up the Academy to any young person. Each reprint of the book will include 2 new essays written by any student (at High School or University) who can communicate the potency and importance of a genuine commitment to virtues and the climate laws that we so urgently need.

#RightToKnow, 'Second after movie' for the Right to Know demonstration/school strike on Children's Rights day, 2018. Filmed and edited by Katriina Surquin (17)

https://youtu.be /48l13eD2w90

essential

reading

Chapter Eight

The Science of Climate Change

Introduction

There is little point mobilising different philosophers to examine climate change if the basic scientific facts are not right. Getting the evidence straight is critical, any book on climate change must be written on a firm scientific base.

Due diligence with the empirical data and the latest conclusions of mainstream science avoids two dangers: It prevents us from being too casual about the severity of the crisis we are in, and it prevents us from undue alarmism.

This chapter summarises the key points of climate science in a step by step way. All the analysis is rooted in the latest research and data, and without compromising that, it hopefully breaks everything down into language and metaphors that can be readily understood.

This is how our boom can go bust, according to climate science.

The size of this bust is important.

What is at stake in our climate crisis is monumentally big. It is neither the kind of bust that might happen in an economic cycle, or even during a global recession, nor is this a bust equivalent to the Bronze Age Collapse or the Fall of the Roman Empire. The type of collapse that could happen will dwarf such events. This is because we have a global population that now stands at over 7.8 billion, and it is because our societies are so interconnected at every level. Moreover, it is not just human societies that may collapse, but entire ecosystems; it will not only affect humans, but all other species too and it is irreversible on human timescales.

It is a bust of massive proportions.

The strength of the science is important.

For anyone who has not yet had the key scientific conclusions explained to them in a clear way, all of this strong language will seem somewhat overcooked. Foreseeing the possible collapse of human civilisation as we know it would normally commit a book to the science-fiction section of bookstores and libraries. Yet, regrettably, we are currently on a pathway towards around 4°C by the end of the century and the conclusions of mainstream science are emphatic. We are moving deeper into a minefield of formidably dangerous trigger points, and the range of disruption and suffering that this will cause to human beings will be unacceptable.

However, it is still possible to avoid this crash, there remains a narrow pathway out of the crisis. Moreover, if we could use our common sense to make the right choices, right now, then we would not only dodge the wrecking ball, but we would also surely gain a much richer life. The status quo is reducing the biosphere's astonishing, diverse beauty down to a world of cattle and cats, cornflakes and coke. It will be hard to save our social body from muscle atrophy as our senses feed off the vividness of a digital screen. Yet, there is so much to win by resetting our priorities and recovering our common sense.

We need to understand the science to do this; literally, we need to understand. We need the humility to accept that there are laws of physics and chemistry that govern us. This humility will serve us well in how we go about the imperative changes to our systems and lifestyles. If we manage to dramatically reduce our emissions, then it could also mean that we will be living in a healthier, more just society too.

This chapter is about understanding the key aspects of that science.

The Absolute Basics

Global Heating

A rise of 2°C average global temperature might not sound like a big deal, but anyone who has had a fever for a few days at 39°C will know how lethargic and grumpy it can make human beings feel. Moreover, doctors inform us that if an elevated temperature is not treated for several weeks, then vital organs can start to break down. A 4°C rise for humans is a medical emergency; vital organ damage occurs and death will follow if the temperature is not lowered. It is called hyperpyrexia.

All life has similar difficulties with movements in temperature outside of their tolerance zone. The parallel between ecological systems and the human body is only a metaphor, given that different organisms experience heat stress differently. However, it gives a good approximation of the deadly consequences that await human civilisation that we are on track to lock-in by the end of this century.

It is crucial to not underestimate the dangers of escalating levels of greenhouse gases in the atmosphere. In 2019, global average temperature was 1.1°C higher than the pre-industrial level; this is consistent with a warming trend of 0.2 °C per decade. Since 1980, each decade has been warmer than any preceding one since 1850.[205] The six warmest years on record have all been in the past six years. It is possible that 2020 has set a new record with 54.4°C (!) being recorded in the USA.[206] Indeed, rising temperature is one marker of climate change, there are many others: rising sea-levels, melting ice, extreme weather events (heat waves, floods, droughts, storms) and wildfires. These markers lead to decreased food security and water availability, increased migration, dramatic changes in ecosystem, decreased biodiversity, health hazards and reductions of economic growth (especially in low developed countries).[207]

Greenhouse Gases

Science has known of the greenhouse gas effect since 1824, through the work of French physicist Joseph Fourier. In 1856, Eunice Foote provided the first key chemical details of this effect when she established that H_2O and CO_2 trap heat.[208]

Modern science can measure, in a remarkably precise manner, which particles make up the atmosphere above our heads. Since 1958, the Mauna Loa Observatory in Hawaii has been measuring the concentration of atmospheric molecules, expressed as parts per million (ppm) or billion (ppb)[209] (the number of molecules of a gas per million/billion molecules of dry air).

---

205 World Meteorological Organization: *Statement on the state of the global climate in 2019*.

206 National Ocean and Atmospheric Administration: *State of the Climate* (August 2020)).

207 World Meteorological Organization: Statement on the state of the global climate in 2019.

208 Foote E., *"Circumstances affecting the Heat of the Sun's Rays"*. Read before the American Association, August 23d, 1856. It is common to credit John Tyndall for this discovery, but his lecture to the Royal Society lecture was delivered 3 years later on June 10th, 1859.

209 The number of molecules of a gas per million/billion molecules of dry air.

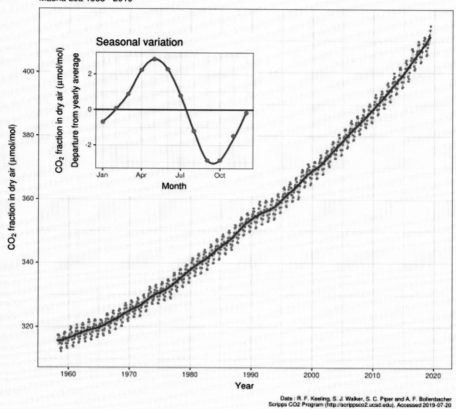

Monthly mean CO$_2$ concentration

Mauna Loa 1958 - 2019

Seasonal variation

Data : R. F. Keeling, S. J. Walker, S. C. Piper and A. F. Bollenbacher
Scripps CO2 Program (http://scrippsco2.ucsd.edu). Accessed 2019-07-20

This data has been plotted onto a graph known as 'The Keeling Curve', so named after the scientist Charles David Keeling, who set it up. The Mauna Loa reading at the time of writing signalled that there were 414 particles of CO$_2$ in every million (414ppm).[210] Nitrogen (N) makes up over three-quarters of the rest with 780,900ppm, alongside Oxygen (O) that occupies 209,500 ppm.

---

210 Monthly average July 2020, 1.5 ppm higher than July 2019.
 Source: https://www.esrl.noaa.gov/gmd/ccgg/trends/monthly.html

Although 414 parts per million[211] does not sound like a lot, a carbon reading of 414 ppm informs us that we have bumped up the level of CO_2 by 46% since the start of the Industrial age.[212]

This is a concentration of CO_2 that is unprecedented in around 4 million years and when geologists look back in time to previous epochs that had the same levels of CO_2 they do not see a world which is compatible with human civilisation as it is now: "Current levels of CO_2 correspond to an equilibrium climate last observed 3-5 million years ago, a climate that was 2-3°C warmer than today, and sea levels that were 10-20 m higher than those today."[213]

It will take us into an utterly alien world for our species. This is a kind of situation that is very hard for us homo sapiens to wrap our heads around.

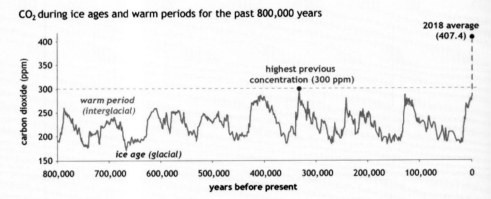

CO_2 during ice ages and warm periods for the past 800,000 years

NDAA Climate.gov Data: NCEI

211 To be exact, the global average for 2019 was 410ppm. The 414ppm that was measured in Mauna Loa is a reading taken at a particular moment in the annual zig-zag of concentrations caused by the four seasons.
212 These figures do not include the other greenhouse gases like methane (CH4), nitrous oxide (N20) and halogens.
213 *World Meteorological Organization Greenhouse Gas bulletin 2017.*

The climate has been so temperate and accommodating in the past. It is hard to imagine that it could switch so dramatically to become such a dangerous enemy. Indeed, human beings have just experienced an unusually balanced climatic period known as the 'Holocene' that lasted from 11,700 BCE until the modern day. This calm interglacial pocket of time provided the favourable conditions that helped Neolithic homo-sapiens to grow up, and it served as the background for our more immediate ancestors' development in the Bronze and Iron Ages.

Looking over the shoulder of the people in the Holocene, and observing the climate for those hominoids who lived in the last 800,000 years of the Palaeolithic Age, we can see that things appear to be more turbulent. With this wider zoom we can see the effects of planet Earth's slowly drifting patterns of orbits, spins and wobbles (more eloquently known as the Milankovitch cycles). Yet, even when these huge rhythmic pulses are examined throughout this age, the level of CO_2 was entrenched in a stable range of between ~180ppm and ~280ppm[214]. Therefore, a reading of over 410ppm is not a historic level; it is a profoundly prehistoric level.

Throwing our whole ecological system out of its long-entrenched equilibrium is unimaginably foolish. The entire biosphere that we are part of has evolved over millions of years into forms of life that are perfectly adapted to this current environment. Anthropogenic climate change is happening at breath-taking speed, 0.2°C per decade, and it is accelerating.[215] This is about 20 times faster than the average rate of ice-age recovery warming.[216] Many species' ability to adapt will be vastly outpaced by climate change.

214 *World Meteorological Organization Greenhouse Gas bulletin 2017.*
215 Intergovernmental Panel on Climate Change, Global Warming of 1.5°C (2018) Executive Summary
216 Nasa Earth Observatory: "As the Earth moved out of ice ages over the past million years, the global temperature rose a total of 4 to 7 degrees Celsius over about 5,000 years." That is about 0.008 to 0.014°C per decade; in other words, current climate change is 14 to 25 (average 20) times faster than the average rate of ice-recovery warming.

The graphs are vertiginous. It is like suddenly doubling the voltage on the power supply to your laptop on which you have all your work, family photos, bank account details and personal files stored. Why would you wilfully do that, especially when there is no back up?

No Common Sense

Why is such a fundamentally important reality so far from our common sense?

Millions of people have an awareness of climate change, but far fewer are aware of how radically dangerous it is at a systemic level. This lack of understanding makes it possible for people to think and act as if more recycling, eating less meat, reduced flying and a reduction of single use plastics are anywhere close to the level of change that is required.

1. Christmas Turkey Syndrome

Spare a thought for the Christmas turkey.

He has been fed so regularly and diligently all year by the farmer; he cannot imagine when he hears the shake of the grain bucket on December 24th that things are going to turn out so badly after breakfast.

Likewise, it is truly difficult for us humans to imagine a different set of coastal maps from the ones that we have all grown up with. It is hard to imagine a whole city going under water because it all seems so concrete. Surely geologists deserve more screen time; it used to be cool to be a geologist in the 19th century, now we tend to think of them in the same kind of category as the fossils that they study and collect. Geologists should garner the respect and the attention that they deserve to make it clear to us that planet Earth can look radically different from what it looks like today.

It was only 'yesterday', in geological terms (c16,000BC), that Doggerland was the one of the busiest hunting grounds in Europe, with grazing mammoth, herds of deer and the odd prowling lion. Today, it is under about 30 meters of water, and it is only really of interest to fishermen who tune into BBC Radio 4 for the Shipping Forecast. Geologists can describe landscapes and climates that are unimaginably alien to us if we really spin the dial of time back on the globe.

We have been pumping these greenhouse gases into the atmosphere for over 200 years and the effects of doing so seem to have only invaded our awareness with intermittent extreme weather events. It would be easy to think, especially in the technologically advanced Western world, that the problem was not so serious. Rather like the COVID-19 virus, the problems of climate change will express themselves with the most damage rather later than the moment at which the problem was established.

To casually imagine that nature will remain essentially favourable to human life is deeply negligent, both of the geological past and of those who have an interest in its future.

2. The difference between a tree and a forest

Climate change is a truth that is essentially non-sensory. The climate can only be seen in scientific graphs. By contrast, we sense the weather because it blows in our face, chills or warms our bodies and gets our clothes wet. The weather happens to us. The distinction between the weather and the climate is very important. It can be made clear by simply thinking about the difference between a tree and a forest.

When you are in the middle of a forest you can only see the trees around you; each tree is like a weather event. By contrast, the whole forest remains out of sight. Not only can you not see the trees hundreds of miles away, but the forest has been around for hundreds, thousands or perhaps millions of years. The forest, in this fullest aspect, is like the climate. One dead tree does not signify anything about the forest, you need to be able to look at the bigger picture. One flood or storm, one cold or warm winter, does not signify anything about the climate. You need to have much deeper and wider data to be able speak scientifically.

Fudging the difference between the climate and the weather is a common tactic used by sceptics to undermine the climate science. It is also true that whilst extreme weather events are typical of what climate change looks like, those who are committed to stopping climate change can make an error by asserting a certain link between a weather event and a climate trend without qualification.

In this rather abstract way, climate change is mostly beyond our common sense.

3. Motion Blindness

By extension, another challenge to our common sense about climate change stems from our inability to experience change. For obvious reasons, the human mind is set up to see the world in the present tense; we just get to see our lives moment by moment, and so observing long term change[217] is generally elusive to us. We are shocked to see an old passport image of ourselves from a decade ago and we are shocked to see relatives after a long break. The imperceptible change, cell by cell, of our faces is not something that we can see in the conventional sense of the verb.

The late Physics Professor Al Bartlett famously gave a lecture about the human inability to grasp change. Starting in 1969, for 36 years he gave his (unchanged) talk about change a total of 1,742 times.[218] He always opened with the same arresting claim: "The greatest shortcoming of the human race is our inability to understand the exponential function." By just playing around with simple arithmetic, he demonstrates the real-world consequences of steady growth rates.

217 The word "change" is used modestly here, out of respect to the deep thoughts of Zeno. This is because as soon as an object changes, it is no longer the same object. So, in the very moment of change the notion of change simultaneously becomes irrelevant, because change implies continuity and as soon as change happens there are two different and clearly distinct objects that have only a tenuous link to each other, arguably they have no link at all.
218 This is an average of 1 lecture every 7.5 days.

For example, he calculated that if the 1999's population growth of 1.3% per year continued, it would lead to a population density of 1 person per square meter on the dry land surface of the earth in 790 years. That is not enough room for anyone to swing a kitten in.

Yet we would have to farm this square meter for all our food, park our car in it, whilst also squeezing our share of all the houses, hospitals, schools, factories and shops into it too.

Similarly, the headlines for climate change sound diminutive; our Greenhouse Gas (GHG) emissions grew on average 1.6% per year since the 1970s. However, what that actually means is that they doubled by 2013[219] - and at this rate they will triple by 2040 and quadruple by 2060.

Thinking about environmental issues in percentages and rates is clearly a necessity for some types of analysis, but it does not always help us to get a common sense of what is actually going on. There would be intense media attention and debate about population growth if it were to become an annual event. Having 81 million[220] extra people disembarking off a giant spaceship every New Year's Day would cause the current residents of Earth to ask some critical questions about how they might be fed and located. Given the current stress marks that can already be seen on the planet's resources, the fact that we are adding the equivalent of the entire population of a country like Germany to a closed mass system every year is one of the most remarkable silences in our current political thinking. This political silence about population growth is equally bewildering when the negative implications for climate change of having to factor an extra 81 million people every year into the carbon emissions calculations are considered.

219 Emissions Database for Global Atmospheric Research (EDGAR),
     EDGAR 5.0 FT2018 (EC-JRC/PBL, 2019)
220 We are currently adding about 81 million people a year (a growth rate of 1.1%). United Nations
     World Population Prospects, the 2019 revision, medium estimate.

Bartlett's point is not that we would ever reach a point of one person per square meter in 790 years, because the stress would snap civilisation and the planet much earlier. His point is that humans have to concentrate to be able to see the real action that is actually occurring inside a steady, long-term trend. This lack of awareness makes humans very prone to making disastrously passive responses to critical issues.

In Munich, a 43-year-old female patient was admitted to hospital in October 1978. Suffering from a lesion in section V5 of her brain; patient 'LM' complained of extreme headaches and vertigo, but more puzzlingly, she could now only see the world in snapshot images. Her disorder is known to medical history now as Gross Akinetopsia.[221] It is more commonly known as 'Motion Blindness'. Patients suffering from Akinetopsia, with their strobe-like vision, find it very challenging to pour a glass of water and cross a road. They have also reported difficulties in following a conversation as the fluent soundtrack does not match the stuttering images of the lips that they see. LM is the only extensively documented case of severe Motion Blindness.

Yet, perhaps we are all suffering from that condition in a sense. We can see the evidence for climate change, but we really struggle to perceive the massive wrecking ball that is coming our way for various cognitive reasons.

221 Zihl J; von Cramon N Mai (1983). "Selective disturbance of movement vision after bilateral brain damage". Brain. 106: 313–340. doi:10.1093/brain/106.2.313.

The Essential Science in 6 Graphs

Science can freeze frame reality. It can pull the past, present and future together into one place, so that we can get a good look at it. The following 6 graphs illustrate the most fundamental facts about climate change. They are made from the baseline data that human civilisation is dependent upon.

Graph One – The cause of Climate Change

These are the long-lived greenhouse gases in the atmosphere. They are the cause of climate change. The graph shows that greenhouse gas concentrations have been increasing and are continuing to rise relentlessly.

Stating the obvious, we are not controlling our emissions. The line on the graph is going up, and new records are being set every year.[222],[223] In the last 30 years, radiative forcing (the technical label for the 'warming effect') has risen 49%. The overall average increase was 0.03 w/m2 per year, but the last 5-year average was 0.04 w/m2 per year.[224] These blunt facts mean that we are not decreasing greenhouse gases in the atmosphere. Conversely, we are accelerating their increase.

A rise from 2.1 to 3.1 W/m2 radiative forcing might not sound like a lot, but when the 1 Watt per square meter increase is cashed out into a different set of units, the reality of it all is rather amazing. A 1W per m2 increase across the entire earth's surface amounts to a 510 trillion-Watt force.

222 *UNEP The Emissions Gap Report 2019,* United Nations Environment Programme (2019).

223 *PBL Tabellen mondiale CO$_2$ en broeikasgasemissions 1990-2018*, PBL Netherlands Environmental Assessment Agency (2019).

224 National Oceanic and Atmospheric Administration Earth System Research Laboratory, *The NOAA Annual Greenhouse Gas Index* (1979-2018).

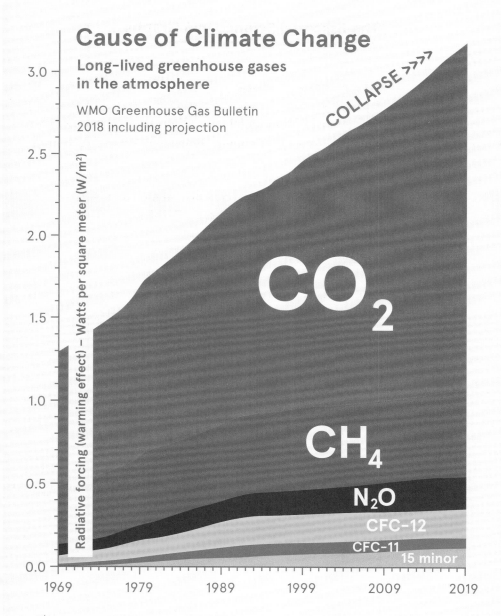

Cause of Climate Change

Long-lived greenhouse gases in the atmosphere

WMO Greenhouse Gas Bulletin
2018 including projection

COLLAPSE >>>>

Radiative forcing (warming effect) – Watts per square meter (W/m²)

3.0

2.5

2.0

1.5

1.0

0.5

0.0

CO$_2$

CH$_4$

N$_2$O

CFC-12

CFC-11

15 minor

1969   1979   1989   1999   2009   2019

WORLD
METEOROLOGICAL
ORGANIZATION

Graph 1: Courtesy of Homo Sapiens Foundation, Our Future Uncompromised, adapted from World Meteorological Organisation Greenhouse Gas Bulletin Figure 1 (2019).

This upturn is the equivalent of 600,000 Hiroshima nuclear bomb explosions per day.[225]

When geologists create images of the planet for how it must have looked in the deep past, as a snowball earth or a greenhouse earth, it is hard to imagine the forces that must have been at work over millions of years to make such transformations possible. When we look at our earth from satellite imagery today and see a giant disco ball, we might simply be reminded of the streetlights at home.

Yet these lights represent another awesome power. They are just a fragment of the energy that human beings are affecting the planet with, on every spin. Seen as a disco ball, those glitzy lights offer a startling reminder of our invasive colonisation of the planet.

Such is our impact on the planet, geologists have proposed that a new section of geological history can be asserted: the Anthropocene (after the Greek for human, ἄνθρωπος, 'anthropos').

A 'Disco Ball Earth' could be a very apt symbol for the Anthropocene.

Image 45. - Disco Ball Earth

225 Increase of 1 W = 1 J / s, earth surface 510.1 trillion m2, thus increase 1 W/m2 equals 510 TJ / s for total earth surface. Energy content of Hiroshima bomb 'Little Boy' is estimated to be equivalent to 63 TJ. Increase of 1 W/m2 is the equivalent of 510 / 63 = 7.6 'little boys' per second or about 600,000 Hiroshima nuclear bombs per day for earth.

Graph 2 – Energy Sources

Our emissions are increasing due to the fact that we are still meeting the large majority of our energy demands with fossil fuels. The chart on the right shows that 81% of all our energy is produced by either coal, oil or gas. These statistics are taken from the latest data of the International Energy Agency. It shows that wind and solar power has dramatically increased from around 110 Twh to over 1,580 Twh since 2005, a whopping 1,450% increase.

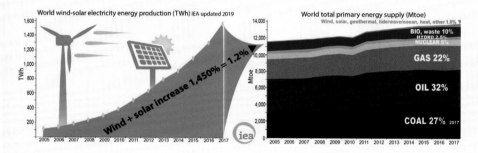

Graph 2: Courtesy of Homo Sapiens Foundation, OurFutureUncompromised.org

However, increasing the size of an apple pip by 1,450% does not change much if it is in competition with slowly inflating Beach Ball or Hopper Ball that had a sizeable head start. In fact, although the use of fossil fuels increased by a much smaller percentage, it outstripped green energy growth by 11 times in absolute terms.

In COP21 in Paris, President Obama proudly underlined the "ambitious investments" [sic] that the USA had made in tackling climate change by talking about the size of his 'apple pip': "Over the last seven years, we've made ambitious investments in clean energy, and ambitious reductions in our carbon emissions. We've multiplied wind power threefold, and solar power more than twentyfold."

Globally, wind, solar, hydro and all other renewable non-emittive energy sources still only account for 4% of humanity's energy supply. Nuclear Power, for all of its other complications, is at least carbon friendly, so we get to 9% with this included. Biomass (which is emittive and has great unsustainability issues) is about 10%.

The impression that we might have, from casually observing solar panels on people's roofs or wind turbines in the open fields by motorways, is that green energies are significantly replacing fossil fuels. Politicians may frequently cite their commitments to huge-percentage increases in green energy supplies.

However, the data that matters shows very clearly that we are not making any inroads into curtailing our reliance on fossil fuel. The word "transition" for the energy sector is a real misnomer: It has never happened. The whole industry is stuck in stasis.[226],[227]

In fact, all of the recent policy commitments to new investments in green energy are not even sufficient to deal with the increased demand for energy that will come in the years ahead from factors such as consumption and population growth. Therefore, fossil fuel use and emissions will continue to increase until 2030 and beyond.[228],[229],[230]

226 T.C.J.Dangerman & A. Grossler, *"No way out? - Analysing policy options to alleviate or derail Success-to-the-Successful in the energy system"*. (2013) https://hdl.handle.net/2066/91359

227 Wainstein, M; Dangerman, J; Dangerman, S, *Energy business transformation & Earth system resilience: A metabolic approach, Journal of Cleaner Production*, 2019, 215 pp. 854 - 869

228 United Nations Framework Convention on Climate Change (UNFCCC) *Updated synthesis report on the aggregate effect of the Intended Nationally Determined Contributions* (INDCs) May 2016.

229 PBL Netherlands Environmental Assessment Agency, Climate Pledge NDC Tool, Global emissions, http://themasites.pbl.nl/climate-ndc-policies-tool.

230 United Nations Emissions Gap Report, 2019, figure ES4.

Graph 3 – Rising Emissions

On 4th June 1992, the United Nations Framework Convention on Climate Change (UNFCCC) opened its doors for the Earth Summit in Rio. By 1994, the UNFCCC entered into force with near universal membership (196 parties).[231] It had become very clear that humanity was stepping into very dangerous territory with global warming. The UN understood that the politicians needed regular updates on the science and regular reviews of the progress made in achieving the Convention's objective. The convention's ultimate decision-making body is the Conference of the Parties (COP) and, as part of their plan, they established annual COP meetings in which these reviews would take place. The first COP meeting took place in Berlin on March 28th, 1995.

The UNFCCC has a singular objective: "To stabilise greenhouse gas concentrations in the atmosphere at a level which would prevent dangerous anthropogenic interference with the climate system".

There have been a long list of negotiated outcomes that often carry the name of the location in which they were agreed upon, and state various purposeful slogans. However, despite all of the signatures, the troubling fact is that not a single COP meeting has made progress in achieving its declared objective. The reason for gathering hundreds of politicians, diplomats and scientists together every year is to achieve the goal that the UNFCCC was set up for, which is "to stabilise emissions".

A list of the meetings is presented on the next page.

231 United Nations Framework Convention on Climate Change timeline.

UNFCCC Conference	Year	Location	Negotiated Outcome	Emission Outcome CO_2 parts per million[232]	Emission Outcome Gigatonnes of CO_2 per year[233]	Emission Outcome Limit for 1.50C Gt of CO_2[234]
COP 1	1995	Berlin	Berlin Mandate	360.0	27.8	1,091
COP 2	1996	Geneva	Geneva Ministerial Declaration Noted	361.8	28.3	1,063
COP 3	1997	Kyoto	Kyoto Protocol	362.9	30.4	1,033
COP 4	1998	Buenos Aires	Buenos Aires Plan of Action	365.5	28.4	1,004
COP 5	1999	Bonn	Bonn Agreement	367.6	29.3	976
COP 6	2000	The Hague	Bonn Agreement Consensus	368.8	29.3	947
COP 7	2001	Marrakesh	Marrakesh Ministerial Declaration Adopted	370.4	29.4	917
COP 8	2002	Delhi	Declaration on Climate Change & Sust. Development	372.4	30.4	887
COP 9	2003	Milan	Climate Change Fund & Least Dev. Countries Fund	375.0	32.0	855
COP 10	2004	Buenos Aires	Complete Marrakesh Accords	376.8	33.1	822
COP 11	2005	Montreal	Global Environmental Facility Guidelines	378.8	33.8	788
COP 12	2006	Nairobi	Nairobi Framework Work	381.0	35.0	753
COP 13	2007	Bali	Bali Roadmap	382.7	35.0	718
COP 14	2008	Poznan	Adaptation Fund	384.8	36.2	682
COP 15	2009	Copenhagen	Copenhagen Accord	386.3	37.4	644
COP 16	2010	Cancun	Cancun Agreements	388.6	38.5	606
COP 17	2011	Durban	Durban Platform for Enhanced Action	390.5	39.6	566
COP 18	2012	Doha	Doha Amendments to the Kyoto Protocol	392.5	40.5	526
COP 19	2013	Warsaw	Warsaw Outcomes	395.2	40.9	485
COP 20	2014	Lima	Lima Call for Climate Action	397.1	41.1	444
COP 21	2015	Paris	Paris Agreement	399.4	41.6	402
COP 22	2016	Marrakech	Marrakech Action Proclamation	402.9	40.8	361
COP 23	2017	Bonn	Fiji Momentum for Implementation	405.0	41.2	320
COP 24	2018	Katowice	Paris Rulebook not finalised	407.4	42.1	278
COP 25	2019	Chile Madrid	Paris Rulebook not finalised	409.9	43.1	235
COP 26	2020	Postponed				

Graph 3 Courtesy Homo Sapiens Foundation – Our Future Uncompromised, adapted

232 Ed Dlugokencky and Pieter Tans, NOAA/GML (www.esrl.noaa.gov/gmd/ccgg/trends.

233 Friedlingstein P. et al, *Global Carbon Budget 2019, Global Budget v1.0.*

234 Cumulative CO_2 emissions until 2100, < 1.5°C, > 67% probability, IPCC (2018) Global Warming of 1.5°C, table 2.2. Limit by the end of the mentioned year.

The red line, which cuts across the years and the places is going up.[235] We have gone from 360ppm of CO_2 to 410ppm, because we have continued to add excessive amounts of CO_2 into the atmosphere. In 1995, the year of the first COP meeting, we added an extra 27.8 gigatonnes of CO_2. This number continued to climb through the nineties and we now emit over 40 extra gigatons of carbon in a year. This is a very basic observation, but it has to be stated repeatedly.

The UNFCCC has many sub-groups, from Climate Finance to Climate Technology, from Deforestation to Gender, but it has one singular overriding objective. It has to keep anthropogenic interference in the atmosphere to a safe level. All of the other targets and outcomes only have any value in how they relate to this central aim.

The UNFCCC is not doing its job.

In Paris at COP21, Obama announced positive news about the bike that we are all travelling on at an impossibly fast speed: "... the good news is this is not an American trend alone. Last year, the global economy grew while global carbon emissions from burning fossil fuels stayed flat. And what this means can't be overstated." When the scientific reality is put squarely against his use of the word "s tabilisation", Obama's statement does actually sound like a major overstatement.

"There is no need to worry!"

In the graph above, it can be seen that there have been some years during which the rate of increase started to flatten out, but this is hardly a comforting fact. If you were to be a child as a passenger on your dad's

---

235 This much hyped 'lull' in energy related CO_2 emissions in 2015-2016 was short-lived. Energy CO_2 emissions grew at 1.5% in 2017, 1.8% in 2018, and so on. The 2020 decrease in emissions because of the global economic slow-down as a result of the COVID measures, is expected to be short-lived. Of course, to stop climate change emissions have to be zero.

bike, and because of his enthusiasm and energy the bike had accelerated at an exponential rate, it would be little comfort if he shouted the message: "There is no need to worry" through the wind-noise.

Slowing down the rate of increase is not enough. Even if your bike stopped increasing in speed and stabilised at 100kmh, it is still going way too fast. Moreover, this is not a flat track, and there are major obstacles and bumps ahead.

What is urgently needed is a firm and sensible application of the brakes to actually slow down the bike to a speed that is compatible with your survival[236].

UNFCCC – A School Report

In the European School system, where my students study, the pass mark is 5 out of 10. A failure to meet this average mark means that they must repeat a year of schooling.[237] Throughout the year, the students are presented with their grades in tests and homework across all of their subjects with marks out of 10. Their continual assessment is provided so that they can know if they are on target, and it helps students, teachers and parents make the right interventions in adequate time. A student with homework scores of 3/10 in Maths and French, a 7/10 in Art, but with 4/10 in all the other subjects will clearly be in danger of having to repeat the year.

It is a clear method of assessment.

236 In fact, to achieve 1.5°C or lower we need to go in reverse,
     but first we have to slow right down and eventually stop.
237 There are some qualifications to this rule.

Going back to Obama's speech at COP21 Paris, this level of clarity is absent: "For our part, America is on track to reach the emissions targets that I set six years ago in Copenhagen. We will reduce our carbon emissions in the range of 17 percent below 2005 levels by 2020. And that's why last year I set a new target: America will reduce our emissions 26 to 28 percent below 2005 levels within 10 years from now." No, there is not a problem with the microphone, there was no problem with the autocue. That is how Obama presented his emission goals.

What is the concrete reality behind these confusing numbers? Do these commitments bring us closer to the UNFCCC's objective or not? If they do, how much closer? Why do the media and the public tolerate being given their information in such a jumbled way, especially for something so fundamentally important to every society?

The USA was not alone in making things cloudy in Paris. Obama was simply following what has become the standard way in which the vital statistics for climate emissions data are released and published. Climate targets continue to be framed like this. For example, in 2020, the EU established the European Green Deal that affirmed its intention to reduce emissions by at least 50% (and towards 55%) by 2030 based on the level of 1990.[238] Japan is committed to reducing its emissions by 26% by 2030 based on the level of 2013, and so on.

By contrast, Economics would not tolerate such numerical ambiguity.

---

238 Proposal for a Regulation of the European parliament and the Council establishing the framework for achieving climate neutrality and amending regulation, European Climate Law (2020/0036 (COD)).

It is informative to make a comparison with another institution. For example, The Bank of England has a clear mandate, much like the UNFCCC. It must keep the UK's inflation (CPI) "as close as possible to 2%". The Bank must write an open letter of explanation to the Chancellor of the Exchequer if the CPI index roams more than one percentage point away from this target in either direction. In the letter, it has to explain how long it expects the inflation rate to remain off target, and the bank must also explain the policy actions it is taking to rectify the problem.

On the homepage of the Bank of England's website, the target inflation rate (2%), the current inflation rate (0.6%, as of July 2020) and two other key statistics (the lending rate and QE) are clearly shown. This is just common sense. In a democratic society, government institutions are accountable to the public and whether they succeed or fail in their goals, everyone has the right to know what is happening. This is especially true with something as fundamentally important to the economy as interest rates and inflation.

Image 46. - Bank of England Homepage

A visit to the UNFCCC website is very different. Anyone (whose interests include treasure hunts and wasting valuable time) could spend several days clicking around the website looking for the key information. There are interesting articles about beating plastic pollution, how people in the Sahel are developing solar energy and so much more. It is a busy webpage with many layers and hundreds of articles that are related to climate change. All of which creates the impression that something is being done.

However, the fundamental question about climate change remains unstated and unanswered.

The essential target for humans is buried far away from the home page, and the essential data that demonstrates our progress towards that target is missing. It is a systemic problem that extends from the webpage to the podium. It is a systemic problem that is also mirrored in the way the media reports on the UNFCCC. For the media, a motivation to get to the roots of a story has been undermined by the commercial imperative to appear interesting and attract clicks.

Image 47. - UNFCCC Homepage

Back to School

There are two school-related issues here.

Firstly, returning to the problem of reporting emissions targets as percentages: imagine that as a parent you receive a report for your child which reads like this: "In History, we expect Madeline to achieve a 26-28% improvement in her grade by 2025 based on the results she attained in 2005" and "In Geography, we expect Madeline to increase her mark by 40% by 2040 based on the level of 1990". Given such a foggy and muddled format, you would rightly insist that the school provide another document. It would be reasonable to ask for the overview to be given in grades like 7/10 and 8/10. It is a notation system that is transparent, and it enables the reader to draw the main conclusions easily. They show where improvements have been made, and where more effort or interventions are needed.

Every child in a class has the right to know how well they are performing, for better or worse. Every citizen has the right to clear information about the atmosphere.

Secondly, many students who fail an exam or an assessment do so because they do not answer the question. When appropriate, my Philosophy students' essays are assessed on a 'shit' scale. At the bottom of this scale is horseshit. These responses are characterised by various features: they cover a large area, they have little shape but a large volume, they don't really smell of anything because their content is rather bland, and they are not very memorable. Although it is a very unpleasant thought, at the top of the scale is dogshit. These are outstanding essays, characterised by a very meaty content, a compact size and a strong impression that is difficult to forget. Most importantly, dogshit essays point somewhere.

If I invited my students to assess any of the speeches made in all of the COP meetings, or indeed any political comments about climate change, they would be graded as horseshit. They simply do not answer the question that they have set out to answer. Although teachers can monotonously repeat the same message about focus, and although many students struggle to see why this is so fundamentally important in an assessment, the dull fact is that not answering the question posed makes all of the knowledge and understanding they might have used irrelevant.

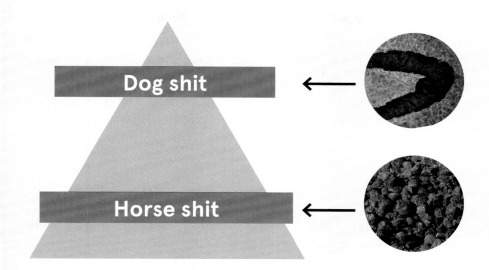

Whilst it might seem tedious, the press must continually hold their politicians accountable to their own mission of "stabilising greenhouse gas concentrations in the atmosphere at a level which would prevent dangerous anthropogenic interference with the climate system".

In order to keep this properly in focus, there are two very simple questions that must be posed: "How many more gigatonnes of carbon can be released before we commit ourselves to a 2°C rise, or 1.5°C?" and "When are we currently projected to exceed that carbon limit?"

The truth is, these are not actually boring questions. In an odd way, they are the most striking questions, because nobody is asking them. It is weirdly mesmerising that every year thousands of delegates, with thousands of scientists, accompanied by thousands of staff, tracked by thousands of reporters, all assemble in one town for 2 weeks – and the main reason for them all being there is not directly addressed or openly discussed.

Graph 4 – The Gigaclock

Here is the answer to the first of those questions:

"How many more gigatonnes of carbon can be emitted before we commit ourselves to a 1.5°C or 2°C rise?"[239]

Researchers are constantly refining their modelling of how the biosphere would respond to heightened CO_2 levels. They have to consider so many variables when making these calculations. These limits come from the 2018 IPCC Report Global Warming of 1.5°C.

The simple point of this graph is to show that there is a limit to what can be put up into the atmosphere. It also shows the accelerating speed with which we go through the budget by the rapidly increasing sizes of subsequent 20-year slices. At 2019 emissions, we are due to spend the 1.5°C budget by 2025, the 2.0°C budget by 2043.

It is a number that should be clearly displayed on the UNFCCC website, as it rolls down to 0.

If we take the Paris Agreement at face value, and assume that all of the nations of the world actually want to limit climate change to well below 2°C, then this carbon budget would be the starting point and the end point of the commitments and the negotiations that follow. The fact that this simple budget does not define either the political or public debate about tackling climate change indicates that we are not yet really serious about the crisis.

We remain lost in a fog of meaningless targets that have been fixed without any reference to this budget.

239 There are some important qualifications to this graph. Firstly, these are for a 67% probability to limit warming to 1.5°C or 2°C since pre-industrial average. It relies on a rapid reduction of other greenhouse gas emissions and accounts for earth feedback systems. It does not include any negative emissions or temperature overshoot (then cooling).

Remaining limit for 1.5°C
5 years of 2019 emissions

Remaining limit for 2°C
23 years of 2019 emissions

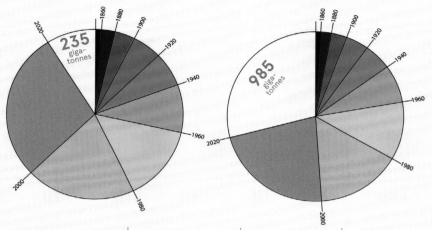

Temperature increase since 1850-1900	Limit 1840–2100	Emitted by 31 Dec. 2019	Remaining by 1 Jan. 2020
~1.5°C	2,635	2,400	235
~2°C	3,385	2,400	985

Graph 4: Courtesy of Homo Sapiens Foundation, OurFutureUncompromised.org

Graph 5 – the state we are in

Where are we now?

The safest interference with the atmosphere would be as close to a 0°C rise as possible. However, the World Meteorological Organization confirmed in 2019 that we have already achieved a 1.1°C increase.[240] Having already overstepped a 1°C rise, human society has passed a threshold that scientists warned us that we should not cross decades ago.

Given that anything over this line carries significant risk, the boundary for a global warming rise was set at COP21 in Paris in 2015. According to the Paris agreement, nearly every nation of the world committed "**...to limit global warming to well below 2°C, preferably 1.5°C**".

However, here is a strange fact. The level of CO_2 that is in the atmosphere now basically guarantees that a rise to 1.5°C will happen in the near future.[241] This is because of what scientists call 'lock in' – certain CO_2 levels 'lock in' temperature rises, even if it takes years to materialise. There is a time-lag between the CO_2 going up into the air and the thermal effects taking place. It is like setting an oven to a certain temperature; we know that it does not get to that temperature immediately, it takes some time.

To avoid a 1.5°C rise, truly gigantic amounts of CO_2 will have to be removed from the atmosphere - something we do not know how to do. There are many other aspects to this issue, that would take too long to open up here, but underneath all of the debates about what is 'plausible' and how they should pin the parameters of stating an 'average' temperature, the bald truth is that unless something close to miraculous happens, 1.5°C is effectively going to happen.

---

240 https://public.wmo.int/en/media/press-release
/2019-concludes-decade-of-exceptional-global-heat-and-high-impact-weather.

241 Rogelj, J. et al. *Energy system transformations for limiting end of century warming to below 1.5 °C.* Nat. Clim. Change 5, 519–527 (2015).

This mechanical detail about the climate system is well understood by science, but this has not been evident at COP meetings. Neither the highest-ranking politicians, nor the media seemed to be aware of the implausibility of even negotiating anything relating to a 1.5°C rise. It was almost surreal to follow the coverage of the COP21 (Paris) back in 2015, given that this most basic fact about the situation was simply not on the table. For example, the BBC's Science Correspondent, Matt McGrath, published an article just before the conference in which he reported that 15 leading Buddhists, including the Dalai Lama, called for the Paris Agreement to limit warming to 1.5°C. However, no comment was made about this ambition being a very improbable goal.[242] A BBC Sport correspondent would not ask a football manager what result he might be hoping for in a match in a post-match interview. He should have watched the game and questioned the manager about the performance and the result.

With 1°C already here, and with 1.5°C coming, the scientists have insisted that the temperature rise caused by current and projected emissions will invite an unmanageable amount of damage and risk for human civilisation. In fewer than 20 years, with Paris fully implemented, GHG in the atmosphere will likely cause dangerous 2°C, the upper limit of the COP21 agreement. Despite this, many major industrialised nations are not even on track to fulfil their Paris commitments.

What are we heading into?

There is a great deal of difference between where we are now, and the policies and action that are required to get "well below 2°C". This gap is known as 'The Emissions Gap'.[243] All nations of the world agreed to put forward their Nationally Determined Contribution (NDC) towards stabilising GHG in the atmosphere. 190 nations made an intended

242 https://www.bbc.com/news/science-environment-34658207.
243 UNEP (2019) *The Emissions Gap Report 2019, United Nations Environment Programme* (UNEP) Nairobi, figure 3.1.

commitment and 173 proceeded to submit their national commitments. Interestingly, Nicaragua neither offered an NDC, nor did it sign the Paris Agreement. This was not because of some delusional leader, but, rather nobly, it was because they simply wanted to point out the size of the emissions gap and they wanted to protest about the lack of serious action.

Indeed, even when all of the NDCs are added up, and assuming that every nation will follow through on its commitments (and most major industrialised nations are failing to meet their pledges[244]), humanity is still heading for a climate that is projected to be an intolerable 3-4°C warmer. This is shown by the two blue sections on the graph; the upper dark blue

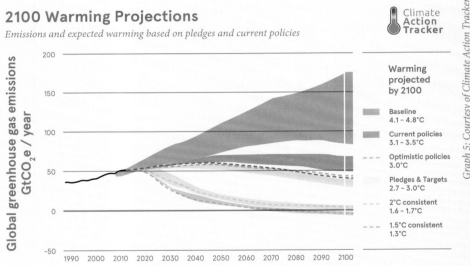

Graph 5: Courtesy of Climate Action Tracker

area represents the current policy commitments, and the lower lighter blue represents the pathway if current targets are met. It might be the case that nations enter into a positive feedback loop with policy making once public opinion swings firmly behind climate action, but it is also true that nations can emphatically swing the opposite direction, such as with the USA and Brazil recently.

244 Victor, D.J. et al. *Prove Paris was more than paper promises.* Nature 548, 25–27 (2017)

That is bad news.

However, this graph is highly misleading.

There is worse news...

Negative Emissions

The climate scenarios that the media use rarely disclose that calculations include 'negative emissions'. Working out negative emissions involves counting the total greenhouse gases that are drawn out of the atmosphere. Trees and plants do this all the time, and so rewilding our landscapes would help boost our negative emissions. However, what the graphs and calculations in the public domain do not admit to is the sheer scale of how much negative emissions capacity is assumed in the numbers – it far exceeds what is currently available. They imagine that we are able to suck CO_2 out of the atmosphere on a truly massive industrial level with technology that does yet exist.[245]

It seems to be neither correct, nor transparent, to have such reductions in greenhouse gases included in the graphs, yet they almost always are. The 2100 Warming Projections graph (previous page) from Climate Action Tracker is no different[246]. It is, therefore, very misleading.

There are two important statements to be made then in conclusion for Graph 5.

---

245 Even if it were to exist, such projects would suffer from the usual objections of NIMBY.
246 The UN also produced a similar graph, with a little more detail, in their *"Emissions Gap Report 2019"*. They also include unproven and misleading levels of negative emissions in their calculations.

Firstly, we are essentially committed to overstepping a 1.5°C rise.[247] This is because without dabbling in the scientifically and ethically dubious potentials of geoengineering, and with carbon capture still a far distant reality for the scale required[248], there is simply no path from the present that can pull us to that safety point from here once the negative emissions have been properly accounted for.

Secondly, if the media reporting was more transparent about the current path that we are on, then the projections would show that we are actually heading for a rise of around 4°C by 2100.

Another way of stating the facts is to acknowledge that the current NDCs only add up to a commitment that is one sixth of what is required.[249],[250]

Graph 6 – Who is responsible?

Most media coverage of climate change points to China as the world's worst emitter of CO_2. The figures require some adjustment to get an exact picture of who is causing the emissions. Given that the atmosphere is shared by every human being, the statistics should show the figures divided on a *per capita* basis. Everyone has an equal right to the earth's resources and, therefore, to an equal share of the atmosphere.

For example, China has 1.42 billion people, 18.5 % of the world's population, and accounts for 28 % of global CO_2 emissions. In comparison, the USA has only 0.3 billion people (4.2 % of the world's population) and accounts for 15% of emissions. In other words, Americans' emissions are 17 tons of

247 Rogelj J., et al. Paris Agreement climate proposals need a boost
     to keep warming well below 2 °C. Nature 534, 631-639 (2016)
248 Anderson, K. & Peters, G., "The trouble with negative emissions."
     Science. 354, 3609, p. 182-183 2 p (2016)
249 United Nations Environment programme, Emission Gap Report 2018
250 These figures were all correct at the time of going to press. As different editions of the book are
     published, these figures will be updated. For updates, see OurFutureUncompromised.org.

CO_2 per person, and Chinese are 7 ton/person per year.[251] This is true for 'territorial' emissions. This calculation of emissions measures the volume of CO_2 that are emitted from within each national boundary of the globe. Indeed, that seems like the common sense way of counting emissions. Portugal and Peru, Bulgaria and Brunei should all be held accountable for what they produce within their territory.

However, the map of emissions looks quite different if the emissions are calculated as 'consumption emissions'. This means that if a European buys a product that was made in China, then the emissions that occur because of their consumption are counted as European, not Chinese. This way of calculating emissions accounts for the major industrial powers 'outsourcing' of the external costs of their lifestyle and is, therefore, fair and representative.

If emissions are only calculated 'territorially', then China has 30% of the volume of CO_2 emissions and Europe has 10%. If emissions are calculated based on consumption, then China only bears 24% responsibility for the CO_2, and the EU (28) bears 12% of the responsibility.By lining up the data in this more realistic way, Luxembourg comes out as the worst country with 41 tons CO_2/*capita* and Rwanda as the least culpable with 0.1 ton CO_2/*capita* per year.[252]

Once all of this has been taken into account, a clearer map emerges of the distribution of CO_2 emissions. Therefore, throughout this book the emissions will be counted both as 'consumptive' and '*per capita*'.

251 Friedlingstein P. et al, Global Carbon Budget 2019, National Emissions v1. Population data: United Nations World Population Prospects 2019 revision. *Per capita* data, Homo Sapiens Foundation.
252 Ibid.

Responsibility for objective failure

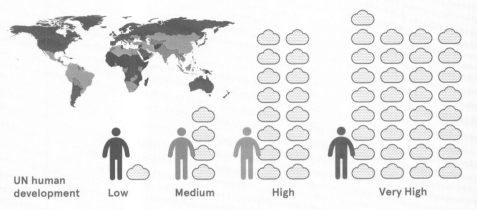

Graph 6: *Courtesy of Homo Sapiens Foundation, OurFutureUncompromised.org adapted.*

Overall, the nations which the United Nations classifies as "Very High Developed" (USA, EU) cause 33 times more emissions *per capita* than those nations classified as "Low" (Nigeria and other African nations), 8 times more than "Medium" (India), and twice the amount of those classified as "High" (China)[253].

Apart from the basic inequity of these proportions, it is also instructive to remember that those countries that contribute the least to the problem also have the fewest resources to stop it from happening.

The final consideration that is required to get the most accurate image of climate change responsibility is 'historical emissions'. Most of the countries classified as "Very High Developed" have a strong economic position because they were the first nations to industrialise their economies. This historical fact means that they had a large head start in filling the atmosphere with CO_2.

253 Calculations OurFutureUncompromised, data United Nations World Population Prospects 2017 Revision (medium estimate) (2017), United Nations Development Programme Human Development Index (2018), Le Quéré C et al. Global Carbon Project, Carbon Budget and Trends (2018).

When this is recognised, the figures show that the "Very High Developed" nations cause 70 times more *per capita* than "Low" Developed nations, they cause 21 times more than "Medium" and 5 times more than "High".[254]

The example of Nicaragua

In an interview covered by Democracy Now![255] during COP21, Paul Oquist, the chief UNFCCC negotiator for Nicaragua expressed his dismay at the progress in Paris: "...3 degrees Celsius is not acceptable. Three degrees Celsius is a disaster. It is catastrophic. So, we think that we have to get out of this spin and back to where the problem can be solved".

During the interview Oquist makes very pertinent points that helps us wrap up this section of key data. He explained that Nicaragua had not signed the Paris Accord[256] for three reasons:

- It was non-binding;
- It was insufficient;
- It was unfair.

254 Calculations OurFutureUncompromised.org, data Boden T. A. & Andres R. J. Carbon Dioxide Information Analysis Center (CDIAC) National Fossil Fuels CO_2 emissions 1751-2014 (2017); Global Carbon Project (2019) National Emissions V1, United Nations Development Programme, Human Development Index (2019), United Nations World Population Prospects 2019 revision

255 https://www.democracynow.org/2015/12/4/we_do_not_want_to_be

256 Nicaragua did eventually accede to the Paris Agreement in October 2017.

11%

Chapter Nine

System Change; Cut11Percent

Science-based laws

All of the principles and explanations from those 6 graphs can now be brought together. They can be embodied into one number. This number indicates what each individual nation of the world needs to do for us all to have a genuinely safe and prosperous future. This singular number for each nation of the world specifies how fast they must reduce their emissions each year, if we really are all committed to staying well below 2°C.

These numbers are needed to inform binding climate laws at a national level. Climate change is a systemic issue, so it requires a systemic response. Laws are the abstract structure to all of our lives and are the only effective way to affect change at a rapid, robust and systemic level. These numbers should, therefore, be used in every nation by those on the streets and by those in the media. They should be used as the standard measure for anyone writing casually or professionally about the climate crisis. These numbers will indicate if we are succeeding or failing to preserve the awesome beauty of this remarkable planet.

This section concerns the most basic level of our solutions to climate change. If we get this solution in place around the world, it will trigger all of the other innovations, improvements and restorations that we would love to see around the globe.

Whether via the courts or via parliaments, these national numbers are essential for judging our progress away from a system collapse and towards a happier world.

They should also be used in climate negotiations in future COP negotiations, but the likelihood of a weak and fragmented structure, such as the current United Nations, making any significant progress is remote. Of course, the objective should be upheld at all times, but the slow crawl of establishing sufficient emission reductions by voluntary consent has failed to achieve any meaningful progress so far and the strong tides of nationalism, protectionism and defensive foreign policy in 2020 do not seem likely to diminish soon.

In any event, the strongest psychological, legal, media and social forces operate at a national level. For example, we are easily triggered by national news events that are reported in the media with a sensitivity to the particular history and characteristics of our nations. National legal systems are also far more developed than those that are emerging in international law. Fighting for climate justice will best happen at this level.

The Numbers

These numbers assume some very basic things:

- There is only one atmosphere;
- Greenhouse gases disperse equally in the atmosphere;
- The atmosphere should be shared equally by all humans. [257]

257 See the 'One Atmosphere Equal Rights' initiative, administered by Homo Sapiens Foundation, supported by many eminent scientists from every nation and discipline, including Nobel Prize winners (OurFutureUncompromised.org).

The numbers are based on the latest data and the conclusions of the best science available in 2020.

Each national number is calculated in the following way:

- It takes the total remaining carbon budget
that limits the warming to 1.5°C or 2°C;
- These budgets do not include unproven reductions of negative emissions achieved by technology that does not yet exist;
- They do not include the possibility of overshooting the targets and then dragging the concentrations back to a safe level at a later date;
- The numbers do include the latest updates to how we understand Earth System sensitivity to greenhouse gas emissions;
- This budget is then divided *per capita*;
- Each nation is then apportioned their fair share
of the reductions, based on emissions generated by the consumption of goods and services by that country;
- The reductions are calculated on a percentage
eduction from the current level of emissions;
- This percentage is to be achieved in the year
starting from now and repeated each year.

After these steps, a few significant numbers are established. At the time of writing (August 2020) the global average reduction in emissions required every year (from now) to keep global warming below 2°C stands at 4.1%. The average for the EU is 7.4%. For the 1.5°C target the numbers are improbably large, with 16.1% annual reductions for the global average and 30.4% annual cuts for the EU 27[258].

A full set of numbers for almost every nation of the world can be found in the appendix and at www.Cut11Percent.org.

---

258 For annually updated data and references, see OurFutureUncompromised.org

The numbers stand in opposition to the way climate targets are set and discussed at the moment. In other words, all of the problems outlined in the previous section have been squeezed out. The figures provided here in this final section are unashamedly different from the whole public and political debate about climate targets. For any policy maker or voter who is reading this, these numbers cannot be related to the current climate targets. They are fundamentally different, and rightly so. The entire game of climate negotiations so far has been profoundly misleading and ineffective. The whole game of % reduction targets for a future date, based on a previous date, with all sorts of hidden assumptions loaded inside has to be bravely called out for what it is by those in power and those on the streets. It is a game that we have all grown up with and become used to, but this accepted norm needs to be urgently replaced by a far simpler, fairer, more honest format of reporting.

Why 11%?

Why 11?

Eleven percent represents the average reduction of greenhouse gas emissions that all Very High Developed (VHD) nations together need to achieve per year, every year, starting from the moment when our initiative started.[259] It is, therefore, a symbolic number that will remain fixed as a statement about the new approach that is needed for climate change debate and policy making.

The numbers for each individual nation in this group are different. The numbers for each nation will either rise with inaction, or fall with strong action. The reason for citing this number as the symbol for the project

259 To limit global warming to $2°C$ with >66% probability accounting for earth system feedbacks, rapid reduction of non-CO_2 forces, and international and intergenerational equity, global carbon emissions from fossil fuels and industry (not including land-use emissions) must be limited to 905 $GtCO_2$ from 1/1/2019 onwards, *IPCC SR1.5 2018, Global Carbon Project 2019.*

is that the VHD nations are the healthiest, wealthiest and best educated nations on the planet, and set the example of 'human development' - a standard of living that all nations want to achieve. The VHD make up 20% of the population, and yet we are responsible for 50% of consumption emissions and for 68% of historic or cumulative emissions (the cause of climate change). They are the ones with the prime responsibility and the capacity to make the change. Once the VHD nations take the lead, the other nations will find it much easier to follow.

Why one percentage number?

The 'Cut11Percent' project provides a base line that is realistic and fair.

Embedded in "Cut11Percent" are the key principles for effective and transparent climate action. Each singular number for each nation then shows the responsibility for exiting the crisis at a national level.

We are in the end game with climate change. It is critical to know as precisely and as clearly as possible where we are up to. In the recent flood of strikes and demonstrations across the globe, there were thousands of poignant and funny banners – but in the end, it all comes down to one core question: "Are we reducing our emissions fast enough?", and there should be an easy way to answer this. It is a basic democratic issue of the 'Right to Know'.

It comes down to one vital statistic, which in 2019 for the VHD was 11%.

If 'midnight' on the Gigaclock represents the moment at which we have emitted enough greenhouse gases to lock in an average rise of 2°C, then we have to be very attentive to how fast the hand is moving towards that position. The following percentage figures can be understood as indicators of how hard we need to press on the brakes to avoid moving past 0 on the Gigaclock. The higher the number, the harder we have to press on the brakes.

We have not yet exhausted the carbon budget to avoid trespassing over the 2°C line, but the following section will explain the measures necessary to do so.

The Extractions and Emissions Table.

The table, which is presented at the start of the tables, graphs and charts section, details what each nation of the world has to do in order to restrict global warming to either a 1.5°C or 2°C rise. It starts with the Very High Developed (VHD) nations; it unpacks the responsibility of each of the VHD nations into fair portions – according to the principles of basic social justice and the mainstream science explained earlier. The table then shows what responsibility all of the other nations have in the crisis.

The VHD nations

Within this group, there are some heavy hitters and these have been colour coded as the Ultra High Developed. The colossal states of Australia (-14%) Canada (-15%) and the USA (-16%) and the diminutively sized Luxembourg (-40%) have the heaviest carbon footprints because of their highly consumptive lifestyles. Of these big players, France (-6.3%) has a lower number because of its nuclear power capacity. By contrast, Portugal (-5.6%) benefits from a Mediterranean climate, a well-developed green energy supply and a more modest level of consumption than most of its EU neighbours.

Despite the general sense in public debates that the EU is a world leader in sustainability, the figures simply do not bear out this claim. Moreover, despite all of the talk about progress with the climate crisis, as we have noted previously, the trends for emissions since 1992 are still upwards. It is still the case that every one of the VHD countries has carbon footprints that far exceed safe levels.

The cause of the elevated emissions is rooted in the resource consumption figures. This first column indicates how many tonnes of resources a VHD lifestyle requires each year. The average American (32 tonnes) and average Singaporean (78 tonnes), the average Brit (23 tonnes) and average Luxembourger (104 tonnes) are ripping up the Earth's crust at a rate that is totally unsustainable. "Earth is a Closed Mass System, energy comes in (sunlight), but no matter (natural resources).[260]"

Just like a spaceship floating in outer-space (but much bigger), our Closed Mass System has a finite supply of stuff that we need to build our cars, ships, trains and planes; to assemble the laptops, phones and lawnmowers; and to construct the bridges, houses, power stations, offices and shops. When it's gone, it's gone[261].

"The alarming evidence is that the destruction of nature by global extraction of natural resources has nearly quadrupled in the last 50 years. Astonishingly, the next 35 years of natural resource extractions and fossil fuel emissions are projected to rise the last 300,000 years (the entire time our species has walked on the Earth)"[262].

Without a radical change to our priorities, we are setting up acute problems for the generations that will follow on after us.

The bottom line with sustainable development and climate change is not just that there are many of us, the issue is that the VHD countries are consuming far too many things, and we set the example for everyone else to follow. Both climate change and excessive resource extraction can cause a collapse of our civilisation. Indeed, the scientific authority on natural resources (The United Nations International Resource Panel) has concluded that for sustainable development, the average person can consume seven tonnes of the Earth's resources per year by 2050[263] –

---

260 Homo Sapiens Foundation, ClosedMass.org
261 Every single element of Planet Earth came from the guts of a supernova.
262 Source: Homo Sapiens Foundation, ClosedMass.org, for references and data.
263 *International Resource Panel, Managing and conserving the natural resource base for sustained economic and social development* (2014).

a sobering conclusion for all those nations who understand themselves as highly developed.

Finally, attentive readers will note that the average emissions reductions required by the VHD since the start of the project have now dipped slightly to 10.3% per year (*per capita*, starting 2020). This is because new countries – with lower consumption levels still – have joined the group of VHD. It is likely that the COVID crisis of 2020 will reduce emissions. However, the short-term drop in consumption should not be allowed to mask the systemic changes that are needed when exiting the COVID pandemic.

The HD, MD and LD nations

In the next group, there are the High Developed (HD) nations who need to make average annual cuts of 4.2% per year from 2020. Ranked 85th in the United Nations Human Development Index, HD China is the biggest emitter of greenhouse gases in the world, with 1.4 billion people. However, its consumption emissions are 6.2 tonnes CO_2 per person, about half that of the VHD average. Whilst they are a world leading investor in green technology, they are still heavily reliant on coal to meet their energy demands.

The Medium Developed (MD) countries need to make annual reductions of -0.9% overall. India (-1.2%) with almost 1.4 billion inhabitants, is the most significant nation in this group. The modest lifestyles of India's huge population means that their per-capita emissions are low, at 1.7 tonnes CO_2 *per capita*. However, if India would follow the same path as the VHD nations into a very high consumptive, fossil fuel-powered economy then it will shunt global emissions into truly dangerous territory.

Finally, the Low Developed (LD) countries could actually accelerate their emissions by 1.9% per year on average until 2100 and it would still be consistent with their 2°C budget because their emissions are so very little per person. On March 15th 2019, the monstrous typhoon Idai slammed into Mozambique (0.6 tonne CO_2 *per capita*, +1.0%). It caused a 4-metre storm surge in Beira and an 'inland ocean' of over 3,000sq kilometres. The extent of the suffering and the damage vividly illustrated the global imbalance in play with climate change. Climate change fits closely to the entrenched plot line of the North-South divide that is so familiar to Human Geographers. There is a stark contrast between the wealth, infrastructure and emissions of the VHD nations and the vulnerability of those nations that have barely contributed to the greenhouse gases that are in the atmosphere. There was also some very heavy-hearted cost counting in the neighbouring countries of Zimbabwe (+0.4%) and Malawi (+2.8%).

Overall, we need to cut our greenhouse gas emissions by an average of 4.1% per year starting from today as a global population.

Visualising the 11%

This chapter's central goal, concerning the science, is to establish the vital statistics for our future on this remarkable planet. These key figures do lead the mind to wonder what such a level of emissions reductions would look like on the ground.

To help visualise what this 11% per year might look like, it could be useful to take the example of Finland. This is because the national emission cuts they need to enact are almost exactly the average for the VHD nations. Finland needs to reduce its emissions by 11% per year starting from now.

Suppose, for the sake of the thought experiment, that the transport industry in Finland makes up about 11% of their overall emissions[264] (this is a fairly standard figure for transport in VHD countries). In order to make an 11% cut, Finland would then require the entire transport sector to be genuinely carbon neutral within one year. Hypothetically, the next

---

264 The example of transport is just illustrative. It is not that far off being correct, but the percentage for each sector of the economy will be very different for each nation. The details do not really matter – but the process illustrates how deep and purposeful the actions we have to take are.

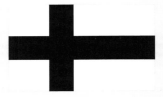

year would require the food industry to be carbon neutral for a further 11% reduction. The next three years would need a massive investment in renewable green energy, followed by intensive tree planting, kelp growing, mangrove planting[265], peat preservation... and so on.[266] A plan should be put in place for everything so that the country could be carbon neutral in time to stay within a 2°C rise.

Once a plan to reduce GHGs for every greenhouse gas emitting sector of the economy is put in place, there would then be a huge argument about which one goes first. Why should the transport sector have to be the first one to act in 2019? Why should the food industry have to achieve all of its reductions in 2020? The role of a competent government would be to take all of those transformations and line them up in a proper sequence, evenly and strategically distributed. Each sector can then fulfil its responsibility for their national economy to complete its role in keeping the global temperature rise under 2°C.

This is not the place to work through the complexities of how this might be done, let alone for each individual economy. Instead, it aims to serve as a taste of the kinds of system thinking that is required; the energy sector would certainly have to move first, because this part of the economy fuels all of the sectors and, therefore, all of the subsequent infrastructure and industry transformations could be achieved with low carbon emissions. Secondly, there are a lot of cross-sector targets that could be done too, such as increasing efficiency and reducing waste. Most importantly, reducing emissions sufficiently will not be possible without drastically reducing energy use and consumption. Indeed, there are thousands of books and academic papers that provide insights and guidance for such challenges.

265 Mangrove forests capture 40 times more CO_2 than a tropical rain forest.
266 A monumental effort must also be made in the background to work out the science of engineered carbon capturing. For the moment, although the price has fallen to around $100 a tonne, the amount of energy required to build these machines, and the rate at which they can sink carbon is far off the progress required.

However, this is not the point to get distracted, given that these types of publications do not provide their advice within a coherent plan that is based squarely on an absolute target provided by science. This short section is just  Image 49. - Union Flag a thought experiment – and this type of writing is frequently used in Philosophy. Thought experiments are not designed as an actual plan; they are deployed to get a clearer picture of the way things are behind the clutter of details. This scenario with 11% emission cuts lined up in a row has been constructed to illustrate the sheer pace of the reforms required and to understand what a genuine effort to deal with climate change would look like.

The UK could be used as a more precise example of how it might actually all work out. Within the VHD group, the UK needs to reduce its emissions by 6.9%. The government is advised to 'reduce beef and lamb' consumption by 50%, which will reduce greenhouse gas emissions by 3%. Stopping food waste will reduce emissions by 0.7%. Many people target air-flights, these are about 7% of GHG emissions in the UK, so halving them would achieve a 3.5% reduction. These 3 actions together would meet UK's 6.9% reduction for 2019. Then the UK would have to plan for the next 6.9% for 2021, then 2022, until the UK is near zero carbon.[267]

In the end, it is a task for each nation state to complete these targets as democratically as possible. In theory, each nation should then come to the global table with their commitments that are rooted in the science and principles above, and then combine their efforts with the same basic logic. Again, now is not the time to delve into the complexities of diplomatic negotiations. The role of Philosophy here is to point out the type of system thinking needed, and to show what is lacking amongst all of the images

267 Theresa May announced her government's commitment to be carbon neutral by 2050. A welcome move forwards, but this commitment allows the government to push back real action to after 2030 after which the sums would simply be utterly unmanageable. It is certainly not a figure that has been worked out from a proper empirical base. The notion that the UK is a world leader in climate action remains an aspiration, not a fact.

of solar panels and grand speeches given at COP meetings, behind all the hugely important (but disparate) ambitions of different NGOs and action groups.

There simply has to be an accountable, realistic, science-based plan that stops the Gigaclock before it ticks down to zero.

The importance of the numbers

This chapter is dedicated to the science and simply points out the very weird truth that although humanity is faced with a total collapse of its civilisation, we still do not have a measurable handle on the situation. This is the case for governments, institutions, the media and throughout society. The data is there if we wanted to look at it, we could frame all of our policies and actions by the realities of science, but for a range of reasons discussed throughout this book, we do not do it.

Of course, it is possible that we might decide that it is all too much effort once we have seen the scope of the changes required. Perhaps it is simply too late to pull public opinion, democratic processes and corporate interests around to a full acknowledgement of the cuts in emissions that are required. If this is so, then we should at least be honest and tell our children that.

However, if we are actually trying to "stabilise greenhouse gas concentrations in the atmosphere at a level which would prevent dangerous anthropogenic interference with the climate system" (UNFCCC Article 2) then we have to do it in an accountable and transparent way. We have to have a scoreboard, upon which we can add up all emission reduction proposals and then measure if we are squeezing the brakes hard enough to stop the Gigaclock ticking past zero. We cannot just wave different initiatives at the problem and hope that they work, like some sort of primitive tribal dance. They are basically meaningless if they do not measure themselves against any non-absolute target

Professor Kevin Anderson, is a world authority in climate science, especially in the field of carbon budgets. After meeting with the Climate Academy and examining the details of the thinking he endorsed the value of 'Cut11Percent', "it is really good to see this level of scientific understanding and political integrity brought together to produce this very challenging but robust target that we all need to be using to inform our policies for the future."

Individual change

It is not without some reluctance that a short attention will be given to the individual. The reason for the hesitancy is that this is overwhelmingly the centre of gravity for our thinking about the problem. Until we throw ourselves without qualification into the struggle for legally binding laws that will provoke system change, any attention given to individual action rapidly siphons away the energy required for the bigger challenges.

Such a hesitancy is not because all of the individual actions are not part of the whole; it is simply a question of remaining consistent. The pull towards the individual and small ecological gestures is so formidably strong in our culture that it seems appropriate to stand in stubborn opposition to it.

There are thousands of books out there about '100 ways to be Green', '50 ways to save the Planet', and so on. There are very few that create a proper perspective on the bigger picture. This book is unashamedly about trying to provide that. It is so easy to get lost in all of the details about climate change and to miss the central points of understanding, and the key points for action. The situation is too urgent for people to still be lost in the details.

I did lose three hours of my life once while in a meeting about the ecological value (or not) of a compost heap in school. The discussion ended without a conclusion and everyone felt deflated. Again, it is not that these small things are not part of the big picture, otherwise I would have happily spent that time eating imported beef from Argentina with a nice bottle of red from Australia. However, there is simply no time left for individuals to work everything out from the bottom upwards. The big carbon footprints in our lives are obvious, and we can deal with them with a few simple choices.

So briefly, with all of those qualifications stated, here is a short analysis of what the 11% reductions in emissions might look like at a private level.

Visualising 11% for the citizens?

An individual with the ambition to live a more sustainable life could think about their lives through a similar process to the example given for Finland. They could do a survey of their household activities and consumption, line them up, and then chop them up into manageable steps. However, there are two problems for households. Firstly, it is very difficult to make realistic plans other than what common sense provides without an easy way to work out how many percent any one person is over budget with their emissions.

Indeed, our lack of awareness about our specific carbon footprint is a significant gap in our democracies. For example, we know precisely how much fat, sugar and carbohydrates are in a packet of crisps; we also know if they have been anywhere near some nuts, but we do not know the size of each snack's carbon footprint. We have a 'Fitbit' that can provide a generally reliable idea about how many steps we took in a day, but we do not have one for the carbon footprint for each of the items we purchase. With the technology available, it would be possible to quantify the embedded emissions that we consume and that would greatly enhance our understanding of the carbon-cost of our lifestyles.

Secondly, and more importantly, our individual emissions are deeply entrenched in the system of our economies. We cannot choose the type of fuel that the bin lorry uses and we cannot decide how our clothes are made, food is produced, buildings, transport, offices, streetlights, data banks, hospitals, factories etc. are powered. Individually, we cannot change the infrastructure of our society: this determines the lion's share of our emissions. We do not directly control the big cogs in the machinery of the state, and those who do control them have proven very reluctant to move forward decisively.

In a recent study, in 'Frontiers in Psychology' the lead author Patrick Sörqvist exposes how poor much of our thinking is when we are trying to act ecologically. He comments: "Some groups have found that people intuitively think the environmental burden of a hamburger and an organic apple in combination is lower than the environmental burden of the hamburger alone".

Image 51. - A Burger and an organic Apple.

We have spent 30 years trying to handle climate change with an individual empowerment approach, where 'every little bit helps'. The problem is that all of the little bits do not add up to achieve the enormous change required. Under 'action fatigue', many people will feel satisfied that 'they have done their bit'. All this is not to undervalue the power of the electorate: we can all be determined to reduce our carbon footprint as much as possible.

Being a citizen, not just a consumer

What we need to do now is throw everything we can at holding each of our country's governments to account about the major issues. We need to put ourselves into the public space as citizens, not just consumers. The big wheels of policy need to start turning to direct the huge investments necessary into effective actions.

Our democracies must be properly informed about the bigger picture.

Again, it is rather odd that this basic set of statistics was not first published decades ago. It is absurd that our democratic societies think that we can function in the face of catastrophic climate change and yet do not show any concern for a reliable update about what is actually required – in hard numbers.

It should be admitted that our understanding of the whole climate system has improved markedly over the last couple of decades – calculating the carbon budget for a 2°C rise is enormously complex. However, there is a more obvious explanation for the absence of this data in the public domain – it clearly suits the big Very High Developed emitters to keep the public debate as foggy as possible. Any clear detail about who is responsible for the greenhouse gases in the atmosphere immediately makes the case for a fair and rapid reduction in emissions.

Banners like "No Planet B!" and the call for "Climate Action!" are all statements of anger and frustration. The sea of commitment and engagement that has poured onto the streets of towns and cities all over the world show the world's leaders just how many millions of people desperately want change. However, until these slogans are accompanied by a precise and informed demand for imperative legal action, they will easily be affirmed and then brushed off by those people who need to make the decisions. For those with a vested interest in the status quo, any open slogans or wide ambitions are fine – it is very easy to appear green in such circumstances. You can put an eco-shampoo bottle in the hotel bathroom, put out a press release about how your company is collecting bottle tops, or have your political party make some vague noises about investing in solar energy.

Making a clear demand

The suffragists had a clear goal – a woman's right to vote. The Civil Rights Movement also had a clear goal – full racial equality before the law. The slogans and speeches of the climate marches are powerful and moving – but until they consolidate around a demand for laws that are based on the reality of the chemistry and physics of the atmosphere, those in power will find it easy to agree with the problemand carry on doing nothing.

Image 52. – Irish Women's Suffrage lapel pin

A medical emergency

A fit and healthy baby that enters the world kicking and crying can score nine or a maximum 10 in the 'AGPAR Test' which is measured by doctors at birth. It was much too quiet when my son was born, he scored only a one. He was taken to an intensive care unit where the doctors and nurses rapidly hooked him up to multi-coloured tubes and wires that fed him and continually measured and monitored all of his body's key indicators 24 hours a day.

The ward was busy with general checks and moments of paperwork, close family visitors were ushered in during the afternoons, sometimes behind portable green curtains, key surgery was carried out. But in the reverential atmosphere of the unit, one thing was always familiar - the background chimes of the monitors that kept watch over every baby's vital statistics. If the oxygen level in their blood dropped below a certain level, the digital numbers would turn blue, a small light would flash, and the tone of a slow ticking chime would start to accelerate and rise in pitch. Someone in a medical uniform would then swiftly appear to make the right adjustments.

Thibault pulled through. On the day of his discharge from the hospital, I took a moment with a coffee in the bar downstairs and thumbed through a copy of 'The Economist'. After skim-reading the articles on 'Orban versus the intellectuals' and 'Zuma versus his people', I absentmindedly reached the back pages. Here, all of the vital statistics of the global economy were presented (perhaps tellingly, just before the Obituaries on the very last page).

The data on these 'Economic and Financial Indicator' pages show all the key signals from around the world, from the Greek GDP to the Columbian CPI, and from the rates of Belgian Bonds to the value of the Russian Ruble. The Nikkei 225 and the CAC 40 are monitored alongside the movements in the dollar price of Gold and West Texas Intermediate Oil. These indices can control the social and political weather - a drop in the price of oil had given a boost to the profit margins of the Pirelli in Italy, but it was causing social unrest in Venezuela. The long-term unemployment data in France and the UK had swollen the numbers of voters on the political edge, especially towards the Right.

However, Thibault was born into a world in which there was no fundamental index to measure our progress with climate change. This remains true today. In the pages of 'The Economist' there was no tracker of how many gigatonnes of carbon we could safely emit before our whole economic system is placed into a situation in which all economic activity will be critically undermined. There was no clear index of the good, the bad and the ugly for emissions and resource consumption.

For all of those millions of people who are deeply concerned about the climate crisis, where do they go to get a reliable update about the state we are in? We all want to hold our governments to account for their inaction, but how can that possibly be measured if there are no established norms for emissions? How do we defend human equality before the law if the law has no international and scientifically informed standard to plug into? How do we uphold universal human rights if we do not make our calculations of emissions on a *per capita* basis? How can we claim to fight for climate justice if we do not use the common sense principles that are embedded in the Cut11Percent figures?

Millions of people ask the following question: "What can I do for climate change?"

The answer has to be that we need to take the protests and actions to a new level – a level with real grip that takes us beyond slogans and sentiments. We must be unified in a demand for clear, systemic change. These numbers embody the most basic principles of fairness and realism. They must be made known and they have to be respected at every level of our home nations. Without this focus, the climate protests will simply become cultural wallpaper.

This chapter is available for free to enable all of this to happen as quickly as possible, and of course, the latest updates are available at www. Cut11Percent.org.

Thank you for using and building upon our common sense.

Chapter Ten

The Climate Academy

In 2011 my understanding of the world was gatecrashed by a powerful lecture on sustainability by Michael Wadleigh. A set of uninvited data and graphs suddenly showed up. Once inside my head, the science went about breaking a lot of false ideas that I had been carrying around rather casually until then. Almost out of nowhere, my view of human life on the planet was assaulted.

Apart from seeing the depth of the crisis for the first time, I struggled to accept that what I had just understood was not common knowledge. How come I had only found out by accident? Still today, a decade later, it is absurd that the systemic threat of climate change remains little known.

These things should not be left to chance. Everyone has the right to know what is happening. Education has been failing us for decades. As a teacher, it is clear to me that there remains a profound mismatch between the reality of climate change and the kind of education that we are providing to our older school children.

Cut11Percent

The Paris Agreement (2015) was a commitment by all the nations of the world[1] to keep global heating "well below 2°C, and to pursue efforts to limit the temperature increase to 1.5°C".

It is fair to assume that they meant it.

Cut11Percent is an annually updated set of figures[2] that shows what is required to meet the objective of the Paris Agreement. It provides the required annual emissions reductions for the 1.5°C target and the 2°C target – for every nation in the world[3].

Without these numbers, how can we hold our governments to account? For COVID, for the economy, for crime, for everything, we measure the success or failure of our governments by examining the key performance data. Indeed, for COVID the sense of urgency led to the creation of dashboards of continually updated data.

So why do we only use slogans or broad arguments for the climate crisis? Why are we so timid? Why do we not ask for results on climate action in the same robust, direct and transparent way?

Our radically softer approach to government performance on this one issue is truly bizarre. There is a carbon budget remaining for both 1.5°C and 2°C heating. It is very well understood by advanced scientific research. It is the most fundamentally important budget for human civilization.

---

1   As of 2020, Iran, Iraq and Turkey have not ratified the agreement. Neither have 4 different war-torn states, Eritrea, Libya, South Sudan (with Sudan) and Yemen. On August 4th 2019, the USA signaled its intention to withdraw from the Paris Agreement as soon as it was legally possible.
2   Figures, data, explanation and updates by Our Future Uncompromised
3   The details behind these numbers are explained in this appendix and on the Cut11Percent website.

Is it not disturbing that this budget is so little known or discussed? Without these national numbers, all our protests about the climate crisis could be treated by our governments as merely cultural wallpaper.

Cut11Percent is all about holding our governments to account, on the streets, in the media, and in courts.

These numbers should be known and used. Getting these numbers out into the democratic space is the core ambition of the Climate Academy.

#Cut11Percent : https://www.youtube.com/watch?v=yRRk7iPc8Lw

Image 54. - Carolina Teixeira

The Return of a Deathly Silence.

Carolina Teixeira, Portuguese, Aged 17

My childhood in Mozambique, followed by four years in Brussels, threw together two entirely different worlds in my mind. Brussels represents centuries of democratic development, with its bureaucracies, legal systems and parliament that have emerged from fighting, dispute and negotiation. Here, fundamental rights, values and principles are advocated and a well-established norm.

In contrast, Mozambique is still struggling to reconcile democracy with a society that is divided by ethnic tensions, gross inequality, environmental pressures and post-colonial scars. As a child, I felt only confusion and helplessness, like it was the established norm. I was driven by emotions but advised to not question openly, later realizing that I lived in a society under implicit censorship. This oppressive atmosphere has had severe social and developmental consequences.

After Cyclone Idai and Cyclone Kenneth hit Mozambique in 2019, I felt helpless once more. The cyclones and their disastrous consequences in Mozambique, Malawi and Zimbabwe demonstrated how the people who have least contributed to climate change can suffer the most. Infrastructure was destroyed, hundreds were killed, and thousands displaced. Life came to a halt. The United Nations (UN) described it as "the worst weather disaster in history in the Southern Hemisphere" and Graça Machel, former Mozambican and South African first lady has stated that Beira,

Mozambique, "will go down in history as having been the first city to be completely devastated by climate change".

When confronted with this I could not help but reflect on the issue of responsibility regarding climate change. People in developing countries have fewer resources to protect themselves when faced with these catastrophic storms but will be the ones affected the most. Across the world, storms are becoming more common, more powerful and more vigorous. Nevertheless, following the cyclones in south-east Africa, there was an almost deafening silence on how we should truly deal with climate change. I continually question myself on what exactly must happen for politicians to acknowledge that our system is failing. Deaths of innocent people are not enough for us to change, even if deep down we know that these are the consequences of our actions, culture and society. For most people, these disasters happen "far away", but what we are facing here are just signs of what is to come in the near future.

As Europeans, we like to think that we live in an open and free society where censorship is reduced to a minimum. But not only are we almost deaf to the depth of suffering in places like Mozambique, we have also censored out of our minds the most devastating horrors of climate change that will hit the global systems within our lifetimes – unless we are brave enough to confront the reality that science so clearly describes.

The Heart of Darkness

History is full of examples of how the greed of a few can brutally crush the lives of millions. Thus, it should not be a surprise to find that a deathly silence is happening today. Our ability to censor disturbing truths remains just as common as our capacity for inhumanity.

The case of Belgium where I now live is an interesting one.

Here I am at the centre of Europe, home to fundamental diplomatic decisions. Europeans are responsible for the majority of the CO_2 that has been added by humans to the atmosphere, and our high consumption lifestyles continue to be one of the leading causes of climate change. However, Europeans like to think of themselves as 'green'.

This strange silence in Brussels over its guilt is not new.

I live close to the "Parc du Cinquantenaire".

The controversial African Museum and the Royal Palace, with its enormous greenhouses, are only a tram ride away. They are all products of King Leopold II's (1835-1909) control over the Congo (at the time, "Congo Free State"). Leopold's and the subsequent Belgian rule over the Congo were ruthless and horrifying. The former gave birth to the first international human rights movement, together with the term "crimes against humanity" which was first used by George Washington Williams (1890) during his investigation.

The African Museum in Tervuren has just opened after five years of renovations, as an attempt to demonstrate the reality of the unscrupulous, obscure regimes. What happened under Leopold II was utterly appalling.

When Leopold acquired the Congolese territory during the Berlin Conference, his stated aim was to "civilise" the people through missionary work. Nonetheless, Leopold's interests were fundamentally economic, as he gave areas of the country over to private enterprises for exploitation – most famously through the celebrity figure of Henry Morton Stanley.

Once a territory had been taken over, "La Force Publique" enforced rubber quotas by torture, flogging and killing. Moreover, they burned entire villages and chopped off the hands of victims to prove that bullets had not been wasted. In 40 years, the population is said to have declined by 10 million .

IN THE RUBBER COILS.
Scene.—The Congo "Free" State.

However, when the true facts of the rule over the Congo were exposed and published in a 150-page document, King Leopold created an organization called the "Western African Missionary Association" to send a heavily censored version to several newspapers. There was a vast difference between the two versions . Indeed, key Belgian documents and information about the time were completely concealed from the public until 1983. Consequently, Belgians had very little idea of the terrors and atrocities happening in the Congo. Censorship and self-censorship happened essentially everywhere during colonisation. It was an endemic and essential characteristic of Belgian rule over the colony.

> **Heart of Darkness** by Joseph Conrad depicts the true reality behind the "progress" and "civilising" narratives imposed on the colonies. Conrad depicts the confrontation with the Congolese environment, together with its implications on the human mind. It illustrates its horror, cruelty and the normalisation of dreadful situations that originate and dictate each character's persona. Although Conrad reveals the inhumanity of the regime, the common humanity between Europeans and the indigenous people is persistently emphasized. Marlow and Kurtz have become symbols of the colonial past and the internal struggle of the individual concerning the ruthlessness of European history.

Today with climate change the same is happening. Governments, media, educational institutes and the international bodies are concealing key information about the environment and sustainability for the short-term corporate interests of a tiny few, notably of Very Highly Developed nations. Just as there was a shadow over the brutality of Belgian rule in the Congo, there is now a shadow over our negligence of climate change.

"...the Horror, the horror", in numbers.

Indeed, this is the censorship of our time, and it is inherent to the infrastructure of our life and our thinking. Our corrosive system has been diminishing our possibilities of solving the most crucial problem of today – climate change. People are being tricked into thinking that recycling and new forms of energy are reducing the colossal amounts of emissions released every year. What they do not know is that only 0,7% of all extracted materials are being recycled globally and that 80% of the economy is still powered by fossil fuels (*IEA Global Energy Review*). Why are we so proud of recycling? Why are we so preoccupied with plastic? If there was any honesty in public life about the horror of the situation we are in with the climate, these actions would just look absurdly limp.

Some people broadly trust their politicians and believe that international agreements are enough to resolve the problem. Do people really understand the dangers of going over nature's tipping points? Why are so few people willing to think about whole systems collapsing? How would they react if they knew how far behind we are in achieving the ambitions of the Paris agreement, to halt temperature rises well below 2°C? How many people know that emissions are still increasing, not falling? Do people understand the issues of responsibility in reducing emissions, and how the amount differs according to whether they are low (LD) or very highly developed countries (VHD)?

Essentially, the most basic facts and information concerning climate change emissions, sustainability, resource extractions and responsibility are not widely communicated and acknowledged. Currently, one of the only moments we really face up to the global problem is when Greta Thunberg speaks and challenges governments, the European Union (EU) and the UN. People have no idea about the past, present and projected complete failures of the UN's Climate Stabilisation and Sustainable Development Objectives. So many NGOs are still pushing to stabilise the temperature at 1.5°C, the preferred Paris limit, but it is already virtually unattainable. At current policies and trends, emissions will lock in a 2°C rise in temperatures around 2036 – a "tipping point" at which humanity loses all influence over the climate. How many people know that on current pathways, over 4°C will be attained in around just 80 years and that this would mean the inevitable collapse of civilisation?

Furthermore, there have been 30 years of Climate Stabilization Objective Responsibility failure and of Sustainable Development Objective Responsibility failure. In cumulative CO_2 emissions (that take history into account), UN Very Highly developed countries such as the US and the EU cause 70 times more *per capita* than Low (such as developing African nations, like Mozambique or the Congo), 21 times more than Medium developed (MD) nations (such as India) and 5 times more than Highly developed nations (HD) (such as China). At current consumption emissions rates (which take imports and exports into account) the Very Highly developed nations cause 30 times more *per capita* than low, 8 times more than Medium and 2 times more than the Highly developed.

Additionally, 1.2 billion of the poorest people consume only 1% of the Earth's resources, while the 1 billion richest consume 72%. There is such injustice in this. The Low Developed countries are responsible for less than 1% of climate-changing emissions; they cannot, therefore, stop climate change – yet they will suffer the most. Conversely, the Very Highly Developed nations, who are responsible for 50% of current emissions have the resources to stop it from happening.

Again, because the countries that contribute the least to climate change are also the ones who have the least resources to stop it from happening, they will be the ones who will suffer the most. I find it unbearable to think that humanity is capable of being passive about this.

Responsibility for objective failure

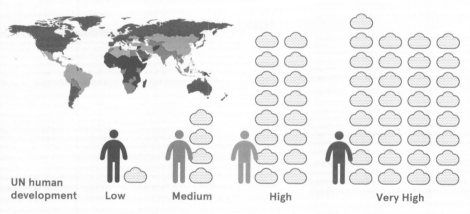

Graph 6: Courtesy of Homo Sapiens Foundation, OurFutureUncompromised.org adapted.

Most importantly, where are the objectives clearly stated? Do we know what percentage of emissions each country needs to reduce each year, so that we can hold our politicians accountable if they do not comply in tackling this issue? In fact, based on current *per capita* responsibility, Very Highly developed nations must reduce emissions by 10.3% per year now to avoid a 2°C temperature rise (67% probability). For instance, Belgium needs to cut by 14.3%; Luxembourg by 39.7.9% and Norway by

8.2%. However, Low Developed countries could emit +1.9% more per year and that would still be consistent with staying below 2°C. For example, Mozambique could emit 1.0% more, Nigeria 1.6% and Rwanda 4%. This should be common knowledge, not something we should have to push so hard to make public .

Getting the truth out

Our generation of the Climate Academy comprehended the scale and the consequences of this censorship through our work with Birgit van Munster and Michael Wadleigh – sustainability experts who founded the Homo Sapiens Foundation. We met them for the first time in 2015 and set up a project that got hundreds of our students to make short social media adverts about the facts of climate change using humour, irony or tragedy. One of the videos made by an Italian student, Pietro Galvinelli (17) went on to win a prize in an Italian Film Festival for "Best Short Film". Then after organising the first climate strike in Belgium in 2018, we set up a website "Cut11Percent.org" that provides all the emissions reduction levels needed for each nation in the world to deal with the crisis.

Therefore, we were doing everything we could to communicate the numbers. Nonetheless, because climate change is a global problem, we needed help from global institutions. Hence, we contacted the UN and asked them to publish key information - which included this responsibility graph that shows what the reality is with emissions calculated *per capita*. However, just like Leopold's rule over the Congo, the truth about climate change is still covered up by 'smart' politics. The details of our attempts will follow shortly.

The UN should be direct and transparent about where we are up to with the climate crisis. This is a question of science that puts our own existence as a species at risk. We should not have to dig around for this kind of information. Everyone has a right to know what is happening so that they can make informed decisions as citizens, voters and consumers.

Keeping things dark

The truth is, in the 25 years that there have been Climate Change conferences (COP meetings), nothing has ever been achieved beyond promises, agreements and vague statements. CO_2 emissions have not decreased but increased by over 60%. Nothing has been achieved beyond inadequate, non-binding commitments.

One major underlying reason why we have not made progress is very simple – the extraction of natural resources. For Leopold II in the Congo it was rubber, for the major powers today it is fossil fuels. Companies whose GDP is greater than some states', such as Exxon Mobil and Shell, have taken over immense areas of influence in politics and the media. Some of it is obvious and explicit. For example, in the United States, House and State deputies receive remunerations in exchange for protection and preference in decision making. This is a relatively obvious example, as the United States' elections campaigns depend on funding and persistence over time. However, this activity is also significant in a lot of countries, such as Brazil and less well known, Portugal - who have recently experienced a conflict between the conservation of nature or the exploration of potential oil sites in the Algarve and the Alentejo.

When the Climate Academy was in Norway in 2018, we visited GRID-Arendal, a non-profit organisation founded by the United Nations Environmental Programme (UNEP) in 1989. Its declared mission is to create "environmental knowledge that encourages positive change". There, we were faced by a rather ironic situation. After a series of powerful presentations from the scientists and really revealing conversations with them afterwards, we were invited to interview the Managing Director of the institute. When questioned on meaningful actions and solutions, he retreated into clichés and platitudes about individual action, recycling and taking public transport. Did he assume we did not know much? Maybe he did not want to overwhelm us? Or maybe he just did not want to start a wide political or economic discussion. Perhaps he was nervous, after all, nobody likes to have a microphone pointed at them... Or maybe, even really good people can become 'institutionalised', where the line of difference between what is real and what you have become used to saying and hearing is blurred.

Indeed, after speaking to several remarkable scientists at the institute, it seemed like this was the deeper general truth. We met so many inspiring people, doing great work in climate science, who desperately want to preserve nature. Yet, in a way, the system does not permit the scientists to really do their work with full independence. It is like an invisible hand that does not allow the core conclusions of the science to come to the surface. So even without explicit pressure or barriers, it is as if they find it hard to forget how the system will react to their work. They naturally predict the political response to their research and tailor their language and requests according to that, rather than the disinterested rules of science. Back then, it was clear very quickly that for institutional reasons they would not be able to make public the simple data we had about the necessary emissions reductions. It was just genuinely weird to think that a body set up by the UN to make environmental science clear, was not able to publish the core data clearly and openly.

It is important to note that the UN is for the greatest part funded by the world's highest emitting nations, as is the UNEP since it depends on the UN. In addition, non-profit research is funded by the UNEP and by the government of the place in which they are settled. There is always intense pressure in research finance. Taking into account that a lot of governments across the world experience oil lobbying and that the UN is dependent on each country for funding, this inevitably results in self-censorship of research foundations' experts in the matter. For instance, Norway receives a lot of money from oil companies that have plants in the North Sea.

The shadow of the IPCC

We were not just in Norway to deepen our understanding of the science of climate change. We were there to develop our own projects and to push through our requests to different global institutions to support us in making the essential facts about climate change clear.

We had spent the summer of 2018 translating our document about the key science conclusions of climate change into all the different languages of the Climate Academy members (German, Lithuanian, Portuguese, French, Latvian, Finnish, Swedish, Dutch...). This document can now be found and downloaded on our Cut11Percent.org website. We had also sent these letters to different UN representatives from our member states asking them to help in publishing the information.

When we had arrived in Norway, we split into different groups and had sessions of emailing, phoning (and so on), in one final burst of effort to get the *per capita* numbers public. We made some progress up their communications chain, but in the end, they presented us with nothing more than silence, tricks of discourse and hypocritical, diplomatic responses. The numbers we asked them to publish are just mainstream science, they are simple, and all the calculations are supported by numerous leading scientists (we now have the endorsement of Professor Kevin Anderson). However, in the end, we failed. The UN still feels the necessity to respect each state's decisions before disseminating any information, or in their words to us, "build support among member states" (email from the spokesperson of António Guterres).

Which is just a very long and political way of saying "no" (we won't).

Because of the different time zones, the calls to the UN in New York happened in the evening, and in the day, we took time to follow up on some European contacts. In the mornings, the team members who were contacting the IPCC were in action. In September 2018, the IPCC was working in Incheon, South Korea.

The problem of hiding key information is especially true of the IPCC. It is full of the world's leading scientists on climate change. There is no question that they are all dedicated to understanding the details of the climate systems as accurately and fully as possible. However, the way in which the UN set up the IPCC was seriously flawed regarding how they put together their summary reports for politicians.

After some persistent messaging, we were eventually able to talk with the IPCC spokesperson, who was snatching moments of time in a very intense week of work. The IPCC was preparing the *"Summary for Policymakers of IPCC Special Report on Global Warming of 1.5°C (SR15)"* and every line of science had to be checked and agreed by the highest-ranking climate scientists, as well as unanimously agreed by government representatives.

And this is where the problem with the IPCC is: in the intense, closed-door meeting, a political representative of each member state is also in attendance, who also has the power to veto any detail that they do not agree with. Thus, unless you are a scientist who reads the full report from the IPCC – which runs into thousands of pages –, you rely on the Policy Maker Summary (PMS) report that has been scrutinized by politicians. Or, you have to trust that Saudi Arabia and the United States will not make sure that in the summary report the main conclusions of the science are not put into the shadows.

This is not an acceptable way to run the public document about science that will determine our future. It is such a serious matter that it can be called "a crime against humanity", to use George W. Williams' phrase concerning the fate of those in the Congo of colonial times.

In the end, the IPCC offered us a meeting in which they would explain their main conclusions to us. We tried to clarify that dividing up the carbon budget *per capita* and calculating the required reductions based on consumption was not that complicated. All we wanted was for them to publish the numbers clearly. We did not get a response. We had one very difficult evening trying to digest how absurd and ridiculous it is that adults block such basic information, let alone start acting on it.

Now almost a year later, how many people know that to keep the warming below 2°C the Very Highly Developed nations need to reduce emissions by a massive 10% per year starting from today? How many people understand how much that is, and what the consequences of not doing it are? How many people know that a 1.5°C rise is basically impossible? Almost none.

Conclusion

How can this be?

It could be expected that following colonisation, World Wars and tyrannical dictatorships, censorship would not exist anymore. Suppression has been used in the past to conceal what was considered "dangerous" information for the government or the social order – and it has most often been covered up with values such as "progress", "freedom", or even, "democracy". We should have learnt our lessons; we should know the game by now. Or perhaps if censorship did exist, it would only be in a very dim way, for truly tricky issues. Nonetheless, this climate change censorship and self-censorship really exist, and they are built into the infrastructure and influences everything.

Returning to the colonial example; what upset colonial powers about knowledge of their actions was the vulnerability they would undergo and the accusations they would suffer from the other powers (even though most of them committed similar horrors in their colonies).

The European countries feared losing colonies and the respect of their enemies. Exposing the truth would just be deeply embarrassing.

Censorship is timeless, but could this really be compared with the present? With all due respect to the past – climate change is uniquely terrifying as it compromises the future of all countries and societies. And currently, climate injustice has become of the utmost relevance, where truth and facts are critical. Censorship is genuinely appalling, because if politicians, the media and the UN do not present the real condition of our society, then who will?

The power of silence has been underestimated. The omission of climate change facts and solutions has prevailed for way too long in our society, and this needs to change immediately. Politicians, the media and institutions self-censor, which leads to a tacit but powerful collective censorship when none of them can afford to step out of line on their own. Nevertheless, people have not yet understood the scale of this censorship and how self-censorship has taken over in the present day. It has become a power that culminates in the control of everyone, everywhere. In fact, it is so ingrained in our society that the population does not seem to either notice it, realise it, or care. And that it is the extraordinary result of censorship – unconsciousness.

We live in an increasingly smaller world, under the impression that it is a more open place, where public and private spheres have blended and become almost indistinguishable. Facing this situation, in this extremely globalised world of mass communication, it is too strange and too tragic that we accept silence about something so crucial.

I only realised when I got to Brussels how many silent rules I had learnt to follow in Mozambique – what could be said, what couldn't be said. I now realise that Brussels is not that much different.

It is easy to feel anxious and depressed about all this, but then we have broken through the silence before so many times. It is possible to change the course of events. Together we can break through this extremely strange and deadly silence.

We can and must do it again, our future is at stake.

Bibliography:

The Guardian (1999) "*The Hidden Holocaust*" [online]
Available at: https://www.theguardian.com/theguardian/1999/may/13/features11.g22 [Accessed 10 July 2020].

Conrad, J. (1983) *Coração das Trevas*. Translated by A. Fernandes.
Lisboa: Editorial *Estampa*, Lda.

Climate Academy, n.d. [online] Available at:
https://www.climateacademy.eu/ (Accessed 10 July 2020)

CollapseStopped.org, n.d. [online] Available at:
http://collapsestopped.org/ (Accessed 10 July 2020)

The Surprising Value of a Broken Mind

Jules Pye, French, Aged 17

Ignoring the latest scientific advancements in 'in-vitro fertilisation', we all have two biological parents. During our childhood they most often become our legal guardians, mentors and are the ones who give us our first set of manners, morality, traditions and beliefs. At birth we are thrown into the world as lost and clueless *tabulae rasae*. There is therefore no way around sucking up our parents' values like dry sponges; even if we were to be pre-pubescent Nietzsches.

However, not only do we accept our parents' view of things as the only and true one and adopt these, we are also completely dependent on them; a dependency which reaches far beyond things material. They teach us the rules of all kinds of social 'games', such as how to efficiently and correctly interact and communicate with other humans. Being able to play by the rules of everyday life is vital for our survival in any society, making us heavily dependent on our parents (or similar equivalents) for our future adult success.

According to 'The School of Life' the ones who loved and cared for us during childhood (most often our parents) also gave us a solid emotional bedrock, equally valuable for later life as the social skills they taught us: "In the course of being loved, we got an encyclopaedic emotional education". These emotions include endurance, self-love, patience and forgiveness and are a very important part of a healthy human's daily life.

Research conducted in 2016, which examined hundreds of children in two US metropolitan areas, found that fatherless children were at a much higher risk of drug and alcohol abuse and that children from single-parent families were twice as likely to commit suicide. (However, children living with their married biological parents were less anxious, depressed and delinquent than children living with one or more non-biological 'parents'. This could suggest that all of the previously mentioned characteristics which we get from our parents, only lead to a stable mental state if they really are our biological ones).

It is this lack of one or both parents that we will analyse, with a focus on the father figure, both on an ontogenic and phylogenic level. For examining the issue of growing up without a father on a personal level, Nietzsche will be used as a 'case study' and Freud will help us to explain the implications and results of it. To bridge the gap between the individual and society we will use Lacan's idea of a good political leader. Then, we will look at the importance of a role model (rather than a father) for a society as a whole, by considering Somalia's anarchy as a case study. Finally, Kierkegaard will be the one to wrap up some conclusions about how a broken mind is perhaps a surprising advantage for solving climate change.

How important are father figures for the individual?

Friedrich Nietzsche was mad. The mental breakdown he suffered in 1889 was only the beginning of 11 years of unhinged behaviour. In the days following his breakdown-day (when hugged a horse) he wrote many letters; these *Wahnzettel* (lit.: 'Notes of craze', known in English as the "Madness Notes") were either signed Dionysus or der Gekreuzigte ('the crucified one', i.e. Jesus). In one of the letters he even claimed to be "Buddha [among the Hindus], in Greece Dionysus" and that "Alexander [presumably the Great] and Caesar were incarnations of [him], as well as the poet of Shakespeare, Lord Bacon. Most recently [he also] was Voltaire and Napoleon, perhaps also Richard Wagner", and many other big declarations and statements were made throughout the series of letters. It is still debated what the exact cause of this mental state of his was, but it almost certainly was the symptom of a physical illness.

Relevant to us is the fact that Nietzsche's father died just before he turned five. His brother's death six months later meant that the only other male in the family was his grandfather. As previously discussed, the absence of one's father whilst growing up can have dramatic consequences.

Image 61. - Nietzsche

And even though this lack of male role-models during Nietzsche's childhood might not be the direct cause of his breakdown, it certainly didn't help. Moreover, it is likely that such a traumatic experience and unique upbringing caused his ability to not only become a philosopher, but to revolutionise the field. It is difficult for us to imagine that a human being – who hadn't had this unique childhood – could come up with ideas as radical as Nietzsche's. Any philosopher must first distance himself from normal common sense and the opinions and widely accepted facts of the majority of society before being able to examine and undermine them. Nietzsche's unusual start in life would have already given him a head start for this.

To try and understand the whole idea of the effects of growing up without a father, we can turn to the founding father of psychoanalysis, Sigmund Freud. Freud divided his rather sexualised view of a child's development into five psychosexual stages, from the oral stage up until the child's first birthday – in which the world is discovered and enjoyed through the mouth – to the genital stage from puberty onwards, in which sexual desires reawaken (yes, re-awaken, as they supposedly first awoke in the phallic stage (when the child is between four and six)).

Nietzsche experienced his father's death in the middle of his phallic stage in which a young boy is supposed to be reducing emotional and sexual tension caused by the Oedipal Complex by imitating his father's behaviour and taking on board his attitudes, values and behaviour – something Nietzsche wouldn't have been able to do having lost his father at an early age. It would have led to a build-up of frustration and have serious effects on Nietzsche's mental health.

According to Freud's theories (of which this following part has remained largely unchanged over the years) such a serious primal wound (i.e. his father's death and the traumatic experiences that surround it) would then lead on to manifest itself in adult life. In Nietzsche's case, the manifestation would be his ideas and writings that led him to become the famous madman he was.

Image 62. - Freud

The second of Freud's theories that could help explain Nietzsche's case and that of many other fatherless geniuses is that of sublimation. Freud argued that we have the ability to transform any kind of egoistic and destructive frustration and disappointment (mainly from childhood) into its exact opposite: a highly positive energy that can be used to, for example, be creative or centring one's life around helping others.

Freud himself lost his father in 1896 which he said caused depressions and neurasthenia, but which also led him to revise many of his theories as well as help him to come up with several new ones, as all of his books were published after that date. In Nietzsche's case, he would have been able to sublimate all of the sadness and male loneliness of his childhood into the creativity – such as poems, music and Philosophy – he excelled at.

But it is Nietzsche's tragic, yet possibly illuminating, start in life that is most interesting when thinking about climate change. Just as Nietzsche revolutionised Philosophy by examining, undermining and criticising then widely accepted realities, we need people with similar courage to do the same with the threats posed by climate change. The consequences of climate change, similar to Nietzsche's new ideas, are uncharted territory for the human race. Nietzsche opens up a radically new space to think in by pushing aside traditional assumptions. The effects of a 'hot house earth' on human life will be like nothing ever experienced by our species before, and Nietzsche can help us to think outside our experience. It takes great courage to take on a society's tenets and even more to challenge seemingly untouchable authorities.

Lacan – A bridge from the individual to society

The French philosopher Jacques Lacan was intellectually very active during the 1960s, a time which was full of protests, revolutions and events of great social change – the Vietnam War, the Civil Rights Movement in the US, the Cuban Missile Crisis, the Space Race, Woodstock and the debuts of 'Star Trek' and 'Sesame Street' being just a few of those. His ideas will help us bridge the gap between the ontogenic and phylogenic level in two ways: with his idea of an ideal political leader and with his 'Name-of-the Father' theory, the latter being based on Freud's Oedipal Complex.

Lacan's Name-of-the-Father is a very clever name for his view of the father's role in his symbolic order: it plays on the nearly identically sounding French phrases 'le nom du père' ('the name of the father') and 'le non du père' (the 'no' of the father) and it was probably intentionally designed as a way to subversively mock the Christian God. In the Oedipal Complex the father's role is a both prohibitive and legislative one. It's up to the father to keep the son's sexual desires for his mother at bay and to install law and order. Lacan makes the link between the individual and society by giving the father figure this importance both on an individual family and on a societal level. He is both the counterpart of the son's sexual incest desires and the one who is responsible for imposing laws; the 'le nom du père' being the one imposing laws and 'le non du père' being the antagonist to his son's repressed desire for his mother.

"It is in the Name-of-the-Father that we must recognize the support of the symbolic function which, from the dawn of history, has identified his person with the figure of the law." (Lacan)

Lacan's message for the student protesters during the '60s was: "What you aspire to as revolutionaries is a new master. You will get one." The ideal political leader (or "master") Lacan thought we all aspire to, is one who is able to convince people of the disappointing nature of reality without causing outrage, protest and uproar from the masses. By doing so, these leaders dare to be adults and are thereby also 'the-ones-who-will-make-everything-ok', the ones who will solve all issues and who will be there in time of disaster. In other words: they are ideal parents. This links the individual's need for a strong and reliable parent to society's need for a similar role-model wonderfully.

Today, with the consequences of the climate crisis looming over us, we need leaders just like Lacan describes. Somebody who is willing to expose the hidden implications of the symbolic order, whilst still upholding some values that we can aspire to. Consumption and a false sense of need, choice and freedom are embedded into the current symbolic order and have to be openly challenged. At the same time, values such as collaboration and humility have to be sustained in order to keep society on the right trajectory.

We are now sitting in a window of prime opportunity for getting our emissions and resource extractions on track to a safe level. This is because the two key features needed for radical change are in place. Firstly, we still have the psychological and political frameworks in place that help us to act in the belief that major action will make a difference. If this basic sense of structure, order and predictability were not there, no individual or government would see the point in doing anything for a lost cause. Secondly, there is a growing pressure and realisation that we are way off track. This awareness has not yet consolidated into robust national targets that are based on the latest science (the numbers can be found at cut11%), but it is increasingly clear to the public that the current path of climate mitigation we are on is far too soft.

We need both a sense of hope that society will remain coherent in the future, but we also need a radical sense of urgency to know that without huge change, it will collapse. If we wait any longer then the many tipping points and feedback loops in nature will put us in a position of very limited control.

We need to be sane, with a little bit of madness.

Somalia: A case study

As we will now see with the example of Somalia and ideas of Thomas Hobbes' there is a certain tipping point that can be reached in a society which, if crossed, can be very difficult to redress. In chaotic, uncoordinated societies that have lost their symbolic order, recovery comes at tremendous expense and effort, a situation that Hobbes famously described as "bellum omnium contra omnes", "the war of all against all".

For fifteen years Somalia went without central government: The ever increasingly unpopular Siad Barre was overthrown by the 'Somali Rebellion' in 1991 and wasn't replaced until the 'Transitional National Government' took power in 2006. It was, in essence, an anarchy: the country was divided into countless fiefdoms controlled by rival warlords, who occasionally clashed for territory. Even though some private companies thrived, the services and products they offered were unaffordable to most of the population and chaos reigned: levels of daily violence were described as "catastrophic" by 'Médecins Sans Frontières', all political institutions broke down, mass migrations and makeshift refugee camps caused the rapid spread of diseases such as malaria, tuberculosis, diarrhoea and dysentery and the country turned into a terrorist haven.

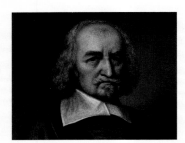

Image 64. - Hobbes

It seemed like an incarnation of Hobbes' stateless state of nature theory: life really was "solitary, poor, nasty, brutish and short" ('*Leviathan*', 1651) and just the fear of violence was enough to cause it. But to get back to our initial point, it could easily be argued that the presence of a strong role model in the form of a political leader would have been able to at least mitigate the chaos and violence during those fifteen years – and thereby prevent the violence of the civil wars that have been going on since 2006. The intertribal conflicts probably took place because of conflicts of beliefs and interests, which set different groups against each other right from the beginning. There was not enough cohesive belief in a shared project or community to hold things together.

During its anarchy, the people of Somalia showed very clearly what Hobbes had predicted the state of nature would look like: Everyone, fuelled by the fear of being the first victim of violence, started to be aggressive to make sure they were the attacker rather than the attacked. Many people think that Hobbes understood people to be fundamentally evil or aggressive, but this was certainly not the case. Violence in a state of nature arises out of simple psychological fear, not because of an intrinsically evil human nature (Something he observed first-hand during the English Civil War).

One former Somali army major even reported being caught in children's holdups: "There is nothing you can do when kids with guns steal everything you have, even your clothes. I'm from a small clan, so I was unable to fight back". Even once the transitional government and its president were all set and ready to go in 2004, the situation was so unstable that they had to wait two years before even being able to enter the country. This particular witness account and the situation the alleged president was in shows just how badly everyone and anyone can be affected by the nervousness that rises without the presence of a strong government.

Somalia provides a good example of what can happen when the symbolic order collapses and there is no given structure for people to operate and cooperate in. The actions taken in such a loose and unstructured space become meaningless and hopeless, because they don't contribute to anything. Society then quickly loses any kind of direction and falls into a vicious cycle of desperation and chaos. In order to prevent our global society from falling into such a situation with the climate crisis, we need a careful balance of confidence, mixed with a little dose of madness.

Kierkegaard – crises as wake-up-calls

The 19th century Danish philosopher Søren Kierkegaard lost all but one of his six siblings by the time he was 22. His traumatic breakup with his fiancée in 1841 and the death of his siblings – even if not that of his father – had a tremendous impact on him and his Philosophy. He is, like many others, a philosopher whose traumatic experiences have enabled him to think outside social norms, common sense and general opinion. In his case his Philosophy has gone towards

Image 65. - Kierkegaard

how we should stop thinking we can know anything. We should stop pretending our lives are comfortable, happy or without mystery or paradoxes in any way. It is Kierkegaard's struggle to come to terms with the reality of life, and his creative responses to it, that will bring this short essay to a close.

As mentioned, one of Kierkegaard's main philosophical aims was to get us to wake up from our safe and cosy emotional illusions around work, love, family and a purposeful and meaningful life. Much like Nietzsche, he wanted us to see that life was wonderful because it was full of contradictions, paradoxes and unanswerable questions. For Nietzsche this ended in an embrace of life and its mysteries, whereas Kierkegaard ended up making his famous 'leap of faith'. Kierkegaard had contempt for systems of thought that were overconfident in human reason – he was especially sharp in his criticisms of Hegel and his System, and of those in the Danish church who followed the Bible with little thought and were just going through the motions. And so, Kierkegaard, instead of trying to resolve the tension between subjectivity and objectivity, just threw himself on God. He described this leap as follows: "To have faith is to lose your mind and to win God".

The 'system-thinking' that Kierkegaard opposed is similar to some of today's ritual recyclers, polar bear mourners, 'make-sure-you-turn-the-light-off-ers', 'technology-will-save-us-ers' and 'our-kids-will-solve-it-ers'. These people lack the depth of thinking and understanding of the scale of the problem that would lead them to realise the banality of their actions and beliefs. When tackling climate change intellectually and in terms of emissions, we need a similar approach to Kierkegaard's: we also need to 'lose our minds', which can happen in two different ways.

Firstly, by thinking outside the box - or rather, outside the system; just like Kierkegaard continuously attacked "the system" of Hegelian idealism. We need to do this because the current one – which is purely focused on economic profit, based on the false assumption that the world has infinite natural resources and is totally tolerant of human interference – won't be able to offer us any feasible solutions. And it isn't just our disastrously consumptive system we need to change, we also need to change our ways of thinking when seeing ourselves as humans in relation to the rest of planet earth. We need to lose our current homocentric state of mind and realise that we, not just the fluffy polar bears and hungry pandas, will be pushed into an unrecognisably hostile environment by a climate that is growing out of control.

The second is to lose our minds by being ready to see how vulnerable we are. In Hobbes' state of nature, there is a certain point of no return, beyond which tremendous effort is required to put the affected society back onto its feet (just like Somalia still hasn't recovered from its time of anarchy). The same tipping points will happen with climate change, mainly on an ecological level. However, since humans are simply part of the world's ecosystems, these breakdowns will pull us with them. The collapse of ecosystems will bring about the collapse of countries and societies; as ever less land is available for a growing demand of food, direct competition and confrontation with people will mount - pressures that will turn us into nervous 'grabbers', prone to aggressive and violent reactions. The potential for collapse must be made clear, so that we do not continue to make superficial responses.

Kierkegaard writes of his philosophical enlightenment: "I opened my eyes and saw the real world, and I began to laugh, and I haven't stopped since." When confronted with the reality of climate change and the necessity to act now due to its width and depth, one might let out a short-lived nervous laugh at the absurdity of the situation (before heading off to go and cry in the corner). When one sees how little has been done in terms of climate mitigation given the fact that the science has been rock-solid for over 50 years, one might laugh at the tiny amount of resolve politicians around the world are showing and how insufficiently and in a twisted manner the situation is covered by the media.

Climate change most definitely is not a laughing matter, but if we are not tempted to laugh at the sheer absurdity of the current situation then we have probably not been looking at it properly. Humanity, thousands of ecosystems and animal and plant species are at risk. We have no time to waste in laughing, unless we use it as a way of dealing with the absurdity of the climate state we are in, whilst keeping a sane and clear mind. Only then will we be able to solve the sixth mass extinction by being laughing children (similar to Nietzsche's third metamorphosis, the child).

We need radical people like Nietzsche and Kierkegaard, who are not afraid to face the truth and live according to it. It is people like them who should become the role models of our societies, the ones who direct us, the ones who teach humanity to handle bare truths, the ones who make us *sapere aude*.

We have seen that different kinds of brokenness can lead to different outcomes. After having analysed Nietzsche's example of a fatherless upbringing and Kierkegaard's traumatic youth and early adulthood and the effects they have had on their philosophies, we have seen that these philosophers have managed to sublimate their tough starts in life into great thoughts and works. They might even be able to help us tackle climate change, as they have found a way of dealing with absurd realities and brutal, devastating facts, whilst still holding on to and celebrating some kind of higher order; in Nietzsche's case life and in Kierkegaard's God. And so, it seems, that broken minds like theirs can help us face reality, react accordingly by seizing the moment and using the opportunity to possibly save us from the jaws of our own egoism.

Kevin Anderson, Professor of Energy and Climate Change, joint chair in the School of Engineering at the University of Manchester (UK) and in Centre for Sustainability and the Environment (CEMUS) at Uppsala University (Sweden). https://youtu.be/cxFUF0LNB8c

end

Image index:

145	Image 34	Steffen et al. "Planetary Boundaries", (2015)
146	Image 35	Guma89 - CC BY-SA 3.0
152	Image 36	*Culturedarm*
157	Image 37	Wakorinda - CC BY-SA 4.0
165	Image 38	Marcus Kauffman
166	Image 39	Rowland Scherman - Public Domain
181	Image 40	Ed Hawkins
183	Image 41	Jona Lendering - Creative Commons CC0 1.0 Universal Public Domain
184	Image 42	Marie-Van Nguyen CC BY-SA 3.0
192	Image 43	Stanley Wolfson - Public Domain

SCIENCE CHAPTER

210	Image 44	Frederik Klanberg
226	Image 46	Screenshot of Homepage of Bank of England at www.bankofengland.co.uk on 01/09/2020
227	Image 47	Screenshot of Homepage of UNFCC at www.unfccc.int on 01/09/2020
250	Image 48	Public Domain - no copyright rule exists
251	Image 49	Public Domain – 100 year rule
253	Image 50	© Climate Academy
255	Image 51	By Evan-Amos - Own work, CC0
257	Image 52	Nancy - CC BY-SA 3.0

STUDENT ESSAY 1

260	Image 53	Katriina Surquin
264	Image 54	Carolina Teixeira
267	Image 55	Daniel Baise - Creative Commons Attribution-Share Alike 3.0 Unported license.
267	Image 56	© John Pye
268	Image 57	Unknown author - Public Domain
268	Image 58	Linley Sambourn {{PD-US}}e.
274	Image 59	©Jules Pye

STUDENT ESSAY 2

280	Image 60	©Samantha Pye
283	Image 61	Public Domain – 100 year rule
284	Image 62	CC BY-SA 3.0 International
285	Image 63	Charles-Henri Favrod - CC BY-SA 3.0 International
288	Image 64	Wellcome Collection Gallery - Creative Commons Attribution 4.0 Intl.
289	Image 65	Brian0918 - The Royal Library, Denmark - Public Domain- 70 year rule

- 298 -

statistics

Here are
the vital statistics
for human civilisation
on the planet.

These simple numbers
are what you get when
the latest scientific data
and basic principles
of common sense
are put together.

These numbers are the work of OurFutureUncompromised.org
and have been approved at the highest level of the scientific world.

	Resource Consumption			CO_2 Emissions from Consumption			
	Per capita 2018	Trend 1993–2018	Reduction for SD	*Per capita* 2017	Trends 1992–2017	Reduction required for	
						1.5°	2°
	Tonnes CO_2	% / yr	% / yr	Tonnes CO_2	% / yr	% / yr	% / yr
ULTRA HIGH	29	1.4%	–5%	13	0.3%	–52%	–12%
VERY HIGH	17	1.8%	–3%	8.9	0.8%	–33%	–8%
HIGH	16	4.6%	–2%	4.8	4.1%	–17%	–4%
HUMANITY	12	2.9%	–1%	4.8	1.9%	–16%	–4%
MEDIUM	4.5	3.6%	+2%	1.5	4.9%	–5%	–1%
LOW	2.3	3.0%	+6%	0.4	4.6%	–0.7%	+2%
1 NORWAY	38	2.5%	–4.9%	9.6	1.1%	–34%	–8.2%
2 SWITZERLAND	32	2.8%	–4.6%	15	1.6%	–62%	–14%
3 IRELAND	22	2.8%	–3.2%	9.1	0.2%	–31%	–7.6%
4 GERMANY	23	0.5%	–4.1%	11	–0.8%	–41%	–9.7%
4 HONG KONG	-	-	-	17	1,2%	–73%	–16%
6 AUSTRALIA	43	2.0%	–5.2%	16	1.9%	–62%	–14%
6 ICELAND *	35	2.3%	–5.0%	11	1.6%	–43%	–10%
8 SWEDEN	32	2.6%	–4.7%	7.4	–0.4%	–25%	–6.3%
9 SINGAPORE	78	5.5%	–7.5%	21	1.7%	–94%	–19%
10 NETHERLANDS	28	1.9%	–4.6%	9.4	–1.3%	–33%	–8.0%
11 DENMARK	25	1.9%	–3.9%	9.5	–0.5%	–34%	–8.3%
12 FINLAND	37	1.5%	–5.5%	12	–0.2%	–46%	–11%
13 CANADA	35	1.2%	–4.6%	17	0.8%	–68%	–15%
14 NEW ZEALAND	25	2.2%	–3.7%	8.8	1.4%	–32%	–7.8%
15 UK	23	1.5%	–3.6%	8.5	–0.7%	–28%	–6.9%
15 USA	32	1.5%	–4.5%	18	0.4%	–77%	–16%
17 BELGIUM	24	1.2%	–4.0%	16	0.7%	–66%	–14%
18 LIECHTENSTEIN *	-	-	-	4.1	–1.4%	–13%	–3.2%
19 JAPAN	26	0.5%	–5.0%	11	0.1%	–41%	–9.6%
20 AUSTRIA	33	1.8%	–5.1%	11	0.6%	–42%	–9.8%
21 LUXEMBOURG	104	3.5%	–7.9%	41	1.7%	>–100%	–40%
22 ISRAEL	24	2.7%	–2.8%	10	1.7%	–35%	–8.3%
22 KOREA	29	2.6%	–5.1%	13	2.5%	–57%	–13%
24 SLOVENIA	24	2.7%	–4.3%	9.2	0.6%	–34%	–8.1%

	Resource Consumption			CO$_2$ Emissions from Consumption			
	Per capita 2018	Trend 1993-2018	Reduction for SD	*Per capita* 2017	Trends 1992-2017	Reduction required for	
						1.5°	2°
	Tonnes CO$_2$	% / yr	% / yr	Tonnes CO$_2$	% / yr	% / yr	% / yr
EU 27	24	1.4%	−4.3%	8.5	−0.5%	−30%	−7.4%
25 SPAIN	24	1.8%	−4.4%	6.6	0.4	−23%	−5.7%
26 CZECHIA	23	2.6%	−4.1%	10	−1.2%	−38%	−9.1%
26 FRANCE	23	0.9%	−3.8%	7.2	−0.4%	−25%	−6.3%
28 MALTA	26	1.2%	−4.5%	12	2.2%	−38%	−9.0%
29 ITALY	22	0.6%	−4.2%	7.9	−0.6%	−27%	−6.7%
30 ESTONIA	30	2.4%	−5.2%	14	−0.5%	−59%	−13%
31 CYPRUS	28	2.7%	−4.2%	7.1	1.4%	−23%	−5.8%
32 GREECE	27	0.8%	−4.9%	6.4	−1.5%	−20%	−5.0%
32 POLAND	25	3.6%	−4.7%	8.3	−0.4%	−30%	−7.3%
34 LITHUANIA	38	3.6%	−6.5%	8.3	−1.6%	−33%	−7.9%
35 UAE	50	7.9%	−6.3%	25	5.4%	>−100%	−23%
36 ANDORRA *	−	−	−	6.3	0.6%	−22%	−5.5%
36 SAUDI ARABIA	12	−0.8%	−1.1%	19	4.2%	−91%	−19%
36 SLOVAKIA	36	1.3%	−5.7%	9.1	−0.2%	−35%	−8.4%
39 LATVIA	24	4.7%	−5.0%	6.8	−0.9%	−25%	−6.2%
40 PORTUGAL	19	0.7%	−3.7%	6.0	0.1%	−22%	−5.6%
41 QATAR	13	3.9%	−1.1%	31	5.6%	>−100%	−33%
42 CHILE	17	2.9%	−2.8%	5.0	4.5%	−17%	−4.3%
43 BRUNEI DAR.	20	1.7%	−3.2%	19	3.9%	−88%	−18%
43 HUNGARY	15	1.0	−3.0%	7.0	−0.5%	−26%	−6.4%
45 BAHRAIN	14	0.4%	−1.2%	13	2.3%	−53%	−12%
46 CROATIA	16	2.5%	−3.6%	5.4	1.3%	−19%	−4.8%
47 OMAN	10	2.6%	−0.3%	14	6.8%	−51%	−12%
48 ARGENTINA	15	2.0%	−2.0%	4.7	2.2	−16%	−4.2%
49 RUSSIAN FED.	10	0.0%	−1.6%	9.7	−0.9%	−35%	−8.3%
50 BELARUS	0.4	2.5%	+9.1%	7.5	2.6%	−27%	−6.7%
50 KAZAKHSTAN	18	−0.8%	−2.4%	13	1.6%	−63%	−14%
52 BULGARIA	13	1.7%	−3.2%	5.9	−0.4%	−20%	−5.0%
52 MONTENEGRO *	28	7.0%	−4.9%	3.3	1.8%	−11%	−2.7%

	Resource Consumption			CO$_2$ Emissions from Consumption			
	Per capita 2018	Trend 1993–2018	Reduc–tion for SD	*Per capita* 2017	Trends 1992–2017	Reduction required for	
						1.5°	2°
	Tonnes CO$_2$	% / yr	% / yr	Tonnes CO$_2$	% / yr	% / yr	% / yr
52 ROMANIA	17	2.9%	–3.7%	3.9	–2.1%	–12%	–3.1%
55 PALAU *	–	–	–	13	0.7%	–56%	–13%
56 BARBADOS *	11	–2.3%	–1.6%	4.6	0.6%	–15%	–3.8%
57 KUWAIT	48	4.2%	–5.5%	22	4.2%	>–100%	–21%
57 URUGUAY	39	5.6%	–5.6%	3.6	2.8%	–11%	–2.9%
59 TURKEY	16	4.4%	–2.4%	5.9	3.2%	–22%	–5.6%
60 BAHAMAS*	21	–0.8%	–2.9%	4.8	0.1%	–14%	–3.4%
61 MALAYSIA	25	3.7%	–3.5%	36	4.9%	–32%	–7.8%
62 SEYCHELLES *	22	1.9%	–3.6%	6.9	5.2%	–32%	–8.0%
63 SERBIA *	17	2.5%	–3.9%	5.3	0.7%	–19%	–4.7%
63 TRINIDAD & TOBAG	5.6	1.8%	0.5%	28	3.8%	>–100%	–38%
65 IRAN	14	2.4%	–1.7%	7.7	4.7%	–28%	–6.9%
66 MAURITIUS	21	1.4%	–3.9%	4.9	2.8%	–18%	–4.6%
67 PANAMA	8.1	2.0%	+0.4%	5.5	7.9%	–17%	–4.3%
68 COSTA RICA	8.3	3.4%	–0.2%	2.6	3.3%	–8.0%	–1.8%
69 ALBANIA	12	4.0%	–2.5%	2.0	2.8%	–6.4%	–1.2%
70 GEORGIA	9.1	–1.9%	–1.5%	2.9	0.7%	–10%	–2.6%
71 SRI LANKA	4.2	5.8%	+1.7%	1.7	6.4%	–6.5%	–1.3%
72 CUBA *	7.7	–1.7%	–0.6%	2.6	1.5%	–8.7%	–2.0%
73 ST KITTS & NEVIS *	–	–	–	4.7	3.1%	–17%	–4.2%
74 ANTIGUA & BARB *	13	–1.0%	–1.7%	6.0	3.0%	–21%	–5.4%
75 BOSNIA & HERZE *	11	0.4%	–2.5%	6.7	2.2%	–24%	–6.0%
76 MEXICO	10	1.9%	0.7%	4.3	1.7%	–14%	–3.5%
77 THAILAND	15	3.4%	–2.9%	4.2	3.3%	–15%	–3.7%
78 GRENADA *	–	–	–	2.5	3.3%	–7.8%	–1.7%
79 BRAZIL	18	3.8%	–3.0%	2.5	3.0%	–8.2%	–1.9%
79 COLOMBIA	11	3.6%	–1.2%	2.2	1.9%	–7.6%	–1.7%
81 ARMENIA	8.4	2.9%	–1.0%	1.9	1.2%	–5.8%	–1.0%

	Resource Consumption			CO$_2$ Emissions from Consumption			
	Per capita 2018	Trend 1993–2018	Reduc-tion for SD	Per capita 2017	Trends 1992–2017	Reduction required for	
						1.5°	2°
	Tonnes CO$_2$	% / yr	% / yr	Tonnes CO$_2$	% / yr	% / yr	% / yr
82 ALGERIA *	3.1	3.7%	+3.8%	3.8	2.6%	−13%	−3.3%
82 N. MACEDONIA *	14	1.5%	−2.8%	3.6	−1.3%	−12%	−2.9%
82 PERU	9.8	3.8%	−0.5%	2.0	4.3%	−6.3%	−1.2%
85 CHINA	21	5.8%	−3.9%	6.2	5.1%	−22%	−5.5%
85 ECUADOR	11	3.6%	−0.6%	2.9	3.3%	−9.8%	−2.4%
87 AZERBAIJAN	6.4	−0.7%	+0.4%	4.2	2.4%	−15%	−3.7%
88 UKRAINE	12	2.3%	−2.8%	5.4	−2.4%	−17%	−4.4%
89 DOMINICAN REP.	6.7	3.2%	+0.7%	2.5	3.4%	−8.1%	−1.8%
89 SAINT LUCIA *	-	-	-	2.4	2.4%	−7.9%	−1.8%
91 TUNISIA	6.4	1.7%	+0.7%	2.6	2.4%	−9.2%	−2.2%
92 MONGOLIA	14	0.5%	−1.5%	8.1	4.1%	−22%	−5.5%
93 LEBANON*	14	4.0%	−2.6%	3.6	3.5%	−13%	−3.2%
94 BOTSWANA	35	2.7%	−3.9%	8.0	7.6%	−54%	−13%
94 ST VINCENT& GRE. *	-	-	-	2.1	3.2%	−7.0%	−1.5%
96 JAMAICA	7.7	0.8%	−0.3%	2.9	0.9%	−9.5%	−2.3%
96 VENEZUELA	8.1	0.4%	+0.3%	4.9	2.2%	−15%	−3.8%
98 DOMINICA *	-	-	-	2.6	4.4%	−8.9%	−2.1%
98 FIJI *	7.5	0.0%	+0.4%	2.5	4.3%	−9.8%	−2.4%
98 PARAGUAY	15	3.6%	−1.9%	1.5	3.8%	−5.4%	−0.8%
98 SURINAME *	14	0.9%	−1.8%	3.2	−0.5%	−9.8%	−2.4%
102 JORDAN	6.7	4.0%	+0.8%	3.6	3.1%	−13%	−3.4%
103 BELIZE *	7.7	1.2%	+1.0%	1.5	1.7%	−5.1%	−0.7%
104 MALDIVES *	13	7.1%	−1.7%	3.0	8.5%	−11%	−2.8%
105 TONGA *	-	-	-	1.3	1.9%	−4.6%	−0.5%
106 PHILIPPINES	4.4	2.6%	+2.4%	1.4	3.4%	−5.4%	−0.8%
107 MOLDOVA *	3.9	16%	+1.1%	1.3	−4.4%	−4.3%	−0.3%
108 TURKMENISTA *	22	4.3%	−3.0%	14	4.4%	−59%	−13%
108 UZBEKISTAN *	6.1	2.1%	+1.3%	2.9	−0.9%	−8.9%	−2.1%
110 LIBYA *	3.8	1.0%	+2.7%	8.3	1.3%	−29%	−7.1%
111 INDONESIA	6.3	3.7%	+0.8%	2.3	4.6%	−7.9%	−1.8%

	Resource Consumption			CO$_2$ Emissions from Consumption			
	Per capita 2018	Trend 1993–2018	Reduction for SD	Per capita 2017	Trends 1992–2017	Reduction required for	
						1.5°	2°
	Tonnes CO$_2$	% / yr	% / yr	Tonnes CO$_2$	% / yr	% / yr	% / yr
111 SAMOA*	8.1	1.2%	+0.4%	1.4	3.5%	−4.9%	−0.6%
113 SOUTH AFRICA	8.4	0.8%	+0.3%	6.1	2.3%	−21%	−5.2%
114 BOLIVIA	5.5	1.8%	+1.7%	1.8	5.1%	−6.6%	−1.3%
115 GABON *	4.3	1.3%	+3.5%	2.6	0.3%	−8.3%	−1.9%
116 EGYPT	4.9	3.0%	+2.7%	2.4	3.9%	−7.7%	−1.7%
117 MARSHALL IS. *	-	-	-	2.6	1.7%	−9.0%	−2.1%
118 VIET NAM	13	9.0%	−2.0%	2.1	9.1%	−7.9%	−1.8%
119 PALESTINE *	-	-	-	0.7	5.1%	−2.1%	+0.9%
120 IRAQ*	2.8	1.7%	+5.0%	5.4	4.8%	−20%	−5.0%
121 MOROCCO	3.9	2.2%	+2.6%	1.9	2.8%	−6.2%	−1.2%
122 KYRGYZSTAN	8.4	2.1%	+0.6%	2.7	0.5%	−8.7%	−2.0%
123 GUYANA *	119	1.6%	−8.9%	3.2	3.4%	−12%	−2.9%
124 EL SALVADOR	6.3	3.0%	+0.5%	1.5	2.7%	−5.0%	−0.7%
125 TAJIKISTAN *	3.8	4.6%	+3.7%	0.6	0.2%	−2.3%	+0.8%
126 CABO VERDE *	8.9	2.6%	−0.2%	1.2	7.2%	−4.1%	−0.2%
126 GUATEMALA	3.9	3.7%	+3.4%	1.2	4.2%	−4.1%	−0.3%
126 NICARAGUA	4.3	3.2%	+2.5%	1.1	3.5%	−3.5%	+0.1%
129 INDIA	4.7	3.4%	+1.8%	1.7	4.9%	−6.2%	−1.2%
130 NAMIBIA	8.6	1.3%	+0.8%	4.1	8.8%	−19%	−4.8%
131 TIMOR-LESTE *	-	-	-	0.4	NaN	−0.8%	+1.8%
132 HONDURAS	3.9	3.7%	+3.0%	1.2	5.0%	−3.9%	−0.2%
132 KIRIBATI *	-	-	-	0.6	3.5%	−2.0%	+1.0%
134 BHUTAN *	11	2.4%	−1.2%	1.6	8.1%	−6.1%	−1.1%
135 BANGLADESH	2.5	3.5%	+3.9%	0.7	6.9%	−2.2%	+0.8%
135 MICRONESIA *	-	-	-	1.4	NaN	−4.6%	−0.5%
137 SAO TOME & P *	5.9	1.1%	+2.6%	0.6	3.9%	−1.6%	+1.2%
138 CONGO *	2.3	2.2	+6.2%	0.6	3.0%	−1.6%	+1.2%
138 ESWATINI *	12	1.4%	−0.4%	1.1	2.1%	−3.0%	+0.3%
140 LAOS	7.9	9.0%	+0.1%	2.4	12%	−15%	−3.8%
141 VANUATU *	7.4	2.1%	+1.8%	0.5	3.7%	−1.6%	+1.2%

	Resource Consumption			CO$_2$ Emissions from Consumption			
	Per capita 2018	Trend 1993–2018	Reduction for SD	Per capita 2017	Trends 1992–2017	Reduction required for	
						1.5°	2°
	Tonnes CO$_2$	% / yr	% / yr	Tonnes CO$_2$	% / yr	% / yr	% / yr
142 GHANA	3.5	3.2%	+4.0%	0.8	6.7%	−2.3%	+0.7%
143 ZAMBIA	3.6	1.6%	+4.8%	0.6	4.0%	−1.9%	+1.0%
144 EQ. GUINEA *	-	-	-	4.5	19%	−13%	−3.2%
145 MYANMAR *	1.5	2.3%	+5.7%	0.5	6.6%	−1.8%	+1.1%
146 CAMBODIA	3.7	4.6%	+2.8%	1.0	8.8%	−4.1%	−0.3%
147 KENYA	3.0	3.1%	+4.7%	0.6	5.1%	−1.8%	+1.1%
147 NEPAL	3.0	3.0%	+3.5%	0.6	9.1%	−1.9%	+1.0%
149 ANGOLA *	3.3	4.6%	+5.5%	1.1	7.4%	−3.5%	+0.1%
150 CAMEROON	1.9	2.2%	+6.7%	0.5	5.6%	−1.6%	+1.2%
150 ZIMBABWE	3.6	4.1%	+4.0%	0.9	-2.2%	−3.0%	+0.4%
152 PAKISTAN	3.0	2.6%	+4.2%	1.1	4.4%	−3.8%	−0.1%
153 SOLOMON ISL *	-	-	-	0.3	0.9%	+0.4%	+2.7%
154 SYRIAN A.R *	3.7	0.9%	+4.3%	1.7	-1,.9%	−4.9%	−0.6%
155 PAPUA N.GUIN *	2.5	-0.1%	+5.2%	0.9	5.2%	−3.4%	+0.1%
156 COMOROS *	-	-	-	0.3	4.7%	+0.2%	+2.5%
157 RWANDA	3.2	3.4%	+4.6%	0.1	3.4%	+1.9%	+4.0%
158 NIGERIA	2.7	3.4%	+5.6%	0.5	3.3%	−1.1%	+1.6%
159 TANZANIA	1.4	2.5%	+8.2%	0.4	7.2%	−0.6%	+1.9%
159 UGANDA	2.6	3.5%	+5.8%	0.2	6.8%	+0.7%	+2.9%
161 MAURITANIA *	2.6	1.4%	+5.8%	0.6	4.3%	−1.8%	+1.1%
162 MADAGASCAR	0.8	2.8%	+9.7%	0.2	5.6%	+0.4%	+2.7%
163 BENIN	4.4	4.4%	+3.9%	0.7	8.3%	−2.1%	+0.9%
164 LESOTHO *	12	5.1%	−1.2%	1.3	2.0%	−4.3%	−0.3%
165 CÔTE D'IVOIRE	0.9	-0,3%	+9.5%	0.6	4.5%	−1.9%	+1.0%
166 SENEGAL	2.5	3.4%	+5.9%	0.8	4.9%	−2.6%	+0.6%
167 TOGO	2.5	2.1%	+5.7%	1.0	7.1%	−2.9%	+0.4%
168 SUDAN *	5.2	29%	+2.8%	0.5	8.5%	−1.4%	+1.3%
169 HAITI *	1.4	1.9%	+6.4%	0.3	6.1%	+0.1%	+2.4%
170 AFGHANISTAN*	1.2	1.7%	+7.9%	0.3	8.1%	+0.4%	+2.7%
171 DJIBOUTI *	2.3	0.5%	+4.6%	0.7	2.6%	−2.0%	+0.9%

	Resource Consumption			CO$_2$ Emissions from Consumption			
	Per capita 2018	Trend 1993–2018	Reduc-tion for SD	*Per capita* 2017	Trends 1992–2017	Reduction required for	
						1.5°	2°
	Tonnes CO$_2$	% / yr	% / yr	Tonnes CO$_2$	% / yr	% / yr	% / yr
172 MALAWI	1.3	3.0%	+8.3%	0.2	3.0%	+0.5%	+2.8%
173 ETHIOPIA	0.8	-1.0%	+9.4%	0.2	7.1%	+0.5%	+2.7%
174 GAMBIA *	2.2	1.8%	+6.3%	0.3	4.4%	+0.1%	+2.4%
174 GUINEA	2.4	1.8%	+6.1%	0.3	4.3%	+0.2%	+2.6%
176 LIBERIA *	1.5	4.0%	+7.6%	0.3	5.3%	-0.6%	+1.9%
177 YEMEN *	1.1	-1.6%	+8.0	0.4	0.6%	+0.5%	+2.7%
178 GUINEA-BISSA *	-	-	-	0.2	2.5%	+0.9%	+3.1%
179 DR CONGO *	2.0	1.2%	+7.2%	0.0	-1.1%	+4.7%	+6.6%
180 MOZAMBIQUE	2.1	3.8%	+6.7%	0.6	6.5%	-2.0%	+1.0%
181 SIERRA LEONE *	7.1	7.2%	+0.9%	0.1	3.5%	+1.5%	+3.6%
182 BURKINA FASO	4.0	4.3%	+4.3%	0.3	7.3%	-0.2%	+2.3%
182 ERITREA *	12	15%	-1.9%	0.2	0.2%	+0.6%	+2.9%
184 MALI *	4.6	5.2%	+4.0	0.2	8.5%	+0.8%	+3.0%
185 BURUNDI *	1.6	1,2%	+7.9%	0.0	3.4%	+3.2%	+5.1%
186 SOUTH SUDAN *	2.0	17%	+5.7%	0.2	8.4%	+0.9%	+3.1%
187 CHAD *	1.5	1.9%	+8.0%	0.1	3.8%	+2.8%	+4.7%
188 C.A.R.	2.6	1.1%	+5.3%	0.1	1.2%	+2.7%	+4.7%
189 NIGER *	3.1	3.8%	+6.3%	0.1	5.5%	+2.0%	+4.0
.. DPR KOREA *	1.0	-5.4%	+6.7%	1.2	-4.5%	-4.1%	-0.2%
.. NAURU *	-	-	-	4.8	-3.2%	-17%	-4.4%
.. SOMALIA *	2.3	2.1%	+6.7%	0.0	0.4%	+3.3%	+5.2%
.. TUVALU *	-	-	-	1.0	1.9%	-3.3%	+0.2%

IPCC CO_2 emission budget to limit global warming to 2°C and 1.5°C (since 1850-1900) 1

Carbon Budget	2°C limit	1.5°C limit
$GtCO_2$ on 1.1.2018[1]	1,070	320
$GtCO_2$ on 1.1.2019[2]	1,028	278
$GtCO_2$ fossil fuels & industry on 1.1.2019[3]	905	245
Tonnes CO_2 per capita 1.1.2019[4]	117	32

National Emissions	Sweden	Tanzania
Tonnes CO_2 per capita per year consumption emissions[5]	7.4	0.4
2°: CO_2 reduction in % per year now (1.7.2020)	-6%	+2%
1.5°: CO_2 reduction in % per year now (1.7.2020)	-25%	-1%

[1] Intergovernmental Panel on Climate Change 2018, Special Report Global Warming 1.5°C, table 2.2 The assessed remaining carbon budget, accounting for "Earth system feedbacks" - permafrost thawing or methane released by wetlands -, percentiles of TCRE: 67th;

[2] Deduct 2018 CO_2 emissions: 42.I $GtCO_2$ (Friedlingstein P. et all, Global Carbon Project (GCP), Global carbon budget 2019 (version 1.0));

[3] Allocate 88% of the budget to fossil fuels & industry emission (landuse change emissions are about 12%) (Friedlingstein P. et all, GCP, Global carbon budget 2019 (version 1.0));

[4] 2019 human population of 7.7 billion, Sweden: 10.0 million, Tanzania 58.0 million (United Nations World Population Prospects 2019 revision);

[5] Consumption emissions per capita (Updated from Peters et al, GCP National Carbon Emissions Global 2019 (version 1.0)).

The Intergovernmental Panel on Climate Change concluded that to limit global warming to the internationally agreed objectiv of 2°C or 1.5°C, CO_2 emissions must be limited to 1,070 or 320 $GtCO_2$ from 1 January 2018 onwards; this is the carbon budhet for a 66% chance, accounting for "earth feedback systems" (100 $GtCO_2$ until 2100), assuming rapid reduction of other greenhouse gases and with no "negative emissions" and no "overshoot". 1

42 $GtCO_2$ were emitted in 2018 2, thus 1,028 or 278 $GtCO_2$ remained by 1 Jan 2019. Land-use emissions are about 12% of total CO_2 emissions and therefor 88% of the budget is allocated to fossil fuels and industry, 905 or 245 $GtCO_2$. Equally divided among humanity (international equity), the per capita limit is 117 tonnes CO_2 for 2°C, 32 tonnes CO_2 for 1.5°C.

With no global government, emissions are allocated to nations, the law-making units. To take a national example, the current per capita consumption emissions of Sweden - an Ultra High Developed nation - are 7.4 tonnes CO_2 per year (decreasing 0.4% per year on a 25 year trend, last year increasing 1.1%). With 10 million people 4 Sweden's "national budget " on 1.1.2019 was 1.2 or 0.3 $GtCO_2$; not exceeding it as of 1.7.2020 requires reducing emissions 6% or 25% per year starting now (intergenerational equity) increasing with inaction.

In comparison, Low Developed Tanzania, with very low per capita emissions of 0.4 tonnes CO_2 must reduce emissions 1% for 1.5°C but can increase emissions 2% for 2°C and not exceed its limit.

If countries have not yet reached zero emissions by 2100, their remaining limit (budget) is at least 20 years od 2100 emissions.

"Justice is what love looks like in public".

- Cornel West -